FRE

IST MEDS

U.J T.

MEDICAL EMBRYOLOGY

MEDICAL EMBRYOLOGY

Human Development — normal and abnormal

Jan Langman, M.D., Ph.D.

Professor of Anatomy, McGill University, Montreal

Illustrations by JILL LELAND

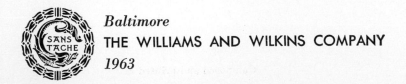

Baltimore
THE WILLIAMS AND WILKINS COMPANY
1963

First Edition, June, 1963

    Reprinted: February, 1964; May, 1964
    Reprinted: July, 1965; August, 1966
    Reprinted: July, 1967

Spanish Edition, December, 1963
French Edition (in preparation)
Russian Edition (in preparation)
German Edition (in preparation)

Library of Congress Catalog Card Number 63-19754

COVER ILLUSTRATION—"La Main de Dieu" (The Hand of God), by August Rodin, 1897. The hand is shaping a mass of formless matter, from which, as from a womb, emerge the bodies of Man and Woman. *Reproduced, with the permission of The Philadelphia Museum of Art, from a charcoal sketch of the bronze in its Rodin Museum.*

Composed and printed at
Waverly Press, Inc.
Mt. Royal & Guilford Aves.
Baltimore, Md., 21202 U. S. A.

To my wife
INA
in appreciation of her great support during
the writing of this book

Preface

Recent advances in embryology, radioautography, and electron microscopy have been so overwhelming that the medical student often has difficulty in grasping the basic facts of development from the highly complicated picture presented to him. The aim of this book, therefore, is to give the future doctor a concise, well illustrated presentation of the essential facts of human development, clarifying the gross anatomical features without omitting the recent advances or changing concepts in the basic sciences. Furthermore, since embryology has become of great practical value because of the enormous progress made in surgery and teratology, each chapter on the development of the organ systems has been complemented by a description of those malformations important to the student in his further training. As a further reflection of the increased clinical importance of embryology an entire chapter has been devoted to the etiology of congenital defects.

Of the many colleagues who have been of help in the writing of this book, I particularly wish to thank Dr. C. P. Leblond for his continuous interest and encouragement; Dr. F. Clarke Fraser, for his help in discussing the various aspects of the congenital malformations; and my friends, Dr. Harry Maisel, Dr. Robert van Mierop, and Dr. Yves Clermont, who have spared no effort in assisting with the design of the drawings and the checking of the text.

I wish to express my sincere thanks to Miss Jill Leland, who prepared all the illustrations in this book, and to Mrs. E. Dawson, who has been of such excellent support to me in setting up the manuscript.

CONTENTS

Part I GENERAL EMBRYOLOGY

Part II SPECIAL EMBRYOLOGY

Index

PART I

GENERAL EMBRYOLOGY

CHAPTER 1

Gametogenesis

- PRIMORDIAL GERM CELLS
- OOGENESIS: *oogonium; primary oocyte; first maturation division; secondary oocyte; second maturation division; mature oocyte*
- SPERMATOGENESIS: *spermatogonium; primary spermatocyte; first maturation division; secondary spermatocyte; second maturation division; spermatid*
- SPERMIOGENESIS: *acrosomic head cap; middle piece, body and tail*
- MEIOSIS
- ABNORMAL GAMETES: *multinucleated oocytes; abnormal spermatozoa*

The development of a new individual commences with fertilization. During this process two highly specialized cells, one from the male, known as the *spermatozoon,* and the other from the female, the *ovum,* unite to give rise to the *zygote,* the first cell of the new organism. In the male the germ cells or spermatozoa arise and mature in the testis; in the female the ova grow and ripen in the ovary.

In preparation for eventual fertilization, both male and female germ cells undergo a series of profound changes that involve the nucleus as well as the cytoplasm of the cells. The purpose of these changes is twofold:

1. To reduce the number of chromosomes in the germ cell to half that in the somatic cell, *i.e.,* from 46 to 23 chromosomes. Hence, the mature germ cells of both male and female contain 23 chromosomes. The reduction in the number of chromosomes is necessary for the maintenance of the species, as otherwise fusion of male and female gametes would give rise to an individual with twice the number of chromosomes of the parent cells. It is accomplished by two highly specialized divisions, known as *meiotic divisions* (see page 11).

2. To alter the shape of the germ cells in preparation for fertilization. The female germ cell, which initially approximates 30 μ in diameter,

enlarges greatly, because of the increase in cytoplasm. At maturity the ovum is about 120 μ in diameter. The male germ cell, on the contrary, loses practically all its cytoplasm, develops a tail, and becomes highly motile.

Since at present it is generally believed that the germ cells as found in the adult are direct descendants of the primitive germ cells as seen in early embryonic life, the discussion on the development of the spermatozoon and ovum will begin with that of the *primordial germ cells*.

Primordial Germ Cells

The primordial germ cells appear in human embryos at the end of the third week of development.[1] They are then located in the wall of the yolk sac near the caudal end of the embryo and from there migrate toward the developing gonads (primitive sex glands), where they arrive at the end of the fifth week.[1-8] (For further details, see Chapter 10.)

It was initially believed that the primordial germ cells died shortly after arrival in the gonads and that new germ cells were formed by the surface epithelium of the glands.[9-13] At present, however, it is evident from genetic, irradiation, and isotope studies that the mature germ cell is a direct descendant of the primordial germ cell in the embryo.[4-7, 14-18] This implies that the predecessors of the mature male and female germ cells produced during reproductive life are present in the embryo and it is thought that some of the primitive germ cells in the female, reaching maturity late in life, may have been dormant for 40 years or more.

Oogenesis

Once the primordial germ cells arrive in the developing female gonad, they divide rapidly and give rise to the *oogonia*, which are considered the most primitive female germ cells. By the third month of development the oogonia are located in the cortical part of the ovary, where they are arranged in clusters surrounded by a layer of flat epithelial cells (fig. 1-1A). It is thought that each cluster is formed by the descendants of a single primordial germ cell and that the surrounding cells originate in the surface epithelium. By the end of the third month some of the oogonia differentiate into the much larger *primary oocytes*, which immediately after their formation enter the prophase of the first meiotic division. By the seventh month, when practically all the oogonia have disappeared and the oocytes have started meiosis, each primary oocyte is surrounded by a layer of flat epithelial cells (fig. 1-1B).[19, 20] A primary oocyte, together with the surrounding epithelial cells, then forms the so-called *primordial follicle* (fig. 1-1B). At birth the primary oocytes have finished the prophase of the first meiotic division and have entered a resting stage (the *dictyotene stage*), in which they remain until sexual maturity is reached (fig. 1-1C).[20, 21]

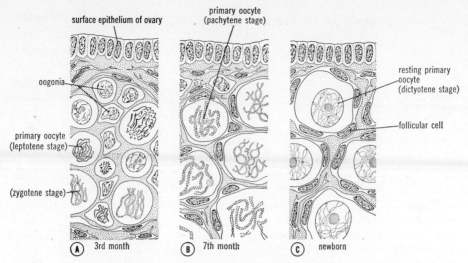

surface epithelium of ovary

primary oocyte
(pachytene stage)

oogonia

resting primary
oocyte
(dictyotene stage)

follicular cell

primary oocyte
(leptotene stage)

(zygotene stage)

(A) 3rd month   (B) 7th month   (C) newborn

Figure 1-1. *Schematic representation of a segment of the ovary at different stages of development. A, At 3 months. The oogonia are grouped in clusters in the cortical part of the ovary. Some show mitosis; others have already differentiated into primary oocytes and have entered the prophase of the first meiotic division (leptotene and zygotene stages). B, At 7 months. Almost all the oogonia are transformed into primary oocytes, which show the pachytene stage of the prophase of the first meiotic division. C, At birth. No more oogonia can be detected. Each primary oocyte is surrounded by a single layer of follicular cells, thus forming the primordial follicle. The oocytes have entered the dictyotene stage in which they remain until maturation. Only then do they enter the metaphase of the first meiotic division (modified after Ohno et al.).*

Only then do they complete the first meiotic division. Although the total number of primary oocytes present at birth is estimated at 40,000 to 300,000, the majority degenerates during further life. After puberty, however, a number of oocytes begin to enlarge with each ovarian cycle, though usually only one achieves full maturity.

As a first indication of further development, the primary oocyte increases in size, while the follicular cells become cuboidal and begin to proliferate, thereby forming an increasingly thick covering around the oocyte (fig. 1-2). In addition, the follicular cells deposit some acellular material consisting of glycoproteins on the surface of the oocyte.[19, 22] This material gradually thickens and forms the *zona pellucida* (fig. 1-3A). Small processes of the oocyte and follicular cells extend into or across the zona pellucida and are thought to be of significance in the transport of materials from the follicular cells to the oocyte during its rapid growth.[19, 23, 24]

As development continues, irregular, fluid-filled spaces appear between the follicular cells. These spaces later coalesce to form the *follicular antrum*, which with time becomes crescent-shaped and filled

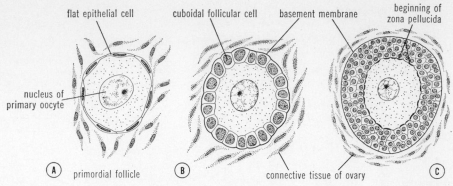

Figure 1-2. *A, Schematic drawing of a primary oocyte surrounded by a layer of flattened epithelial cells (primordial follicle). B, With increase in size of the primary oocyte the follicular cells become cuboidal and show a distinct basement membrane. C, With further growth of the oocyte, the follicular cells form an increasingly thick layer around it. The zona pellucida is visible in irregular patches between the surface of the oocyte and the columnar follicular cells (modified after Shettles).*

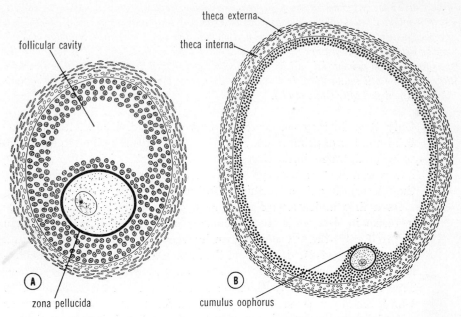

Figure 1-3. *Schematic representation of a maturing follicle. A, The oocyte surrounded by the zona pellucida is eccentrically located; the follicular antrum has developed by coalescence of intercellular spaces. Note the arrangement of the cells of the theca interna and the theca externa. B, Mature Graafian follicle. The antrum has enlarged considerably, is filled with follicular fluid, and is surrounded by a layer of follicular cells. The oocyte is surrounded by a mound of follicular cells, the cumulus oophorus.*

General Embryology

with follicular fluid containing estrogenic hormones secreted by the follicular cells (fig. 1-3*A*). Those follicular cells massed around the oocyte itself are known collectively as the *cumulus oophorus* (fig. 1-3*B*). In its mature state the follicle is known as the *Graafian follicle*. It is then surrounded by two layers of connective tissue: an inner vascular layer, the *theca interna*, and an outer fibrous layer, the *theca externa* (fig. 1-3*B*). As the follicle nears maturity the cumulus oophorus becomes more elevated, until finally the oocyte is supported by a column of follicular cells.[24] The follicle then varies in size from 6 to 12 mm., and is found immediately adjacent to the surface of the ovary.

Toward the end of development of the primordial follicle into the mature Graafian follicle, the primary oocyte finishes its *first meiotic* or *maturation division*, which was started during prenatal life. The result of this division is the formation of two daughter cells, each with 23 chromosomes but of unequal size (fig. 1-4*A*, *B*). One receives almost all the cytoplasm of the mother cell and is known as the *secondary oocyte*; the other receives hardly any and forms the *first polar body*.[25] The latter lies between the zona pellucida and the cell membrane of the secondary oocyte (fig. 1-4*B*).

As soon as the first maturation division has been completed and before the nucleus of the secondary oocyte has returned to its resting stage, the cell starts a *second maturation division*. This division results in the formation of a large, mature oocyte and a second polar body. At the moment that the secondary oocyte shows the spindle formation, ovulation occurs and the oocyte is shed from the ovary (fig. 1-4*C*).[26] It is thought that the second maturation division is completed only if the

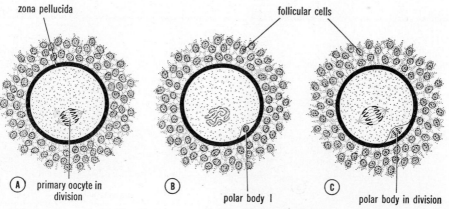

Figure 1-4. *Maturation of the oocyte. Although this process occurs inside the follicle, as shown in figure 1-3, in this drawing only a few layers of follicular cells are represented. A, Primary oocyte, showing the spindle of the meiotic division. B, Secondary oocyte and polar body I. C, Secondary oocyte, showing the spindle of the second maturation division. Polar body I likewise shows spindle formation (adapted from several sources).*

oocyte is fertilized, otherwise the oocyte degenerates approximately 24 hours after ovulation. Whether the first-formed polar body always undergoes a second division is not known for certain, but fertilized ova accompanied by three polar bodies have been observed.[24]

Spermatogenesis

During the fifth week of development the primordial germ cells enter the developing male gonad, where they are incorporated into the *primitive sex cords*. These irregularly shaped cords are composed of cells derived from the surface epithelium of the gland.[27]

At birth the sex cords are solid and contain two types of cells (fig. 1-5*A*). The larger of the two is located along the basement membrane and has a large, lightly staining, spherical nucleus with one or more nucleoli. These cells are believed to be the primordial germ cells.[18] The other cell type is likewise found along the basement membrane, but it is much smaller and characterized by nuclei with coarse chromatin granulations. These cells proliferate actively and are known as the *supporting cells*.[28] After birth they cease to divide and become typical *Sertoli cells* (*sustentacular cells*), a nonspermatogenic cell type derived from the surface epithelium (fig. 1-5*B*).

Recently it has been shown that some of the primordial germ cells die in the course of development but that the others develop into spermatogonia which later give rise to the spermatozoa.[18, 29-31]

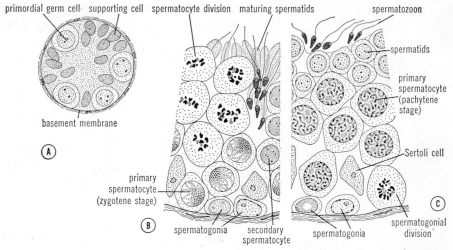

Figure 1-5. *A, Transverse section through testis cord in the newborn, showing the primordial germ cells and supporting cells surrounded by the basement membrane. B and C, Two different segments of the adult seminiferous tubule shown in transverse section. Each segment shows a different stage of the maturation of the male germ cells (derived from Clermont).*

In the course of postnatal development the sex cords obtain a lumen and become known as *seminiferous tubules*. The spermatogonia close to the basement membrane of the tubule then begin to divide and give rise either to new spermatogonia (the so-called type A spermatogonia which include the stem cells), or to a more differentiated type (type B), which develop into *primary spermatocytes* (figs. 1-5 and 1-6).[32-35] The latter have a spherical nucleus with fine chromatin granulations either free in the nucleoplasm or attached to the nuclear membrane. The primary spermatocytes then start the long lasting prophase of the *first meiotic* or *maturation division* (fig. 1-6). As in the case of the primary oocyte, this division is characterized by a reduction in the number of chromosomes. The primary spermatocyte thus gives rise to two *secondary spermatocytes*, each containing half the number of chromosomes of the mother cell. Contrary to the oocyte, however, both secondary spermatocytes receive an equal amount of cytoplasm (see fig. 1-9*B*).

The secondary spermatocytes have a very short life span and almost immediately after their formation start a *second maturation division*. The cells resulting from this division are called *spermatids* (figs. 1-5 and 1-6). Hence, each primary spermatocyte gives rise theoretically to four spermatids, which then develop into spermatozoa (fig. 1-9*B*).

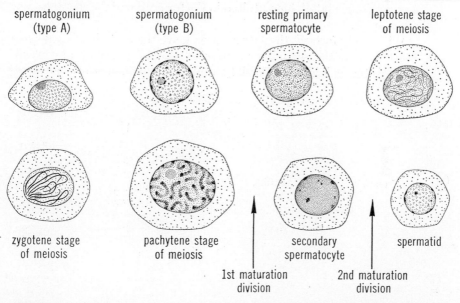

spermatogonium (type A)   spermatogonium (type B)   resting primary spermatocyte   leptotene stage of meiosis

zygotene stage of meiosis   pachytene stage of meiosis   secondary spermatocyte   spermatid

1st maturation division   2nd maturation division

Figure 1-6. *Schematic representation of the spermatogenesis in man. Note the leptotene, zygotene, and pachytene stages of the prophase of the first meiotic division (derived from Clermont).*

Spermiogenesis

As soon as the spermatids are formed they undergo a series of profound changes which result in the production of the spermatozoa.

Initially the spermatid has a spherical nucleus, a clearly visible Golgi zone, and a large number of mitochondria (fig. 1-7A). The first noticeable change occurs in the Golgi zone, where a densely staining area, the *acrosomic granule*, becomes visible (fig. 1-7B).[36] This granule subsequently gives rise to a thin membrane which spreads over the surface of the nucleus, forming the so-called *head cap* (fig. 1-7C). With time, the head cap extends over half the nuclear surface, while the remaining portion of the Golgi zone moves to the other side of the cell (fig. 1-7D, E, F).[37]

The centrioles meanwhile migrate to the pole of the nucleus opposite the head cap and give rise to the *flagellum* or *axial filament*, which later forms the body and tail of the spermatozoon. The nucleus itself is displaced within the cytoplasm, becomes condensed, and assumes a slightly flattened, elongated shape (fig. 1-7E, F).

Simultaneously, the mitochondria move toward the flagellum, where they become arranged in collar-like fashion around the filament (fig. 1-7F, G, H). Distally, this mitochondrial collar is bounded by a ring-like structure and, together with the centriole, they form the *middle piece* of the spermatozoon. At the end of spermiogenesis the cytoplasm and the Golgi material not utilized in the formation of the spermatozoon are cast off.

When fully formed, the spermatozoa leave the Sertoli cells and enter the lumen of the seminiferous tubules. From here, they are pushed toward the epididymis, possibly under the influence of contractile

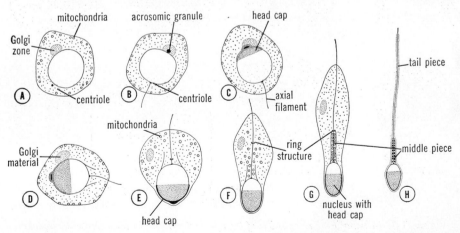

Figure 1-7. *Schematic drawings showing the successive stages in the transformation of the human spermatid into the spermatozoon (derived from Clermont and Leblond).*

       General Embryology

elements in the wall of the seminiferous tubules.[38] Though initially only slightly motile, the spermatozoa obtain full motility in the epididymis.[39]

Meiosis

The human somatic cell contains 46 chromosomes, of which 44 are known as autosomes, and two as sex chromosomes.[40-42] In the female, the latter are represented by two X chromosomes, and in the male, by one X and a much shorter Y chromosome. Close examination reveals that the 46 chromosomes are arranged in 23 pairs, the members of each pair, the *homologs*, being morphologically identical, with the exception of the X-Y pair in the male. Hence the human somatic cell contains 23 pairs, or a diploid (*diplous*, double) number of chromosomes.

Like the somatic cells, the oogonia and spermatogonia contain 46 chromosomes. When they divide to give rise to the primary oocytes and spermatocytes, each chromosome forms a replica of itself and appears double-stranded. One strand goes to each daughter cell, which thus receives the same number of chromosomes as the mother cell, that is, 46. Such a division is a typical *mitotic division*.

When subsequently the primary oocytes and spermatocytes divide to give rise to secondary oocytes and spermatocytes, the division of the chromosomes is quite different. Each of the newly formed daughter cells now receives only 23 chromosomes, that is, the haploid (*haplous*, single) number. This type of division is known as *meiosis* or *reduction division*.

Meiosis is divided into several phases which correspond to those of mitosis, except that in a meiotic division the prophase is considerably extended and subdivided into a number of stages. In the first or *leptotene stage*, the 46 chromosomes appear as single, slender threads. In the second or *zygotene stage*, the homologous chromosomes approach each other and become paired longitudinally so that only 23 components, called *bivalents*, are visible (*synapsis*) (fig. 1-8A). In the third or *pachytene stage*, each chromosome becomes double-stranded, except at the centromere, which does not divide (fig. 1-8B). At this stage the chromosomal strands frequently break and recombine with strands from the homologous chromosome. In the next or *diplotene stage*, the homologous strands separate, but when recombination has occurred the diplotene structure has an X appearance known as *chiasma* (fig. 1-8C). In the metaphase the bivalents become orientated on the spindle, and when the cell divides the members of each pair move toward opposite poles (fig. 1-8D). Hence, after the first meiotic division, each daughter cell contains a haploid number of chromosomes,

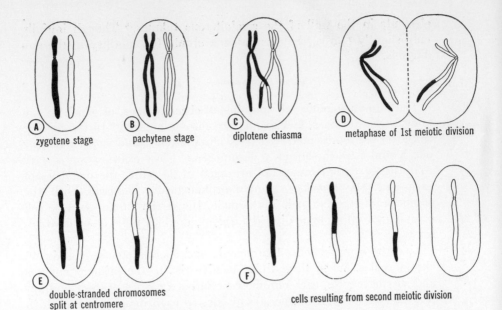

Figure 1-8. *Schematic representation showing the fate of two homologous chromosomes during the first and second meiotic divisions. A, The chromosomes approach each other closely (zygotene stage). B, The chromosomes become double-stranded (pachytene stage). C, Recombination of homologous strands (diplotene chiasma). D, Metaphase of the first meiotic division, in which each of the double-stranded homologous chromosomes moves to an opposite pole. E, The double-stranded chromosomes in each of the newly formed cells divide at the centromere. F, Completion of the second meiotic division, resulting in four new cells; note that the chromatids in each of the four cells are different from each other.*

each of which is double-stranded except at the centromere, which is single.

In case of the primary oocyte, which contains 44 plus 2 X chromosomes, this means that each daughter cell receives 22 plus 1 X chromosomes (fig. 1-9). In case of a primary spermatocyte, it means that one secondary spermatocyte receives 22 plus X chromosomes, and the other 22 plus Y chromosomes.

When subsequently the secondary oocytes and spermatocytes divide, each of the 23 double-stranded chromosomes divides at the centromere (fig. 1-8E). Hence, each of the newly formed daughter cells again receives a haploid number of chromosomes (fig. 1-8F and 1-9).

If a mature oocyte containing 22 plus X chromosomes is fertilized by a spermatozoon with a 22 plus X chromosomal complement, the result is the restoration of the diploid number of chromosomes and the embryo will be female. On the other hand, if fertilization is accomplished by a spermatozoon with a 22 plus Y chromosomal complement, the result is a male embryo.

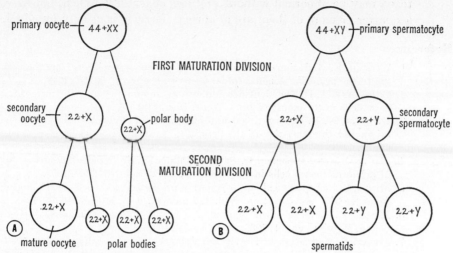

Figure 1-9. *Diagram showing the reduction in the number of chromosomes during the maturation divisions. A, In the female germ cell. B, In the male germ cell.*

Abnormal Gametes

In man as well as in most mammals it happens occasionally that one follicle contains two or three clearly distinguishable primary oocytes (fig. 1-10A).[25] Although they are thought to be a possible source of twin or triplet pregnancies, usually these oocytes degenerate before reaching maturity. Rarely does one primary oocyte contain two or even three nuclei (fig. 1-10B). When they do, however, these bi- or trinucleated oocytes die before reaching maturity.

Contrary to atypical oocytes, abnormal spermatozoa are seen frequently. An anomaly may affect the head or tail of the spermatozoon; they may be giants or dwarfs and sometimes are even joined (fig. 1-10C).[43] There is evidence suggesting that 10 per cent of the sperma-

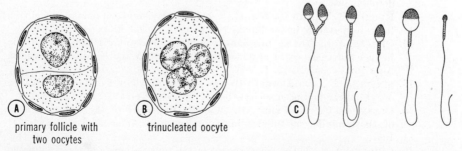

Figure 1-10. *Drawings showing abnormal germ cells in the female and male. A, Primary follicle with two oocytes. B, Trinucleated oocyte. C, Various types of abnormal spermatozoa.*

tozoa may be abnormal without any loss of fertility. When, however, a quarter or more of them are abnormal, fertility is usually impaired.

References

1. WITSCHI, E. Migration of the germ cells of the human embryos from the yolk sac to the primitive gonadal folds. Contrib. Embryol., 32: 67, 1948.
2. CHIQUOINE, A. D. The identification, origin, and migration of the primordial germ cells in the mouse embryo. Anat. Rec., 118: 135, 1954.
3. EVERETT, N. B. Observational and experimental evidences relating to the origin and differentiation of the definitive germ cells in mice. J. Exp. Zool., 92: 49, 1943.
4. MINTZ, B., AND RUSSELL, E. S. Gene induced embryological modificatons of primordial germ cells in the mouse. J. Exp. Zool., 134: 207, 1957.
5. MINTZ, B. Embryological development of primordial germ cells in the mouse; influence of a new mutation, $W\gamma^1$. J. Embryol. Exp. Morph. 5: 396, 1957.
6. MINTZ, B. Embryological phases of mammalian gametogenesis. J. Cell. Comp. Physiol., 56: 31, 1960.
7. MINTZ, B. Formation and early development of germ cells. In *Germ Cells and Development* (Symposium, Inst. Intern. d'Embr.), pp. 1–24. Fondaz. A. Baselli, 1960.
8. McKAY, D. G., HERTIG, A. T., ADAMS, E. C., AND DANZIGER, S. Histochemical observations on the germ cells of human embryos. Anat. Rec., 117: 201, 1953.
9. LATTA, J. S., AND PEDERSEN, E. S. The origin of ova and follicle cells from the germinal epithelium of the ovary of the albino rat as demonstrated by selective staining with Indian ink. Anat. Rec., 90: 23, 1944.
10. STIEVE, H. Die Entwicklung der Keimzellen und der Zwischenzellen in der Hodenanlage des Menschen. Ein Beitrag zur Keimbahnfrage. Z. Mikroskopischanat. Forsch., 10: 253, 1927.
11. ZUCKERMAN, S. The number of oocytes in the mature ovary. Recent Progr. Hormone Res., 6: 63, 1951.
12. BRAMBELL, F. W. R. Ovarian changes. In *Marshall's Physiology of Reproduction*, Ed. 3, edited by A. S. Parkes, Vol. 1, Part 1, p. 397. Longmans, Green and Co., London, 1956.
13. GAILLARD, P. J. Sex cell formation in explants of the foetal human ovarian cortex. I and II. Konink. Ned. Akad. Wetenschap., 53: 1300, 1950.
14. WITSCHI, E. *Development of Vertebrates*, p. 40. W. B. Saunders Co., Philadelphia, 1956.
15. RUDKIN, G. T., AND GRIECH, H. A. On the persistence of oocyte nuclei from fetus to maturity in the laboratory mouse. J. Cell Biol., 12: 169, 1962.
16. OEHLER, J. E. Beitrag zur Kenntnis des Ovarialepithels und seiner Beziehungen zur Oogenese. Untersuchungen an fetalen und Kindlichen Ovarien. Acta Anat. (Basel), 12: 1, 1951.
17. SIRLIN, J. L., AND EDWARD, R. G. Timing of DNA synthesis in ovarian oocyte nuclei and pronuclei of the mouse. Exp. Cell Res., 18: 190, 1959.
18. CLERMONT, Y., AND PEREY, B. Quantitative study of the cell population of the seminiferous tubules in immature rats. Amer. J. Anat., 100: 241, 1957.
19. CHIQUOINE, A. D. The development of the zona pellucida of the mammalian ovum. Amer. J. Anat., 106: 149, 1960.
20. OHNO, S., KLINGER, H. P., AND ATKIN, N. B. Human oogenesis. Cytogenetics, 1: 42, 1962.

General Embryology

21. OHNO, S., MAKINO, S., KAPLAN, W. D., AND KINOSITA, R. Female germ cells in man. Exp. Cell Res., 24: 106, 1961.
22. KEMP, N. E. Protoplasmic bridges between oocytes and follicle cells in vertebrates. Anat. Rec., 139: 324, 1958.
23. SHETTLES, L. G. The nourishment of the human ovum. Bull. Sloane Hosp. Women, 4: 34, 1958.
24. SHETTLES, L. G. Ovum Humanum. Urban and Schwarzenberg, Munich and Berlin, 1960.
25. HAMILTON, W. J. Phases of maturation and fertilization in human ova. J. Anat., 78: 1, 1944.
26. ALLEN, E., ET AL. Human tubal ova; related early corpora lutea and uterine tubes. Contrib. Embryol., 22: 45, 1930.
27. CLERMONT, Y., AND HUCKINS, C. Microscopic anatomy of the sex glands and seminiferous tubules in growing and adult male albino rats. Amer. J. Anat., 108: 79, 1961.
28. MANCINI, R. E., NARBAITZ, R., AND LAVIERI, J. C. Origin and development of the germinative epithelium and Sertoli cells in the human testis; cytological, cytochemical and quantitative study. Anat. Rec., 136: 477, 1960.
29. HARGITT, G. T. The formation of the sex glands and germ cells of mammals. II. The history of the male germ cells in the albino rat. J. Morph., 42: 253, 1926.
30. BOOKHOUT, C. G. The germ cell cycle in the guinea pig. II. The postnatal development of the testis. Z. Zellforsch., 25: 749, 1937.
31. BRYSON, V. Spermatogenesis and fertility in mus musculus as affected by factors at the T locus. J. Morph., 74: 131, 1944.
32. CLERMONT, Y., AND LEBLOND, C. P. Renewal of spermatogonia in the rat. Amer. J. Anat., 93: 475, 1953.
33. CLERMONT, Y., AND LEBLOND, C. P. Differentiation and renewal of spermatogonia in the monkey. Amer. J. Anat., 104: 237, 1959.
34. OAKBERG, E. F. Degeneration of spermatogonia of the mouse following exposure to x-rays, and stages in the mitotic cycle at which cell death occurs. J. Morph., 97: 39, 1955.
35. OAKBERG, E. F. A description of spermiogenesis in the mouse and its use in analysis of the cycle of the seminiferous epithelium and germ cell renewal. Amer. J. Anat., 99: 391, 1956.
36. LEBLOND, C. P., AND CLERMONT, Y. Spermiogenesis of rat, mouse, hamster and guinea pig as revealed by the "periodic acid-fuchsin sulfurous acid" technique. Amer. J. Anat., 90: 167, 1952.
37. CLERMONT, Y., AND LEBLOND, C. P. Spermiogenesis of man, monkey, ram and other mammals as shown by periodic acid-Schiff technique. Amer. J. Anat., 96: 229, 1955.
38. CLERMONT, Y. Contractile elements in the limiting membrane of the seminiferous tubules. Exp. Cell Res., 15: 438, 1958.
39. BLANDAU, R. J., AND RUMERY, R. E. Fertilizing capacity of rat spermatozoa recovered from various segments of the epididymis. Anat. Rec., 139: 209, 1961.
40. FORD, C. E., JACOBS, P. A., AND LAJTHA, L. G. Human somatic chromosomes. Nature (Lond.), 181: 1565, 1958.
41. TJIO, J. H., AND LEVAN, A. The chromosome number in man. Hereditas, 42: 1, 1956.
42. FORD, C. E., AND HAMERTON, J. L. The chromosomes of man. Nature (Lond.), 178: 1020, 1956.
43. HOTCHKISS, R. S. Fertility in Men. J. B. Lippincott Co., Philadelphia, 1944.

CHAPTER 2

First Week of Development (Fertilization to Implantation)

NORMAL DEVELOPMENT
- FERTILIZATION
- CLEAVAGE
- BLASTOCYST FORMATION: *embryoblast, trophoblast, and blastocele*

CHANGES IN THE FEMALE GENITAL TRACT
- OVARIAN CYCLE
- UTERINE CYCLE: *menstrual, follicular, and progestational phases*

ABNORMALITIES
- *Abnormal ova; abnormal implantation sites*

Normal Development

In the days immediately preceding ovulation, the Graafian follicle expands rapidly to a diameter of approximately 15 mm., stretching the overlying surface of the ovary. As the follicular fluid increases further, the overlying surface layer becomes avascular and the follicle ruptures. With the sudden release of tension in the follicle the oocyte is torn from its attachment and together with a number of cumulus oophorus cells— the *corona radiata*—is discharged from the ovary (fig. 2-1*A*).[1, 2]

During ovulation the musculature of the Fallopian tube contracts rhythmically while its vascularized fimbriae sweep over the surface of the ovary. It is believed that the oocyte is caught by the fimbriae almost immediately after being shed from the ovary and that it is drawn into the tube by suction.[3-5] Once in the Fallopian tube, the oocyte is passed along toward the uterine lumen by contractions of the muscular wall and the ciliary beat of the epithelial lining.[6-8] The human oocyte remains viable for approximately 12 to 24 hours and if, during this period, it is not fertilized, degeneration follows rapidly.

Fertilization

Fertilization, that is, fusion of male and female gametes, probably occurs in the ampullary region, or at least in the distal third of the Fallopian tube.[9] Although it has been suggested that in some mammals the oocyte and spermatozoa are attracted to each other by chemical influences, studies *in vitro* have shown that human spermatozoa, though swimming close to the oocyte, may pass by without any apparent attraction.[10, 11] However, once the spermatozoon touches the oocyte, it becomes firmly attached and starts to penetrate the zona pellucida toward the ooplasm. In the human both the head and tail enter the oocyte (fig. 2-1B). Although only one of the 200 to 300 million spermatozoa deposited in the female genital tract is needed for fertilization, it is thought that others aid the fertilizing sperm to penetrate the oocyte by detaching the layer of corona radiata cells by enzymatic action.[12, 13] Some of these have been found embedded in the zona pellucida but do not seem to play a role in fertilization (fig. 2-1B).[14]

As soon as the spermatozoon enters the oocyte, the latter finishes its second maturation division and its chromosomes (22 plus X), arrange themselves in a vesicular nucleus known as the *female pronucleus* (fig. 2-1B).[15] At the same time, the ooplasm shrinks and a *perivitelline space* containing the polar bodies becomes visible.

The spermatozoon meanwhile moves forward until it lies close to the female pronucleus.[14] Its head becomes swollen, forming the so-called *male pronucleus*, which is morphologically indistinguishable from the female pronucleus. The tail meanwhile is detached from the head, and the anterior centriole is transformed into a centrosome which later divides in two, each half moving to opposite poles of the new spindle (fig. 2-1C).

Each pronucleus loses its nuclear membrane and resolves its chromatin into a complete single (haploid) set of chromosomes which become organized on the spindle. The chromosomes then split longitudinally and the resulting halves move to opposite centrosomes, thus restoring to the human somatic cell its full (diploid) number of chromosomes (fig. 2-1D, E). While this occurs a deep furrow appears on the surface of the cell, gradually dividing the cytoplasm in two (fig. 2-1E). Each cell of the newly formed individual, usually referred to as the *zygote*, contains 46 chromosomes, that is, the diploid number.

The main results of fertilization are: (1) restoration of the diploid number of chromosomes; (2) determination of the sex of the zygote (see Chapter 1); and (3) initiation of a series of mitotic divisions known as cleavage divisions.

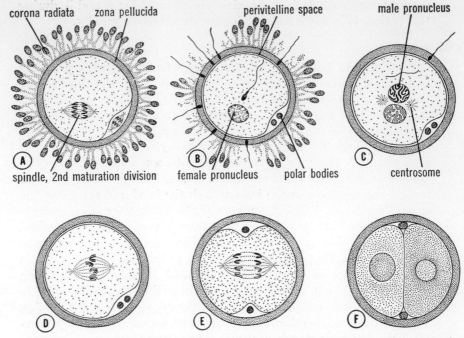

Figure 2-1. *A, Schematic drawing of the oocyte immediately after ovulation, showing the spindle of the second maturation division, the zona pellucida, and the corona radiata (modified after Hamilton). B, A spermatozoon has penetrated the oocyte, which has finished its second maturation division and extruded its second polar body. The chromosomes of the ovum are arranged in a vesicular nucleus, the female pronucleus. The cells of the corona radiata are partly detached and the heads of several spermatozoa are stuck in the zona pellucida. C, Stage of male and female pronuclei. Note the two centrosomes, derived from the anterior centriole. D and E, The chromosomes become organized on the spindle, split longitudinally, and move to opposite centrosomes. F, The two-cell stage; the two blastomeres differ in the size of the nuclei.*

Although it is generally accepted that a female gamete cannot produce an organized embryo without the participation of a male gamete, it has been suggested that the human oocyte may undergo its first cleavage divisions without being fertilized.[16, 17] When this occurs, however, the oocytes are found in the ovary, and as they develop they give rise to an ovarian teratoma.[18]

Cleavage

Once the fertilized oocyte reaches the two-cell stage it undergoes a series of mitotic divisions, resulting in an increase in the number of cells. These cells, which become smaller with each cleavage division, are known as *blastomeres* (fig. 2-2). Only a few human cleavage stages

General Embryology

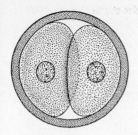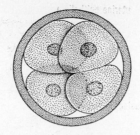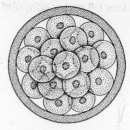

Figure 2-2. *Schematic representation of the development of the zygote from the two-cell stage to the late morula stage. The two-cell stage is reached approximately 30 hours after fertilization; the four-cell stage at approximately 40 hours; the 12- to 16-cell stage at approximately 3 days; and the late morula stage at approximately 4 days. During this period the blastomeres are surrounded by the zona pellucida, which disappears at the end of the fourth day.*

are known. Hertig and co-workers[19] recovered a two-cell stage with two polar bodies and a zona pellucida from the Fallopian tube (fig. 2-1F). Its age is unknown, but experiments *in vitro* have shown that the human zygote reaches the two-cell stage approximately 30 hours after fertilization.[20] This seems to be in accordance with the two-cell stage in the monkey which was recovered from the Fallopian tube 29½ hours after ovulation.[21] At this stage one cell is usually larger and probably divides first, resulting in a three-cell stage. Subsequently, the small cell divides and the zygote then consists of two large and two small cells (fig. 2-2). *In vitro*, the four-cell stage is reached 40 to 50 hours after fertilization.[20]

As cleavage progresses the zygote passes down the Fallopian tube, and when the 12- to 16-cell stage is attained it is called a *morula* (fig. 2-2). The morula consists of a group of centrally located cells, the *inner cell mass*, and a surrounding layer, the *outer cell mass*. Although at this stage of development all the cells of the morula appear similar, from studies on further development it is known that the inner cell mass gives rise to the tissues of the embryo proper, and the outer cell mass forms the trophoblast which later develops into the placenta. The morula is thought to reach the uterine cavity at about the 12- to 16-cell stage, which *in vitro* is reached approximately 60 hours after fertilization. Indeed, a human 12-cell morula, aged 3 days, has been recovered from the uterine cavity.[22]

Blastocyst Formation

While the morula continues to divide, fluid from the uterine cavity passes into the intercellular spaces of the inner cell mass. As the result of a continuous increase of fluid these spaces become confluent, finally forming a single cavity, the *blastocele* (fig. 2-3A). The zona pellucida

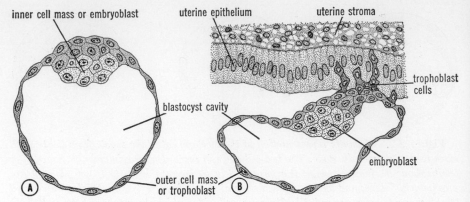

inner cell mass or embryoblast   uterine epithelium   uterine stroma

trophoblast cells

blastocyst cavity

embryoblast

A   outer cell mass or trophoblast   B

Figure 2-3. *A, Schematic representation of a section through a human blastocyst recovered from the uterine cavity at approximately 4½ days. Note the light cells of the inner cell mass or embryoblast, and the dark cells of the outer cell mass or trophoblast (modified after Hertig and Rock). B, Schematic drawing of a section of a Macaque monkey blastocyst at the ninth day of development. The trophoblast cells located at the embryonic pole of the blastocyst begin to penetrate the uterine mucosa (modified after Wislocki and Streeter). The human blastocyst begins to penetrate the uterine mucosa probably by the fifth or sixth day of development.*

has disappeared by this time and the zygote is known as the *blastocyst.* The cells of the inner cell mass, now referred to as the *embryoblast,* stick together and are located on one pole, while those of the outer cell mass, or *trophoblast,* flatten and form the wall of the blastocyst (fig. 2-3A).

Two human blastocysts, consisting of 58 and 107 cells with an estimated age of 4 and 4½ days, respectively, have been recovered from the uterine cavity and, *in vitro,* a well advanced blastocyst has been found approximately 100 to 140 hours after fertilization.[20, 22] The 107-cell blastocyst contained an embryoblast with eight large vacuolated cells, and the remaining 99 belonged to the trophoblast. Of the latter, 69 formed the wall of the blastocele, and 30 were grouped over the embryoblast. Although in the human the early attachment between the blastocyst and the uterine mucosa has not been observed, in all probability this occurs about 5½ to 6 days after ovulation.[22] It is thought that this implantation process is comparable to that in the Macaque monkey, in which the earliest attachment occurs 9 days after ovulation.[23] At this time the trophoblastic cells over the embryoblast pole begin to penetrate between the epithelial cells of the uterine mucosa (fig. 2-3B). It is probable that the penetration and subsequent erosion of the epithelial cells of the mucosa results from proteolytic enzymes produced by the trophoblast. Undoubtedly, however, the uterine mucosa supports the trophoblastic action of the blastocyst, so

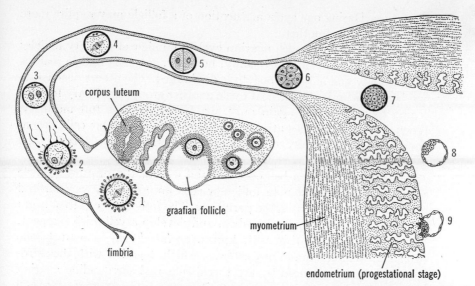

Figure 2-4. *Schematic representation of the events taking place during the first week of human development. (1) Oocyte immediately after ovulation. (2) Fertilization approximately 12 to 24 hours after ovulation. (3) Stage of the male and female pronuclei. (4) Spindle of the first mitotic division during which the diploid number of chromosomes is restored. (5) Two-cell stage (approximately 30 hours old). (6) Morula containing 12 to 16 blastomeres (approximately 3 days old). (7) Advanced morula stage reaching the uterine lumen (approximately 4 days old). (8) Early blastocyst stage (approximately 4½ days old). (9) Early phase of implantation (blastocyst approximately 6 days old). The ovary shows the transformation of a primary follicle into a Graafian follicle as well as a corpus luteum. The uterine endometrium is depicted in the progestational stage.*

that implantation is the result of mutual action.[24] Hence, by the end of the first week of development, the human zygote has passed through the stages of morula and blastocyst formation and has begun its implantation in the uterine mucosa (fig. 2-4).

Changes in the Female Genital Tract

Ovarian Cycle

It is generally accepted that ovulation occurs once in a cycle, although the precise time in any given cycle is variable. At present, there is much evidence indicating that ovulation occurs approximately 14 days ± 1 day before the beginning of the following menstrual bleeding, independent of the length of the menstrual cycle.[25, 26] Although the time between ovulation and the succeeding menstrual bleeding is constant, the time between ovulation and the preceding menstruation is highly variable and depends on the length of time the follicle needs to mature. During one cycle maturation of a follicle may require more time than during another.

At the beginning of each ovarian cycle a number of primary follicles begin to grow and mature. Usually, however, only one follicle reaches full maturity and only one oocyte is discharged. The others degenerate and become atretic. In the next cycle another group of primary follicles begins to mature and again only one follicle reaches full maturity. When a follicle becomes atretic, the oocyte and follicular cells degenerate and are gradually replaced by connective tissue, forming the *corpora atretica.*

As soon as ovulation has occurred the wall of the ruptured follicle collapses and the remaining follicular cells are gradually vascularized by vessels growing in from the periphery. The follicular cells then begin to hypertrophy, become polyhedral, and develop a yellowish pigment. These modified yellowish cells, known as *luteal cells,* constitute the *corpus luteum* and secrete progesterone which, together with the estrogenic hormones produced by the thecal cells and surrounding ovarian tissue, brings the uterine mucosa to its progestational stage (figs. 2-5 and 2-6).[27]

If fertilization fails to occur the corpus luteum reaches maximum development approximately 9 days after ovulation, and is then easily recognized as a yellowish projection on the surface of the ovary, surrounded by a hyperemic area.[28] From then on, the corpus luteum decreases rapidly in size as a result of degeneration of the luteal cells. The progesterone secretion likewise decreases, precipitating the menstrual bleeding. Finally, the corpus luteum is transformed into a mass of fibrotic scar tissue known as *corpus albicans.*

If the ovum is fertilized, the trophoblast secretes a gonadotropic hormone; this prevents the degeneration of the corpus luteum, which continues to grow, forming the *corpus luteum of pregnancy.* By the end of the third month this structure may constitute as much as one-third to one-half of the total size of the ovary. The luteal cells continue to secrete progesterone until the end of the fourth month, but thereafter regress slowly. Whether during this period new luteal cells are added to the periphery by differentiation of the surrounding stroma cells or by active division of the existing luteal cells is unknown. Removal of the corpus luteum of pregnancy before the fourth month usually results in abortion.[29]

Uterine Cycle

Whereas the rhythmic changes in the ovary constitute the ovarian cycle, those in the uterus, involving mainly the mucosa or *endometrium,* are known as the *uterine cycle.* Since this cycle terminates in a phase of hemorrhagic destruction of the endometrium, *menses* or *menstruation,*

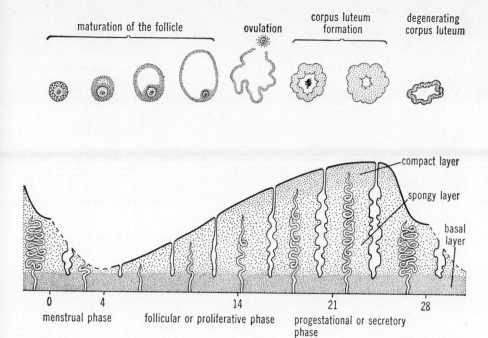

Figure 2-5. *Schematic representation of the changes taking place in the uterine mucosa correlated with those in the ovary.*

it is also called the *menstrual cycle*. This cycle is divided into several phases and the first day of bleeding is taken as the first day of the cycle.

Menstrual Phase

This phase is probably induced by a temporary constriction of the spiral arteries in the endometrium, resulting in ischemia of the superficial layers.[30, 31] When later these arteries dilate, blood escapes from their damaged superficial branches into the intercellular spaces beneath the surface epithelium, and small fragments of stroma and broken glands are lifted off. During the following 3 or 4 days, the endometrium is shed down to the basal layer and is expelled from the uterus in small pieces (fig. 2-5). By the end of the menstrual phase the endometrium may be reduced to one-fifth or one-tenth its maximum thickness. The discharge, consisting of blood, epithelial cells, and detritus resulting from degeneration of the stroma does not normally clot because of proteolytic enzymes which destroy the proteins needed for blood coagulation. Experimental evidence obtained chiefly from monkeys has shown that the menstrual bleeding is caused by the withdrawal or decrease of the progestational and estrogenic hormones. The average amount of blood lost is 50 to 60 cc.

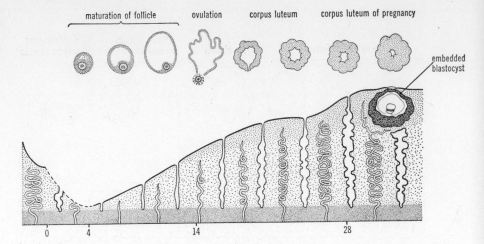

maturation of follicle ovulation corpus luteum corpus luteum of pregnancy

embedded blastocyst

0 4 14 28

Figure 2-6. *Schematic representation of the changes taking place in the uterine mucosa in case of fertilization. The secretory activity of the endometrium is increased considerably as a result of the large amounts of progesterone produced by the corpus luteum of pregnancy. Note the spiral arteries and the large, dilated uterine glands.*

Follicular Phase

This phase, also referred to as the *proliferative phase*, is characterized by the repair and subsequent growth of the endometrium and corresponds to the follicular phase of the ovarian cycle on which the menstrual cycle depends (figs. 2-5 and 2-6). During the first few days of this phase epithelial cells from the stumps of the glands spread over the denuded endometrial stroma, and by the fifth or sixth day the endometrial surface is usually re-epithelialized. Meanwhile, the cells in the basal layer of the endometrium begin to multiply, circulation is reestablished, and the glands become simple and straight, leading from the basal layer to the surface of the endometrium. During the later stages of the follicular phase all parts of the endometrium show active growth and the surface epithelium becomes columnar. The epithelial cells making up the lining of the glands show some serous secretion while the glands acquire a corkscrew appearance. A dense superficial layer (the *compact layer*), an intermediate, loosely arranged layer (the *spongy layer*), and a deep layer (the *basal layer*) can now be recognized in the endometrium (fig. 2-5). All the above-mentioned changes of the endometrium are attributed to the estrogenic hormones which produce their maximum effect until ovulation occurs.

Progestational Phase

The progestational phase, also known as the *secretory phase*, is caused by the action of progesterone produced by the corpus luteum and a

General Embryology

simultaneous increase in the amount of estrogenic hormones. The first signs of this hormonal action are clearly recognizable 2 or 3 days after ovulation. The endometrium reaches its maximum thickness, which varies from 5 to 7 mm. at approximately day 21 of the menstrual cycle.

During this phase the epithelial cells lining the glands show active secretion and discharge their products, including mucin and glycogen, into the lumen. Like the glands, the arteries become very tortuous and are known as *spiral arteries*. The endometrium itself becomes highly edematous and is usually pale in color as a result of the accumulation of intercellular fluid. During the last 2 or 3 days before the onset of menstruation, the endometrial intercellular edema is reabsorbed, with a resultant decrease in the thickness of the endometrium. The glands are greatly dilated and filled with secretion products and cellular debris, while the venules and sinusoidal spaces are packed with blood cells. With impending menstruation an extensive diapedesis of red and white blood cells into the stroma is seen.

If, however, the oocyte is fertilized the secretory activity of the endometrium increases considerably as a result of the large amounts of progesterone produced by the corpus luteum of pregnancy (fig. 2-6). The uterine mucosa is then ready to receive the blastocyst.

Abnormalities

Abnormal Ova

Abnormal zygotes of the pre-implantation stage have been described by a number of authors.[20, 32] Of a total of eight zygotes recovered by Hertig et al.[22] from the uterine tube, four appeared to be normal, whereas the other four were definitely abnormal. The abnormal zygotes, which varied from 3 to 5 days of age, showed multinucleated blastomeres and, in addition, some showed variable degrees of cellular degeneration. Although it is doubtful that these zygotes were able to implant, all four were recovered from patients of normal fertility.

Abnormal Implantation Sites

The human blastocyst normally implants in the endometrium along the posterior wall of the body of the uterus, where it becomes attached between the openings of the endometrial glands or occasionally in the mouth of one of the glandular ducts.

Not infrequently, however, the blastocyst implants in abnormal locations outside the body of the uterus, and when this occurs it usually leads to the death of the embryo and severe hemorrhage of the mother during the second month of pregnancy. Implantation of the blastocyst outside the uterus is known as *extra-uterine* or *ectopic pregnancy* and may occur at any place in the abdominal cavity, ovary, or Fallopian

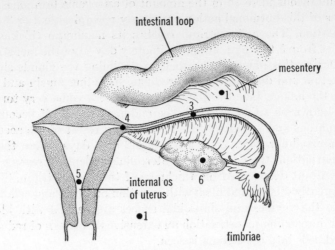

Figure 2-7. *Drawing to show the abnormal implantation sites of the ovum.* (*1*) *Implantation in the abdominal cavity. The ovum most frequently implants in the Douglas' pouch, but may implant at any place covered by peritoneum.* (*2*) *Implantation in the ampullary region of the tube.* (*3*) *Tubal implantation.* (*4*) *Interstitial implantation, that is, in the narrow portion of the uterine tube.* (*5*) *Implantation in the region of the internal os, frequently resulting in placenta praevia.* (*6*) *Ovarian implantation* (*modified after Hamilton, Boyd, and Mossman*).

tube (fig. 2-7). In the abdominal cavity the blastocyst most frequently attaches itself to the peritoneal lining of the recto-uterine cavity (Douglas' pouch), demonstrating that the blastocyst does not necessarily need the progestational endometrium for implantation. The blastocyst also may implant in the peritoneal covering of the intestinal tract or in the omentum. Rarely does an extra-uterine embryo come to full term.

Sometimes the blastocyst develops in the ovary proper (*primary ovarian pregnancy*), or in the Fallopian tube (*tubal pregnancy*), one of the most common sites of ectopic pregnancies. In the latter case, the tube ruptures at about the second month of pregnancy and a severe internal hemorrhage of the mother results.

Occasionally implantation in the uterus itself may lead to serious complications. This is particularly so when the blastocyst implants close to the internal os. The placenta then overbridges the os (*placenta praevia*), and causes severe bleeding in the latter part of pregnancy and during delivery.

References

1. ELERT, R. Der Mechanismus der Eiabnahme im Laparoskop. Zbl. Gynaek., 69: 38, 1947.

2. Markee, J. E., and Hinsey, J. C. Observations on ovulation in the rabbit. Anat. Rec., **64**: 309, 1936.

3. Westmann, A. Investigations into the transit of ova in man. J. Obstet. Gynaec. Brit. Emp., **44**: 821, 1937.

4. Decker, A. Culdoscopic observations on the tubo-ovarian mechanism of ovum reception. Fertil. Steril., **2**: 253, 1951.

5. Doyle, J. B. Tubo-ovarian mechanism: observation at laparotomy. Obstet. Gynec. **8**: 686, 1956.

6. Black, D. L., and Asdell, S. A. Transport through the rabbit oviduct. Amer. J. Physiol., **192**: 63, 1958.

7. Harper, M. J. K., Bennett, J. P., Boursnell, J. C., and Rowson, L. E. A. An autoradiographic method for the study of egg transport in the rabbit Fallopian tube. J. Reprod. Fertil., **1**: 249, 1960.

8. Pincus, G., and Saunders, B. Unfertilized human tubal ova. Anat. Rec., **69**: 163, 1937.

9. Hamilton, W. J. Phases of maturation and fertilization in human ova. J. Anat., **78**: 1, 1944.

10. Austin, C. R. Fertilization and development of the egg. In *Reproduction in Domestic Animals*, edited by H. H. Cole and P. T. Cupps, Vol. 1. Academic Press, Inc., New York, 1959.

11. Tyler, A. Gametogenesis, fertilization and parthenogenesis. In *Analysis of Development*, edited by B. H. Willier, P. A. Weiss, and V. Hamburger. W. B. Saunders Co., Philadelphia, 1955.

12. Pincus, G. *The Eggs of Mammals*. The Macmillan Co., New York, 1936.

13. Bishop, D. W., and Tyler, A. Fertilization in mammalian eggs. J. Exp. Zool., **132**: 575, 1956.

14. Shettles, L. B. The living human ovum. Obstet. Gynec. (N. Y.), **10**: 359, 1957.

15. Hamilton, W. J. Early stages of human development. Ann. Roy. Coll. Surg. Engl., **4**: 281, 1949.

16. Balfour-Lynn, S. Parthenogenesis in human beings. Lancet, **1**: 1071, 1956.

17. Beatty, R. A. *Parthenogenesis and Polyploidy in Mammalian Development*. Cambridge University Press, London, 1957.

18. Simard, L. C. Polyembryonic embryoma of the ovary of parthenogenetic origin. Cancer, **10**: 215, 1957.

19. Hertig, A. T., Adams, E. C., and Mulligan, W. J. On the pre-implantation stages of the human ovum; a description of four normal and four abnorma specimens ranging from the second to the fifth day of development. Contrib. Embryol., **35**: 199, 1954.

20. Shettles, L. B. *Ovum Humanum*, Hafner Publishing Co., New York, 1960.

21. Lewis, W. H., and Hartman, C. G. Early cleavage stages of the egg of the monkey (*Macacus rhesus*). Contrib. Embryol., **24**: 187, 1933.

22. Hertig, A. T., Rock, J., and Adams, E. C. A description of 34 human ova within the first 17 days of development. Amer. J. Anat., **98**: 435, 1956.

23. Heuser, C. H., and Streeter, G. L. Development of the Macaque embryo. Contrib. Embryol., **29**: 15, 1941.

24. Fawsett, D. W., Wislocki, G. B., and Waldo, C. M. The development of the mouse ova in the anterior chamber of the eye and in the abdominal cavity. Amer. J. Anat., **81**: 413, 1947.

25. Farris, E. J. *Human Ovulation and Fertility*. J. B. Lippincott Co., Philadelphia, 1956.

26. Speck, G. The determination of the time of ovulation. Obstet. Gynec. Survey, **14**: 798, 1959.

27. DEMPSEY, E. W., AND BASSETT, D. L. Observations on fluorescence, bire-fringence and histochemistry of rat ovary during the reproductive cycle. Endocrinology, **33**: 384, 1943.

28. WHITE, R. F., HERTIG, A. T., ROCK, J., AND ADAMS, E. Histological and his-tochemical observations on the corpus luteum of human pregnancy, with special reference to corpora lutea associated with early normal and abnormal ova. Contrib. Embryol., **34**: 55, 1951.

29. AMOROSO, E. C. Comparative aspects of the hormonal functions. In *The Placenta and Fetal Membranes*, edited by C. A. Villee. The Williams & Wilkins Co., Baltimore, 1959.

30. BARTELMEZ, G. W. Premenstrual and menstrual ischemia and the myth of endometrial arteriovenous anastomoses. Amer. J. Anat., **98**: 69, 1956.

31. MARKEE, J. E. Morphological basis for menstrual bleeding. Bull. N. Y. Acad. Med., **24**: 253, 1948.

32. SHETTLES, L. B. The ovum in infertility, abortion, and developmental anomaly. Fertil. Steril., **7**: 561, 1956.

Second and Third Weeks of Development (Bilaminar and Trilaminar Germ Discs)

NORMAL DEVELOPMENT IN THE SECOND WEEK

- **EIGHTH DAY OF DEVELOPMENT:** *trophoblast—cytotrophoblast and syncytiotrophoblast; embryoblast—formation of entodermal and ectodermal germ layers (bilaminar germ disc)*
- **NINTH DAY OF DEVELOPMENT:** *lacunar stage of trophoblast development; formation of primitive yolk sac or exocoelomic cavity*
- **ELEVENTH TO TWELFTH DAYS OF DEVELOPMENT:** *trabecular stage of trophoblast development; beginning uterotrophoblastic circulation; formation of extra-embryonic coelom and extra-embryonic mesoderm*
- **THIRTEENTH DAY OF DEVELOPMENT:** *formation of primary stem villi; formation of secondary yolk sac*

NORMAL DEVELOPMENT IN THE THIRD WEEK

- **FORMATION OF THE TRILAMINAR GERM DISC:** *formation of the notochord and mesodermal germ layer*
- **FURTHER DEVELOPMENT OF THE TROPHOBLAST:** *formation of secondary stem villi*

ABNORMALITIES

During the second and third weeks of development the blastocyst becomes firmly embedded in the uterine mucosa, and its two parts, the trophoblast and embryoblast, each differentiate in their own manner. The cells of the *trophoblast* penetrate deep into the endometrium and give rise to the future *placenta*; those of the embryoblast give rise to the *ectodermal, entodermal,* and *mesodermal germ layers,* the three basic layers of the embryo proper. In this chapter a description is given of the major events in the development of the trophoblast and embryoblast. It must be kept in mind, however, that embryos of the same fertilization age do not necessarily develop at the same rate; therefore considerable difference in their rates of growth may be found.

Normal Development in the Second Week

Eighth Day of Development

By about the eighth day of development the blastocyst is partially embedded in the endometrial stroma (fig. 3-1).[1] At the embryonic pole of the blastocyst, that is, the area over the embryoblast, the trophoblast forms a solid disc composed of an inner layer of pale, discrete, mononucleated cells, the *cytotrophoblast*, and an outer, multinucleated, darker zone without distinct cell boundaries, the *syncytiotrophoblast* or *syncytium* (fig. 3-1). At the opposite or abembryonic pole, the trophoblast remains undifferentiated temporarily, forming a thin mesothelial membrane (fig. 3-1). Abundant mitoses are usually found in the cytotrophoblast but never in the syncytium, yet the thickness of the latter increases considerably, suggesting that it is most probably derived from the cytotrophoblast.[2] The endometrial stroma adjacent to the implantation site is edematous and highly vascular and its large tortuous glands secrete glycogen and mucus.

The cells of the embryoblast differentiate into two distinct cell layers: (1) a layer of small, flattened, polyhedral cells which delaminate from the surface facing the lumen and is known as the *entodermal*

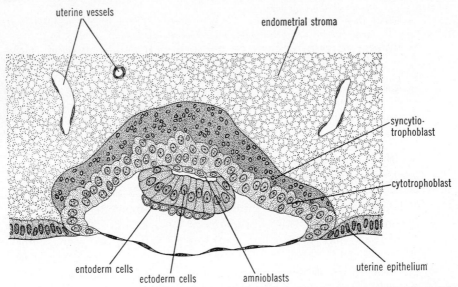

Figure 3-1. *Schematic drawing of a 7½-day human blastocyst partially implanted in the endometrial stroma (modified after Hertig and Rock). The trophoblast is composed of an inner layer with pale mononuclear cells, the cytotrophoblast, and an outer layer without distinct cell boundaries, the syncytiotrophoblast. The embryoblast is composed of the ectodermal and entodermal germ layers; the amniotic cavity appears as a small cleft. Note the mesothelial membrane forming the original lining of the blastocyst cavity.*

germ layer; and (2) a layer of high columnar cells, the *ectodermal germ layer*, temporarily in contact with the trophoblast. The ectodermal as well as the entodermal cells appear as a disc and together form the so-called *bilaminar germ disc*.

The ectodermal cells are initially attached to the proliferating cytotrophoblast, but with further development small intercellular clefts appear between the two layers; when these coalesce, they give rise to the *amniotic cavity*. Along the trophoblastic border of this newly formed cavity are large, flattened cells, the *amnioblasts*, presumably derived from the trophoblast; the floor of the cavity is formed by the ectodermal germ disc. The junction of the two is known as the *amnio-ectodermal junction* (fig. 3-1).

Ninth Day of Development

By the ninth day of development the blastocyst is more deeply embedded in the endometrium, and the penetration defect in the surface epithelium is closed by a fibrin coagulum.[1] The trophoblast, which now surrounds the blastocyst completely, shows further differentiation, particularly at its embryonic pole. Isolated intracytoplasmic vacuoles appear in the outer layer of the syncytium, and when these vacuoles fuse they give rise to large lacunae (fig. 3-2). Hence this phase of trophoblast development is known as the *lacunar stage*. The endometrial stroma surrounding the trophoblast shows vascular congestion, and its cells are rich in glycogen.

At the abembryonic pole, meanwhile, flat mesothelial cells delaminate from the inner surface of the cytotrophoblast and form a thin membrane, known as *Heuser's membrane* (fig. 3-2). This membrane is continuous with the edges of the entoderm and together they form the lining of the *exocoelomic cavity* or *primitive yolk sac*. Although most authors accept that the cells of Heuser's membrane are of cytotrophoblastic origin, others suggest that, as in the Macaque monkey, this membrane is formed by migration of the primitive entoderm cells.[3-5] Whatever their origin, it is evident that the lining of the exocoelomic cavity is composed of two different cell types: a roof of polyhedral cells from the entodermal germ disc and the remainder of flattened cells from Heuser's membrane.

The germ disc has a simple bilaminar appearance and is composed of columnar ectodermal cells and a layer of polyhedral entodermal cells with large nuclei. Compared to the 7½-day blastocyst the amniotic cavity is much larger and new amnioblasts are continuously derived from the adjacent cytotrophoblast.

Eleventh to Twelfth Days of Development

By the 11th to 12th day of development the blastocyst is completely embedded in the endometrial stroma, and the surrounding surface

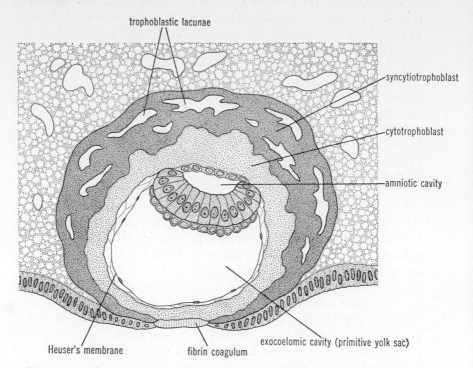

trophoblastic lacunae

syncytiotrophoblast

cytotrophoblast

amniotic cavity

Heuser's membrane

fibrin coagulum

exocoelomic cavity (primitive yolk sac)

Figure 3-2. *Schematic drawing of a 9-day human blastocyst (modified after Hertig and Rock). The syncytiotrophoblast shows a large number of intracytoplasmic lacunae (lacunar stage in trophoblast formation). Note the flat mesothelial cells which have delaminated from the inner surface of the cytotrophoblast to form Heuser's membrane. The bilaminar germ disc consists of a layer of high columnar ectodermal cells and a layer of small polyhedral entodermal cells. The amniotic cavity is well delineated. The original surface defect is closed by a fibrin coagulum.*

epithelium begins to cover the original defect in the epithelial lining of the uterine mucosa. The blastocyst lies in the stratum compactum and produces a slight swelling on the inner surface of the uterus.

The organization of the trophoblast has made considerable progress in comparison to the 9-day stage, and the lacunar spaces in the syncytium form an intercommunicating network. This is particularly evident at the embryonic pole, where the syncytium assumes a trabecular appearance (*trabecular stage*); at the abembryonic pole close to the uterine lumen, however, the trophoblast consists mainly of cytotrophoblastic cells and does not yet have many lacunar spaces (fig. 3-3).

Around the implantation site the maternal capillaries are congested and dilated and begin to form scattered capillary sinusoids. These sinusoids originate from anastomoses between the spiral arterioles and

General Embryology

endometrial veins. It is thought that the trophoblast produces a substance capable of dilating blood vessels, thus aiding in the formation of the sinusoids.[6-8]

In the meantime the syncytial cells penetrate deeper into the stroma and begin to erode the endothelial lining of the maternal sinusoids. The syncytium then becomes continuous with the remaining endothelial cells of the vessels, and maternal blood enters the lacunar system, establishing the future *uteroplacental circulation* (fig. 3-3). As the trophoblast continues to invade the stroma, more and more sinusoids are invaded and eventually the lacunae become continuous with the

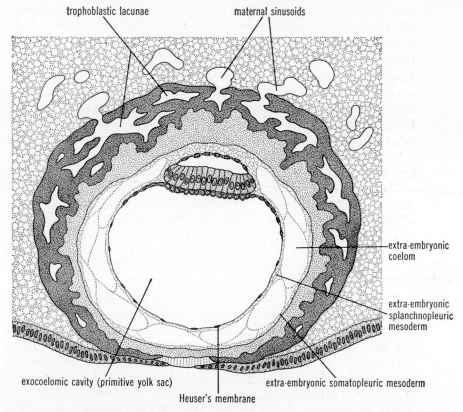

Figure 3-3. *Schematic drawing of a human blastocyst of approximately 12 days (modified after Hertig and Rock). The trophoblastic lacunae at the embryonic pole are in open connection with the maternal sinusoids in the endometrial stroma. The trophoblast at the abembryonic pole shows little differentiation. Cells continue to delaminate from the cytotrophoblast to form the extra-embryonic mesoderm, which lines the inner aspect of the trophoblast (extra-embryonic somatopleuric mesoderm), and the primitive yolk sac (extra-embryonic splanchnopleuric mesoderm). Note the spread of entodermal cells over the inside of Heuser's membrane.*

Second and Third Weeks of Development

arterial and venous capillaries. As a result of the difference in pressure between the arterial and venous capillaries, maternal blood begins to flow through the trophoblastic lacunar system.

The stroma cells, meanwhile, become polyhedral and loaded with glycogen and lipids; the intercellular spaces become edematous and filled with extravasate. This transformation, known as the *decidual reaction*, is at first confined to the area immediately surrounding the implantation site but soon spreads throughout the endometrium.

Differentiation of the trophoblast is not only restricted to the syncytial portion but also involves the cytotrophoblast. On the inner surface of this layer, cells continue to delaminate, thereby forming a fine, loose network. This tissue, known as the *extra-embryonic mesoderm*, fills the expanding space between the trophoblast externally and the amnion and primitive yolk sac internally (fig. 3-3). Soon, large cavities develop in this tissue and when these subsequently become confluent, a new space, known as the *extra-embryonic coelom*, is formed. This cavity surrounds the blastocyst except where the extra-embryonic mesoderm forms the future connection, the *connecting stalk*, between the germ disc and the trophoblast (figs. 3-3 and 3-4). The extra-embryonic mesoderm lining the cytotrophoblast and amnion is called the *extra-embryonic somatopleuric mesoderm*; that covering the yolk sac is known as the *extra-embryonic splanchnopleuric mesoderm*.

The growth of the bilaminar germ disc is relatively slow compared to that of the trophoblast, but by about the end of the 12th day cells originating in the entodermal germ disc begin to spread over the inside of Heuser's membrane which lines the exocoelomic cavity or primitive yolk sac (fig. 3-3).

Thirteenth Day of Development

By the 13th day of development the epithelial surface defect has usually healed. Occasionally, however, bleeding may occur at the implantation site as a result of increased blood flow into the lacunar spaces at the abembryonic pole. Since this bleeding occurs at about the 28th day of the menstrual cycle, it may be confused with normal menstrual bleeding and so cause an inaccuracy in the determination of the expected delivery date.

The trophoblast shows further organization, particularly at the embryonic pole. The lacunae and syncytial trabeculae, arranged irregularly at first, now become orientated in such a manner that they radiate out from the cytotrophoblast (figs. 3-4 and 3-10). The cytotrophoblastic cells project into the syncytial trabeculae, which are then known as the *primary stem villi*. These newly formed structures have a cytotrophoblastic core covered with syncytium and are surrounded by lacunae (figs. 3-4 and 3-10).

General Embryology

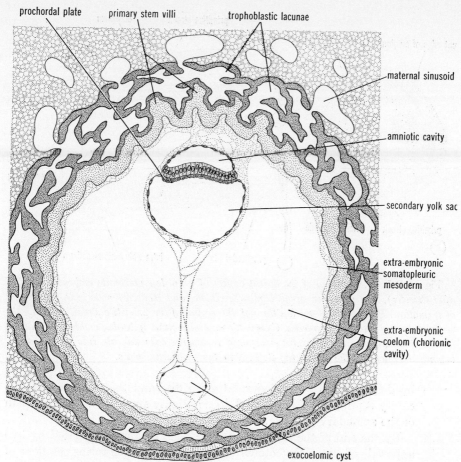

prochordal plate   primary stem villi   trophoblastic lacunae

maternal sinusoid

amniotic cavity

secondary yolk sac

extra-embryonic somatopleuric mesoderm

extra-embryonic coelom (chorionic cavity)

exocoelomic cyst

Figure 3-4. *Schematic drawing of a 13-day human blastocyst completely embedded in the endometrium (modified after Hertig and Rock). The trophoblastic lacunae are now present at the embryonic as well as at the abembryonic pole, and the uteroplacental circulation has begun. Note the formation of the primary stem villi and the extra-embryonic coelom. The secondary yolk sac is entirely lined with entoderm and the exocoelomic cyst in the extra-embryonic coelom forms a remnant of the primitive yolk sac or exocoelomic cavity.*

The entodermal germ layer, which in the 12-day blastocyst started to form a layer of flat epithelial cells along the inside of Heuser's membrane, continues to proliferate and gradually lines a new cavity known as the *secondary yolk sac* (fig. 3-4). This yolk sac is much smaller than the original exocoelomic cavity or primitive yolk sac and it is believed that during its formation large portions of the exocoelomic cavity are pinched off. These portions are represented by so-called *exocoelomic cysts*, often found in the extra-embryonic coelomic cavity (fig. 3-4).[9] Other authors, however, believe that the secondary yolk sac develops

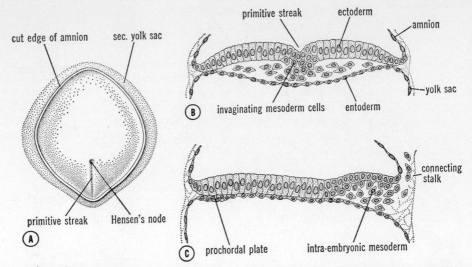

Figure 3-5. *A, Drawing of the dorsal aspect of a 16-day presomite embryo (modified after Streeter). The primitive streak is clearly visible, and Hensen's node is in the process of formation. B, Transverse section through the region of the primitive streak, showing the invagination of the mesoderm cells. C, cephalo-caudal section of 16-day embryo just lateral to the primitive streak. The intra-embryonic mesoderm cells migrate into the extra-embryonic mesoderm of the connecting stalk. Note the prochordal plate.*

by dehiscence of the entodermal germ disc and that the exocoelomic cavity is pinched off *in toto* and does not play any role in the formation of the secondary yolk sac.[10, 11]

By the end of the second week the germ disc is represented by two apposed cell discs: the ectodermal germ layer which forms the floor of the continuously expanding amniotic cavity, and the entodermal germ layer which forms the roof of the secondary yolk sac. In its cephalic region the entodermal disc shows a slight thickening known as the *prochordal plate*. This is a localized area in the mid-cephalic region of the embryonic disc and consists of columnar cells closely connected to the overlying ectodermal disc (figs. 3-4 and 3-5C). Its appearance confers a bilateral symmetry on the embryonic disc by establishing a cephalo-caudal axis.

Normal Development in the Third Week

Formation of the Trilaminar Germ Disc

The next important phase in the development of the germ disc is the formation of the third or *mesodermal germ layer*. At the end of the second week, and becoming more evident by the beginning of the third week, ectodermal cells in the caudal region of the germ disc become spherical, begin to proliferate, and migrate toward the midline. These changes result in the formation of the *primitive streak*, which is clearly visible in a 15- to 16-day embryo and is characterized by a narrow groove with slightly bulging regions on either side (fig. 3-5*A*, *B*). On the basis of findings in the lower vertebrates, it is believed that in the human embryo also, the modified ectodermal cells move toward and invaginate in the region of the primitive streak, and from there migrate between the ectodermal and entodermal germ layers (fig. 3-5*B*).[12, 13] The newly formed intermediate cell layer is known as the *mesodermal germ layer* and is the last embryonic layer to develop.

As more and more surface cells are added to the mesodermal germ layer, the latter begins to spread laterally until eventually it becomes continuous with the extra-embryonic mesoderm covering the amnion and secondary yolk sac (fig 3-5*B*). In addition, the mesoderm cells migrate in cephalic direction on each side of the midline until they meet in the most cephalic part of the germ disc in front of the prochordal plate (fig. 3-6). The midline region extending between the primitive streak and prochordal plate, however, is not occupied by intra-embryonic mesoderm but by the *notochordal process* (fig. 3-6).

During the lateral and forward migration of the intra-embryonic

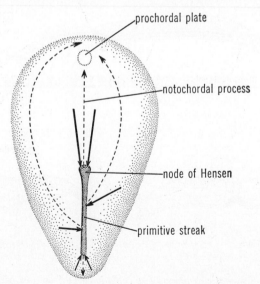

prochordal plate

notochordal process

node of Hensen

primitive streak

Figure 3-6. *Schematic representation of the dorsal aspect of the germ disc, indicating the movement of the surface cells toward the primitive streak and node of Hensen (solid arrows), and their subsequent migration between the entodermal and ectodermal germ layers (broken arrows). The notochordal process occupies the midline region from the prochordal plate to the node of Hensen.*

mesoderm, the cephalic end of the primitive streak shows a marked thickening, known as *Hensen's node* (figs. 3-5 and 3-8). It consists of the small, central, *primitive pit* at the cephalic end of the primitive streak and is surrounded by a slightly elevated area. The primitive pit is believed to be caused by the invagination of surface cells which then migrate along the midline in cephalic direction until they reach the prochordal plate (figs. 3-6 and 3-7*A*). In this plate the ectoderm and entoderm layers are so tightly adherent that the forward-migrating cells are unable to separate them. In 17-day embryos the newly formed midline structure, extending from the node of Hensen to the prochordal plate, is clearly distinguishable and is known as the *notochordal* or *head process*. It contains a small, central canal considered as the forward extension of the primitive pit.

By the 18th day of development the notochordal process fuses with the underlying entoderm and subsequently, beginning in the cephalic region, the notochordal-entodermal plate disappears (fig. 3-7*A, B*). Thus the lumen of the notochordal process is connected to the yolk sac cavity, and since the former is in open connection with the amniotic cavity in the region of Hensen's node, a temporary canal, the *neurenteric canal*, connects the yolk sac and amniotic cavities. The notochordal process then forms a narrow plate of cells, intercalated in

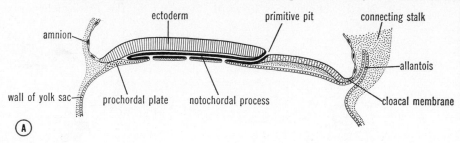

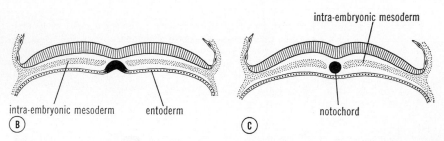

Figure 3-7. *A, Schematic drawing of a cephalo-caudal section of an 18-day embryo, showing the notochordal process extending from the primitive pit to the prochordal plate and fused with the entoderm. The notochordal-entodermal plate gradually disappears and the remaining part of the notochord then is intercalated in the entodermal germ layer (B). C, Transverse section through the cephalic part of a 19-day presomite embryo, showing the definitive notochord flanked by the intra-embryonic mesoderm.*

General Embryology

the entodermal germ layer (fig. 3-7*B*). Soon the notochordal plate folds along a longitudinal axis, thereby forming a solid cord known as the *definitive notochord* (fig. 3-7*C*). While this folding proceeds from the cephalic to the caudal end of the embryo, the entoderm becomes detached and once again forms an uninterrupted layer in the roof of the yolk sac (fig. 3-7*C*).

The entodermal germ layer meanwhile establishes firm contact with the ectoderm in the region immediately behind the primitive streak, and a bilaminar membrane, the *cloacal membrane*, is formed (fig. 3-7*A*). Hence, by the middle of the third week the cephalic part of the embryonic disc is characterized by the *prochordal plate*, which later gives rise to the *buccopharyngeal membrane*, while the caudal part is characterized by the cloacal membrane, which forms the *urogenital* and *anal membranes*. Concomitantly with the formation of the cloacal membrane, the posterior wall of the yolk sac gives rise to a small diverticulum which extends into the connecting stalk. This diverticulum, the *allanto-enteric diverticulum*, or *allantois*, appears by about the 16th day of development (fig. 3-7*A*). Although in some lower vertebrates the allantois becomes a large organ serving as a reservoir for the excretion products of the renal system, it remains rudimentary in man and plays no role in development.

The external appearance of the embryonic disc, initially round or oval-shaped, has become elongated and by the 18th day is pear-shaped, with a broad cephalic and narrow caudal end (fig. 3-8). In comparison to the younger stages it is evident that expansion is taking place particularly in the cephalic region, whereas the region of the primitive streak remains more or less the same size. It must be realized, however, that much of the growth and elongation of the cephalic part of the disc is due to a continuous migration of cells from the primitive streak in cephalic direction. Although after the 19th day of development the primitive streak regresses caudally, invagination of surface cells and subsequent migration of these cells in forward and lateral directions continue until the end of the fourth week. At that stage the primitive streak and node of Hensen show regressive changes and rapidly diminish in size. The fact that the caudal end of the disc continues to supply new cells up to the end of the fourth week has an important bearing on the further development of the different parts of the embryo. In the cephalic part the three germ layers begin their further specific development by the middle of the third week, whereas in the caudal part they continue to segregate up to the end of the fourth week.

Further Development of the Trophoblast

By the beginning of the third week the trophoblast is characterized by a great number of primary stem villi which consist of a cytotropho-

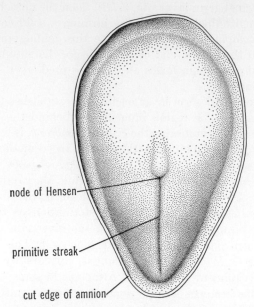

node of Hensen

primitive streak

cut edge of amnion

Figure 3-8. *Schematic drawing of the dorsal aspect of an 18-day presomite embryo (modified after Heuser). The embryo has a pear-shaped appearance and shows at its caudal end the primitive streak and node of Hensen.*

blastic core covered by a syncytial layer (figs. 3-4 and 3-9A). From this time on, mesodermal cells either originating from the extra-embryonic somatopleuric mesoderm or from the cytotrophoblastic cells themselves start to penetrate the core of the villi toward the decidua.[14, 15] The newly formed structure, the *secondary stem villus*, is composed of a loose connective tissue core covered by a layer of cytotro-

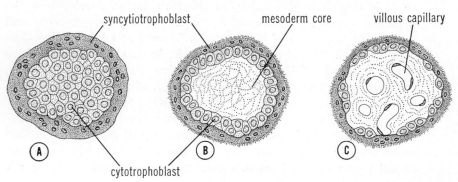

syncytiotrophoblast   mesoderm core   villous capillary

A   B   C

cytotrophoblast

Figure 3-9. *Schematic drawings to show the development of the villus. A, Transverse section of a primary stem villus, showing a core of cytotrophoblastic cells covered by a layer of syncytium. B, Transverse section of a secondary stem villus with a core of mesoderm covered by a single layer of cytotrophoblastic cells, which in turn is covered by syncytium. C, The mesoderm of the secondary villus shows a number of capillaries.*

General Embryology

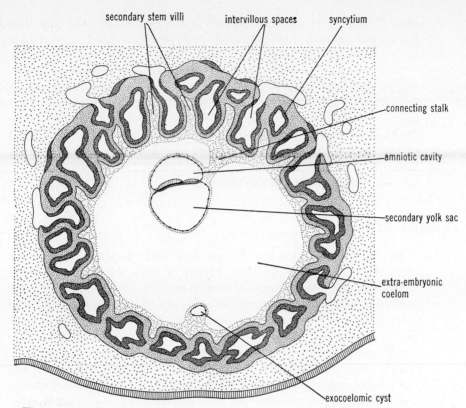

secondary stem villi   intervillous spaces   syncytium

connecting stalk

amniotic cavity

secondary yolk sac

extra-embryonic coelom

exocoelomic cyst

Figure 3-10. *Diagram showing a presomite embryo and the trophoblast at the end of the third week. The secondary stem villi give the trophoblast a characteristic radial appearance. The intervillous spaces are found throughout the trophoblast and are lined with syncytium. Note how the cytotrophoblastic cells surround the trophoblast entirely and are in direct contact with the endometrium. The embryo is suspended in the extra-embryonic coelom by means of the connecting stalk.*

phoblastic cells, which in turn is covered by the syncytium (figs. 3-9*B* and 3-10).

By the end of the third week the mesodermal core begins to differentiate and small capillaries arise (fig. 3-9*C*). This villous capillary system is soon connected to capillaries developing in the extra-embryonic mesoderm covering the inside of the trophoblast and in the connecting stalk. These vessels in turn establish contact with the intra-embryonic circulatory system during the fourth week of development (see Chapters 4 and 11).

Meanwhile the cytotrophoblastic cells at the decidual tip of the villi penetrate progressively into the syncytium until they reach the maternal endometrium. Here they establish contact with similar extensions of neighboring villous stems, thus forming a thin *outer cytotrophoblastic shell*. This shell at first is localized on the embryonic pole only, but from there expands toward the abembryonic pole until it surrounds the trophoblast (fig. 3-10).[6]

The extra-embryonic coelomic cavity meanwhile becomes larger, and by the 19th or 20th day the embryo is attached to its trophoblastic shell by a narrow connecting stalk only (fig. 3-10). This stalk is composed of extra-embryonic mesenchyme continuous with that lining the inner surface of the trophoblast and is attached at the caudal end of the embryo. The connecting stalk, also known as the *body stalk*, later develops into the umbilical cord, which forms the connection between the placenta and the embryo.

Abnormalities

In 1956, Hertig, Rock, and Adams[9] described a series of 26 implanted blastocysts varying in age from $7\frac{1}{2}$ to 17 days. All these specimens were recovered from patients of normal fertility, and surprisingly, nine (34.6 per cent) of these appeared to be abnormal. Some consisted of syncytium only, whereas others showed variable degrees of trophoblastic hypoplasia. In two of them the embryoblast was absent and in some the germ disc showed an abnormal orientation.

It is likely that the most abnormal ones would not have caused any evidence of pregnancy, as their trophoblast was of such inferior quality that the corpus luteum could not have persisted. These ova presumably would have been aborted with the following menstrual flow. Others, however, may have been able to survive for some time, presumably to be aborted at a later stage of pregnancy.

In some cases the trophoblast is characterized by overactivity. These cases result in the formation of noninvasive *hydatidiform moles* or highly malignant tumors, known as *chorionepitheliomas*.

References

1. Hertig, A. T., and Rock, J. Two human ova of the previllous stage, having a developmental age of about seven and nine days respectively. Contrib. Embryol., **31**: 65, 1945.
2. Wimsatt, W. A. New histological observations on the placenta of the sheep. Amer. J. Anat., **87**: 391, 1950.
3. Hertig, A. T., and Rock, J. Two human ova of the previllous stage, having an ovulation age of eleven and twelve days respectively. Contrib. Embryol., **29**: 127, 1941.
4. Heuser, C. H., and Streeter, G. L. Development of the Macaque embryo. Contrib. Embryol., **29**: 15, 1941.
5. Wislocki, G. B., and Streeter, G. L. On the placentation of the Macaque (*Macaca mulatta*) from the time of implantation until the formation of the definitive placenta. Contrib. Embryol., **27**: 1, 1938.

6. HAMILTON, W. J., AND BOYD, J. D. Development of the human placenta in the first three months of gestation. J. Anat., **94**: 297, 1960.
7. HAMILTON, W. J., AND BOYD, J. D. Phases of human development. In *Modern Trends in Obstetrics and Gynaecology*, edited by K. Bowes. Butterworth & Co., Ltd., London, 1950.
8. WISLOCKI, G. B., AND BENNETT, H. S. The histology and cytology of the human and monkey placenta with special reference to the trophoblast. Amer. J. Anat., **73**: 335, 1943.
9. HERTIG, A. T., ROCK, J., AND ADAMS, E. C. A description of 34 human ova within the first 17 days of development. Amer. J. Anat., **98**: 435, 1956.
10. STRAUSS, F. Gedanken zur Entwicklung des Amnions und des Dottersackes beim Menschen. Rev. Suisse Zool., **52**: 213, 1945.
11. STARCK, D. Die Frühphase der Menschlichen Embryonalentwicklung und ihre Bedeutung fur die Beurteilung der Säugerontogenese. Ergebn. Anat. Entwicklungsgesch., **35**: 133, 1956.
12. HOLTFRETER, J., AND HAMBURGER, V. Embryogenesis; progressive differentiation. In *Analysis of Development*, edited by B. H. Willier, P. A. Weiss, and V. Hamburger, p. 230. W. B. Saunders Co., Philadelphia, 1955.
13. McCRADY, E. The evolution and significance of the germ layer. J. Tenn. Acad. Sci., **19**: 240, 1944.
14. HERTIG, A. T. Angiogenesis in the early human chorion and in the primary placenta of the Macaque monkey. Contrib. Embryol., **25**: 37, 1935.
15. WISLOCKI, J. B., AND STREETER, G. L. Placentation of the Macaque. Contrib. Embryol., **27**: 1, 1938.

Fourth to Eighth Weeks of Development (Embryonic Period)

- GERM LAYERS AND THEIR DERIVATIVES: *mesodermal, entodermal, and ectodermal germ layers*
- EXTERNAL APPEARANCE OF THE EMBRYO DURING THE SECOND MONTH OF DEVELOPMENT

During the fourth to eighth weeks of development, a period known as the *embryonic period,* the shape of the embryo changes greatly and by the end of the second month all the major features of the external body form are recognizable. Moreover, each of the three germ layers starts its own typical course of differentiation and gives rise to a number of specific tissues and organs, so that by the end of this period all the main organ systems have been laid down.

Under normal conditions each germ layer adheres rather rigidly to its own developmental scheme. When, in experimental work on vertebrates, the interrelationship of the germ layers was altered, it appeared that each germ layer had a far greater potentiality than what it actually accomplished. Also, it was found that even under normal conditions the concept of absolute specificity of the germ layers is untenable. For instance, mesenchyme or young connective tissue, initially thought to be predominantly of mesodermal origin, may also develop from the ectodermal and entodermal germ layers.[1, 2]

In this chapter a brief description is given of the main structures and organs arising from each of the three germ layers. Since the external contours of the embryo during the first phase of the embryonic period (the *somite period* from the 20th to 30th day of development) are greatly influenced by the formation of a series of mesodermal blocks on each side of the midline (the *somites*), the fate of the mesodermal germ layer will be discussed first.

Germ Layers and Their Derivatives

Mesodermal Germ Layer

Initially the mesodermal cells form a thin sheet of loosely woven tissue on each side of the midline (fig. 4-1*A*). By about the 17th day of development, however, the cells in the cephalic part of the embryo immediately lateral to the notochord proliferate and form a thickened mass of tissue known as the *paraxial mesoderm* (fig. 4-1*B*). More laterally, the mesoderm layer is known as the *lateral plate*, and, with the appearance and subsequent coalescence of numerous intercellular cavities, this plate is divided into two layers (fig. 4-1*B, C*): one, continuous with the extra-embryonic mesoderm covering the amnion, is known as the *somatic* or *parietal mesoderm*; and the other, continuous with the mesoderm covering the yolk sac, is the *splanchnic* or *visceral mesoderm* (fig. 4-1*C, D*). Together, these layers line the newly formed cavity, the *intra-embryonic coelomic cavity*, which on each side of the embryo is continuous with the extra-embryonic coelom. The tissue initially connecting the paraxial mesoderm and the lateral plate is known as the *intermediate mesoderm* (fig. 4-1*B, C*).

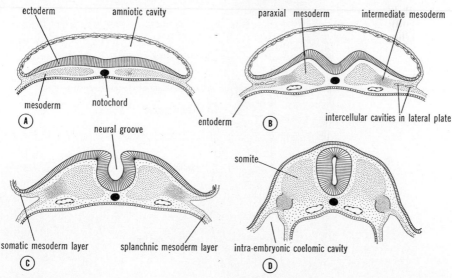

Figure 4-1. *Transverse sections through an embryo, showing the development of the mesodermal germ layer. A, At day 17; B, day 19; C, day 20; D, day 21. The original thin mesodermal tissue sheet gives rise to the paraxial mesoderm (the future somites), the intermediate mesoderm (the future excretory units), and the lateral plate, which is split into the somatic and splanchnic mesoderm layers lining the intra-embryonic coelomic cavity.*

Fourth to Eighth Weeks of Development

By the end of the third week the paraxial mesoderm forms a bilateral, longitudinal strip of solid tissue which gradually breaks up into segmented blocks of epithelioid cells, the *somites*. The first pair of somites arises in the cephalic part of the embryo just caudal to the tip of the notochord, and from here new somites appear in craniocaudal sequence, until by the end of the first month approximately 40 pairs are present.[3] Their formation molds the contours of the embryo, giving it a segmented appearance (figs. 4-2 to 4-4). The size of the embryo is usually expressed in the number of somites, since during this time the somites form one of its most characteristic external features. Based on embryos described by a number of authors,[9-11] table 4-1 represents the approximate age of the embryo correlated to the number of somites.

SOMITES. By the middle of the fourth week the cells of the ventromedial portion of the somite, known collectively as the *sclerotome*, lose their epithelioid shape, become polymorphous, and migrate toward the midline, forming a loosely woven tissue, the *mesenchyme* or *young connective tissue*. The cells of this tissue in turn give rise to connective tissue, cartilage, and bone (see "Formation of the Somite," Chapter 7, and "Skeletal System," Chapter 8).

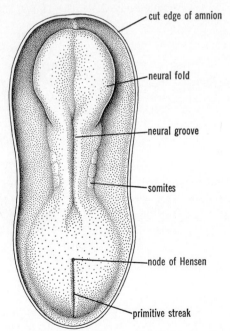

cut edge of amnion

neural fold

neural groove

somites

node of Hensen

primitive streak

Figure 4-2. *Dorsal view of a human embryo at approximately day 20 (modified after Ingalls). Note the appearance of the first somites and the formation of the neural groove and folds.*

General Embryology

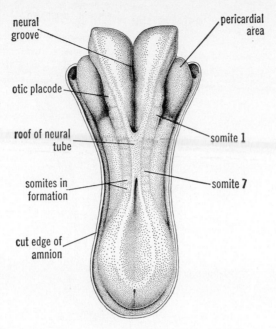

neural groove

pericardial area

otic placode

roof of neural tube

somites in formation

cut edge of amnion

somite 1

somite 7

Figure 4-3. *Dorsal view of a human embryo at approximately day 22 (modified after Payne). Seven somites are visible on each side of the neural tube.*

The remaining dorsolateral portion of the somite is known as the *dermomyotome*. The medially located cells of this portion differentiate into *myoblasts* which in turn give rise to *muscle cells*, while the lateral cells become mesenchymatous and spread under the overlying ectoderm to form the *dermis* and *subcutaneous tissue of the skin* (see "Muscular System," Chapter 9, and "Integumentary System," Chapter 18).

INTERMEDIATE MESODERM. This tissue, which temporarily connects the paraxial tissue and the lateral plate, differentiates in a manner entirely different from that of the somites. In the cervical and upper thoracic regions it forms segmentally arranged cell clusters, whereas more caudally it forms an unsegmented mass of tissue known as the *nephrogenic cord*. The excretory units of the urinary system are later formed from this partly segmented, partly unsegmented intermediate mesoderm (see "Urinary System," Chapter 10).

SOMATIC AND VISCERAL MESODERM LAYERS. These layers, derived from the lateral plate and lining the intra-embryonic coelom, later form the *mesothelial* or *serous membranes* of the peritoneal, pleural, and pericardial cavities (see "Coelomic Cavity and Mesenteries," Chapter 13).

CARDIOVASCULAR SYSTEM. The cardiovascular system, an important

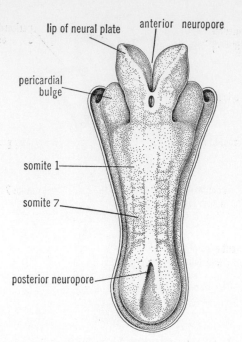

lip of neural plate   anterior neuropore

pericardial
bulge

somite 1

somite 7

posterior neuropore

Figure 4-4. *Dorsal view of a human embryo at approximately day 23 (modified after Corner). It is characterized by the presence of 10 pairs of somites. Note the pericardial bulge on each side of the midline in the cephalic part of the embryo.*

Table 4-1. *Number of Somites Correlated to Approximate Age in Days*

Approximate Age	No. of Somites	Approximate Age	No of Somites
days		*days*	
20	1–4	25	17–20
21	4–7	26	20–23
22	7–10	27	23–26
23	10–13	28	26–29
24	13–17	30	34–35

organ system derived from the mesodermal germ layer, arises at about the middle of the third week. At that time mesodermal cells located in front and on each side of the most cephalic part of the embryo differentiate into blood and vessel-forming cells which become arranged in isolated clusters, the *angiogenetic cell clusters* (fig. 4-5). These clusters later become canalized by confluence of intercellular clefts, the centrally located cells giving rise to the primitive blood cells and those on the periphery forming the endothelial cells lining the *blood islands*. The blood islands subsequently approach each other rapidly by

General Embryology

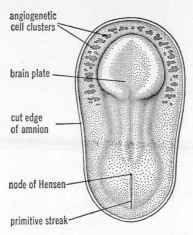

angiogenetic
cell clusters

brain plate

cut edge
of amnion

node of Hensen

primitive streak

Figure 4-5. *Dorsal view of a late presomite embryo, showing the angiogenetic cell clusters in front and on each side of the cephalic portion of the embryo (modified after Davis). The angiogenetic cell clusters are formed from mesodermal cells and later give rise to the primitive blood cells and blood vessels.*

sprouting of the endothelial cells, and after fusion give rise to small blood vessels (fig. 4-9*A*).

While this occurs the embryonic disc begins to bulge into the amniotic cavity, probably as a result of the formation of the somites and the development of the central nervous system (fig. 4-6*A*). By the seven-somite stage (approximately day 21), the bulging of the disc becomes more marked and the *head* and *tail folds* are established (fig. 4-6*B*). The cephalocaudal folding of the embryonic disc has a profound bearing on the position of the intra-embryonic blood vessels and particularly on that of the heart. The angiogenetic cell clusters initially located in front of the prochordal plate in the most cephalic part of the embryo are finally located on the ventral aspect of the embryo (fig. 4-6*C*). Concomitantly with the cephalocaudal folding of the embryo the germ disc is gradually lifted from the yolk sac, thus producing lateral folds so that the angiogenetic cell strands on each side of the embryo approach each other ventrally in the midline (fig. 4-7*A*, *B*, *C*, *D*). During the fourth week these cell cords obtain a lumen and fuse in the midline, thus establishing a single primitive heart tube, suspended in the pericardial cavity. By the end of the fourth week the pericardium forms a conspicuous bulge on the ventral aspect of the embryo, known as the *pericardial swelling* (fig. 4-8).

The formation of blood cells and blood vessels is not restricted to the intra-embryonic mesoderm but also occurs in the extra-embryonic mesoderm of the villous stems, of the connecting stalk, and in the wall of the yolk sac (fig. 4-9*A*). These extra-embryonic vessels, formed in

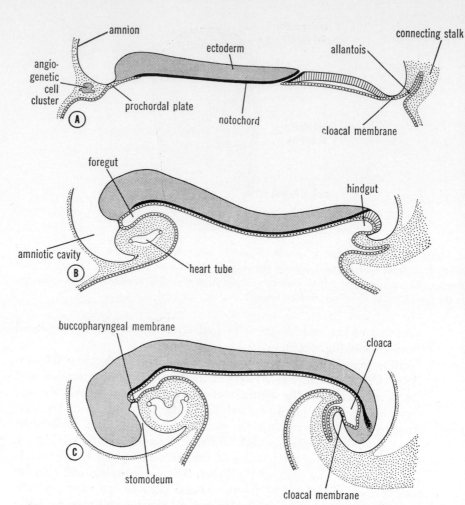

Figure 4-6. *Schematic drawing of mid-sagittal sections through embryos at various stages in development, showing the cephalocaudal flexion and its influence on the position of the heart and the entoderm-lined cavity. A, Presomite embryo; B, seven-somite embryo; C, 14-somite embryo (adapted from several sources).*

a manner similar to those inside the embryo, are known as the *umbilical* and *vitelline vessels.* By continuous budding they penetrate the embryo proper, where they come in contact with the independently developing intra-embryonic vascular system (fig. 4-9B) (see "Cardiovascular System," Chapter 11).

PHARYNGEAL ARCHES. The pharyngeal arches, also derived from proliferating mesodermal tissue, form a conspicuous feature of the external form of the embryo during the somite period. In a 10-somite embryo a distinct bilateral swelling, the *first pharyngeal* or *branchial*

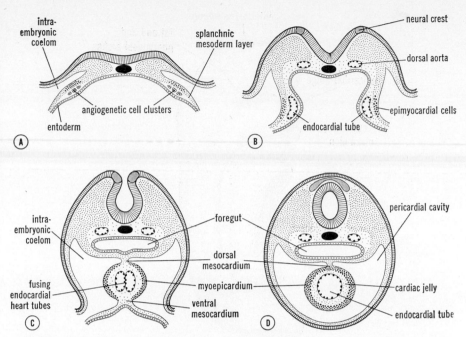

Figure 4-7. *Schematic representation of transverse sections through embryos at different stages of development, showing the formation of the single heart tube from paired primordia. A, Early presomite embryo (approximately 17 days); B, late presomite embryo (approximately 18 days); C, four somites (approximately 21 days); D, eight somites (approximately 22 days) (adapted from several sources). Note how the angiogenetic cell clusters located in the splanchnic mesoderm layer (see also fig. 4-5) gradually obtain a lumen, approach each other in the midline, and then fuse to form the heart tube.*

arch, can be seen just caudal to the head fold (fig. 4-8). Together with the head fold and pericardial swelling these arches bound a depression, the *stomodeum*, the floor of which is formed by the *buccopharyngeal membrane*, the former prochordal plate (fig. 4-6C).

By the 14-somite stage the first arch has differentiated into dorsal and ventral portions, the *maxillary* and *mandibular swellings*, respectively, while the second or *hyoid arch* begins to appear. The two arches are separated by the first pharyngeal cleft (fig. 4-8). By the 25-somite stage a third arch, separated from the second by the second pharyngeal cleft, is well established (fig. 4-10). The mesoderm of the pharyngeal arches later gives rise to connective tissue, ligaments, muscles, and cartilaginous and bony components (see discussion of pharyngeal arches in Chapter 12).

Although only the main derivatives of the mesodermal germ layer have been described, it must be noted that the following tissues and organs are considered to be of mesodermal origin: (1) connective tissue,

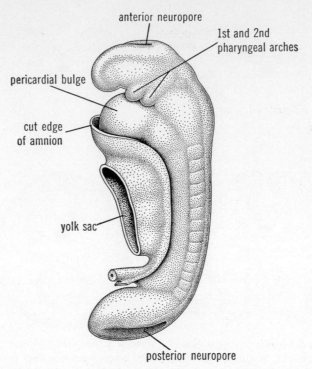

anterior neuropore

1st and 2nd
pharyngeal arches

pericardial bulge

cut edge
of amnion

yolk sac

posterior neuropore

Figure 4-8. *Left lateral view of a 14-somite embryo (approximately 25 days). Note the bulging pericardial area and the first and second pharyngeal arches separated by the first pharyngeal groove (modified after Heuser).*

cartilage, bone, and joints; (2) smooth and striated muscles; (3) blood and lymph cells and the walls of the heart, blood and lymph vessels; (4) serous membranes; (5) kidneys, gonads, and corresponding ducts; (6) the cortical portion of the suprarenal gland; and (7) the spleen.

Entodermal Germ Layer

The entodermal germ layer initially forms the roof of the secondary yolk sac. With the cephalocaudal folding of the embryo, a portion of the yolk sac at the cephalic as well as the caudal end of the embryo is incorporated into the body of the embryo proper and forms the *primitive foregut* and *hindgut*, respectively (fig. 4-6). Since the embryonic disc also undergoes a lateral folding, the foregut and hindgut become blind-ending tubes lined with epithelium of entodermal origin. At its cephalic end the foregut is temporarily bounded by an ectodermal-entodermal membrane, the *buccopharyngeal membrane*, whereas the hindgut terminates at the *cloacal membrane*. At the end of the third week the buccopharyngeal membrane ruptures, establishing an open connection between the amniotic cavity and the primitive gut; the

General Embryology

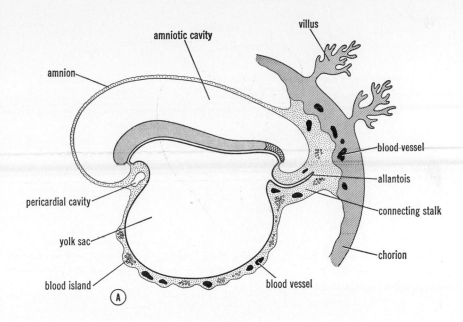

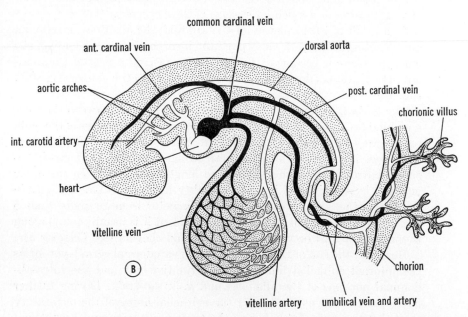

Figure 4-9. *A, Schematic drawing showing blood vessel formation in the extra-embryonic mesoderm of the trophoblast, connecting stalk, and wall of the yolk sac in a presomite embryo of approximately 19 days (modified after Keibel and Elze). B, Schematic drawing of the main intra- and extra-embryonic blood vessels in a 4-mm. embryo. Only the vessels on the left side of the embryo are shown.*

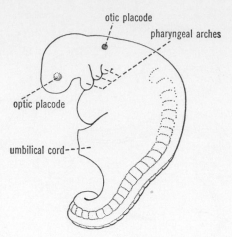

otic placode

pharyngeal arches

optic placode

umbilical cord

Figure 4-10. *Schematic drawing showing the left side of a 25-somite embryo approximately 28 days old. The first three pharyngeal arches and the optic and otic placodes are clearly visible (modified after Streeter).*

cloacal membrane which gives rise to the *urogenital* and *anal membranes* ruptures at a much later stage of development.

As a result of the formation of the tail fold, the allantois, initially an outpocketing of the yolk sac is partially incorporated in the body of the embryo, where it becomes attached to the ventral aspect of the hindgut. The distal portion of the allantois remains in the connecting stalk (fig. 4-6).

The *midgut*, that part of the primitive gut located between the fore- and hindgut, remains temporarily in open connection with the yolk sac by way of a broad stalk, the *omphalomesenteric* or *vitelline duct*. This duct is initially wide, but with elongation of the embryo it becomes narrow and at the same time lengthens rapidly. In man, the yolk sac is vestigial and in all probability has a nutritive role only in the early stages of development. Its diameter is never more than 5 mm., and in the second month of development it is usually found along the umbilical cord between the amnion and chorion (see Chapter 5).

Hence, at the end of the first month the entodermal germ layer forms the internal epithelial lining of the primitive gut and the intra-abdominal portions of the allantois and yolk sac stalk. During further development it gives rise to: (1) the epithelial lining of the respiratory tract; (2) the epithelial lining of the tympanic cavity and Eustachian tube; (3) the epithelial lining of part of the bladder and urethra; and (4) the parenchyme of the tonsil, thyroid, parathyroids, thymus, liver, and pancreas (see "Digestive Tube and Derivatives," Chapter 12).

General Embryology

Ectodermal Germ Layer

Initially the ectodermal germ layer forms a flat epithelial disc which continues peripherally into the amniotic ectoderm (see figs. 3-1 and 3-4). Shortly after the formation of the notochord, however, and presumably under its inductive influence, the ectoderm gives rise to the central nervous system, which forms a prominent feature on the dorsal aspect of the embryo during the somite period.

By the end of the third week the nervous system appears as an elongated, slipper-shaped plate, the *neural plate*, overlying the notochord and part of the paraxial mesoderm (fig. 4-2). During the next few days the neural plate invaginates, forming the *neural groove* which is lined on each side by a *neural fold* (fig. 4-3). These folds approach each other in the midline where they finally fuse, giving rise to the *neural tube*. This fusion begins in the region of the fourth somite, that is, the future neck region, and from there proceeds in cephalic and caudal directions. At the cranial and caudal ends of the embryo the tube temporarily remains in open connection with the amniotic cavity by way of the *anterior* and *posterior neuropores*, respectively (fig. 4-4).

Closure of the anterior neuropore occurs at the 18- to 20-somite stage, whereas the posterior neuropore closes at the 25-somite stage. The central nervous system then appears as a closed tubular structure with a narrow cylindrical portion, the *spinal cord*, and a broader cephalic portion, the future *brain* (see "Central Nervous System," Chapter 14).

At the end of the somite period another ectodermal derivative, the *otic placode*, is visible. It is situated dorsal to the second pharyngeal cleft and forms a distinct surface marking on the lateral aspect of the

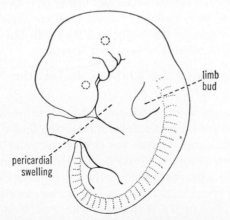

Figure 4-11. *Schematic drawing of a 5-week human embryo seen from the left. Crown-rump length is approximately 7 mm. Note the paddle-shaped limb buds. The otic and optic vesicles are indicated by broken circles (modified after Streeter).*

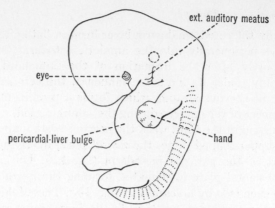

eye

ext. auditory meatus

pericardial-liver bulge

hand

Figure 4-12. *Schematic drawing of a 6-week human embryo seen from the left. Crown-rump length is approximately 13 mm. The upper limb buds show a flattened terminal portion with four radial grooves. Note the formation of the eye and external auditory meatus flanked on each side by three hillocks derived from the mandibular and hyoid arches (modified after Streeter).*

embryo. Soon the otic placode invaginates, forming the *otic pit*, which by about the end of the fourth week is closed over by the surface ectoderm, thus forming the *otic vesicle* (figs. 4-11 and 4-12). In addition, the *optic vesicle*, an outpocketing of the forebrain, can be seen through the overlying ectoderm (see "The Eye," Chapter 15, and "The Ear," Chapter 16).

In summary, the ectodermal germ layer gives rise to: (1) the central nervous system; (2) the peripheral nervous system; (3) the sensory epithelium of the sense organs. In addition, the following structures are formed by the ectoderm during further development: the epidermis, including the hair, nails, and subcutaneous glands; the hypophysis; the enamel organs of the teeth; and the epithelial linings of a number of other organs which are described later.

External Appearance of the Embryo during the Second Month of Development

During the second month the external appearance of the embryo is greatly influenced by the formation of the limbs, face, ear, nose, and eyes. Although the somites are clearly recognizable until the end of the sixth week, during the second month of development the age of the embryo is usually expressed as the crown-rump (C.R.) length. This is the measurement from the vertex of the skull to the midpoint between the apices of the buttocks. Owing to the considerable variation in the degree of flexure from one embryo to another, it is understandable that the measurements presented in table 4-2 can be only an approximate indication of the real age of the embryo.[12]

Table 4-2. *Crown-Rump (C.R.) Length Correlated to Approximate Age in Weeks*

C.R. Length	Approximate Age	C.R. Length	Approximate Age
mm.	*weeks*	*mm.*	*weeks*
5–8	5	17–22	7
10–14	6	28–30	8

Figure 4-13. *Schematic drawing of a 7-week human embryo seen from the left. Crown-rump length is approximately 18 mm. The upper extremities are more advanced in development than the lower ones (modified after Streeter).*

Figure 4-14. *Schematic drawing of an 8-week human embryo seen from the left. Crown-rump length is approximately 30 mm. Note the size of the head in comparison with the remaining part of the body. The eye lids are not present and the eyes are wide open (modified after Streeter).*

Fourth to Eighth Weeks of Development

By the beginning of the fifth week the fore- and hindlimbs appear as paddle-shaped buds (fig. 4-11). The former are located dorsal to the pericardial swelling at the level of the fourth cervical to the first thoracic somites, thus explaining their later innervation by the brachial plexus. The hindlimb buds appear slightly later just caudal to the attachment of the umbilical stalk at the level of the lumbar and upper sacral somites. With further growth the terminal portion of the buds flattens and becomes separated from the proximal, more cylindrically shaped, segment by a circular constriction. Soon four radial grooves separating five slightly thicker areas appear on the distal portion of the buds, foreshadowing the formation of the digits (fig. 4-12). While the fingers and toes are being formed a second constriction divides the proximal portion of the buds into two segments, and the three parts characteristic of the adult extremities can be recognized (figs. 4-13 and 4-14). During their formation the limb buds undergo a profound change in orientation. Initially they project at right angles to the body, but with the development of the elbow and knee joints the distal portions bend ventrally. Finally, the upper and lower extremities undergo a 90° torsion along their longitudinal axis, but in opposite directions so that the elbow points dorsally and the knee ventrally.

References

1. McGRADY, E. The evolution and significance of the germ layers. J. Tenn. Acad. Sci., **19:** 240, 1944.
2. OPPENHEIMER, J. M. The non-specificity of the germ layers. Quart. Rev. Biol., **15:** 1, 1940.
3. AREY, L. B. The history of the first somite in human embryos. Contrib Embryol., **27:** 233, 1938.
4. INGALLS, N. W. A human embryo at the beginning of segmentation with special reference to the vascular system. Contrib. Embryol., **11:** 61, 1920.
5. LUDWIG, E. Über einen operative gewonnenen menschlichen Embryo mit einem Ursegmente. Morphol. Jahrb. **59:** 41, 1928.
6. PAYNE, F. General description of a 7-somite human embryo. Contrib. Embryol., **16:** 117, 1924.
7. CORNER, G. W. A well preserved human embryo of 10 somites. Contrib. Embryol., **20:** 81, 1929.
8. HEUSER, C. H. A human embryo with 14 pairs of somites. Contrib. Embryol., **21:** 135, 1930.
9. STREETER, G. L. Developmental horizons in human embryos: age group XI, 13–20 somites, and age group XII, 21–29 somites. Contrib. Embryol., **30:** 211, 1942.
10. STREETER, G. L. Developmental horizons in human embryos: age group XIII, embryos 4 or 5 mm. long, and age group XIV, indentation of lens vesicle. Contrib. Embryol., **31:** 26, 1945.
11. DAVIS, C. L. Description of a human embryo having 20 paired somites. Contrib. Embryol., **15:** 1, 1923.
12. STREETER, G. L. Developmental horizons in human embryos: age groups XV, XVI, XVII, and XVIII (the third issue of a survey of the Carnegie Collection). Contrib. Embryol., **32:** 133, 1948.

CHAPTER 5

Third to Tenth Months
of Development (Fetal Period)

- DEVELOPMENT OF THE FETUS
- DEVELOPMENT OF THE PLACENTA
- FUNCTION OF THE PLACENTA
- AMNION AND UMBILICAL CORD

Development of the Fetus

The period from the beginning of the third month to the end of intra-uterine life is known as the *fetal period*. It is characterized by the rapid growth of the body, while further differentiation of the tissues is of minor importance.[1] During this time the age of the fetus is usually expressed as the crown-rump (C.R.) length (sitting height), or the crown-heel (C.H.) length, the measurement from the vertex of the skull to the heel (standing height). Based on measurements derived from various sources, table 5-1 shows the age of the fetus in lunar months correlated to the C.R. and C.H. lengths. In addition, the average weight is given.

One of the most striking changes taking place during fetal life is the relative slowdown in the growth of the head compared to the rest of the body. At the beginning of the third month the head constitutes approximately one-half of the C.R. length; by the beginning of the fifth month, about one-third; and at birth, approximately one-fourth (fig. 5-1). During the third month the face becomes more human-looking. The eyes, initially directed laterally, become located on the ventral aspect of the face; the ears come to lie close to their final position at the side of the head; the limbs reach their relative length in comparison to the rest of the body, although the lower limbs are still a little shorter and less developed than the upper extremities; and the

Table 5-1. *Growth in Length and Weight during the Fetal Period*

Age	Crown-Rump Length	Crown-Heel Length	Weight
lunar months	*cm.*	*cm.*	*gm.*
3	5–6	7	20
4	10	15	120
5	15	23	300
6	20	30	640
7	23	35	1230
8	27	40	1700
9	30	45	2300
10	34	50	3250

external genitalia develop to such a degree that the sex of the fetus can be determined by external examination.

During the fourth and fifth months the fetus lengthens rapidly, and at the end of the first half of intra-uterine life its standing height (C.H. length) is approximately 23 cm. (C.R. length, 16 cm.), that is, about half the total length of the newborn. The weight of the fetus, however,

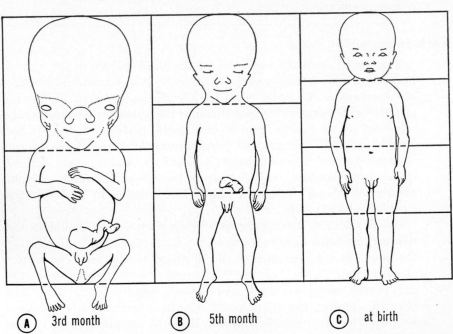

(A) 3rd month   (B) 5th month   (C) at birth

Figure 5-1. *Schematic drawing showing the size of the head in relation to the rest of the body at various stages of development. A, Note the swelling of the umbilical cord at its attachment to the abdominal wall. This is caused by herniation of the intestinal loops into the extra-coelomic cavity in the umbilical cord (see fig. 5-7).*

General Embryology

increases little during this period and by the end of the fifth month is less than 500 gm. Fetal movements are usually felt by the mother during the fifth month.

During the second half of intra-uterine life the weight of the fetus increases considerably, particularly during the last $2\frac{1}{2}$ months, when 50 per cent of its full term weight (approximately 3200 gm.) is added. The fetus has a wrinkled appearance at first, because of the lack of underlying connective tissue, but during the last couple of months obtains well rounded contours as the result of deposition of subcutaneous fat. By the end of intra-uterine life the skin is covered by a whitish, fatty substance, the *vernix caseosa,* composed of the secretion products of the sebaceous glands.

By the end of the 10th lunar month, when the fetus is approximately 50 cm. long and weighs about 3200 gm., the skull still has the largest circumference of all parts of the body, an important fact in regard to its passage through the birth canal. At birth, the testicles have usually descended into the scrotum and the umbilical cord is attached near the center of the abdominal wall.

Development of the Placenta

By the beginning of the second month the *trophoblast,* later referred to as the *chorion,* is characterized by a great number of secondary villi which give it a striking radial appearance (fig. 5-2). The villi are anchored in the mesoderm of the chorionic plate and attached peripherally to the maternal decidua by way of the outer cytotrophoblastic shell. Their surface is formed by the syncytium, resting on a layer of cytotrophoblastic cells which in turn cover a core of vascular mesoderm (fig. 5-3*A*). This mesoderm is at first found on the chorionic side of the villi but gradually penetrates toward the decidual side. The capillary system in the core of the villous stems develops during the fourth week and soon comes in contact with the capillaries on the inner surface of the chorion and connecting stalk, giving rise to the extra-embryonic vascular system (fig. 4-9). This system in turn establishes contact with the intra-embryonic vessels and thus connects the embryo to its future placenta.

From now on numerous small extensions sprout from the existing villous stems into the surrounding *lacunar* or *intervillous spaces.* These newly formed villi initially have the same layers as the stem villi, but by the beginning of the fourth month the cytotrophoblastic cells as well as some of the connective tissue core disappears, leaving only the syncytium and the endothelial wall of the blood vessels to separate maternal and fetal circulations (fig. 5-3*B*). The disappearance of the cytotrophoblastic cells progresses from the smaller to the larger villi, although some always persist in the stem villi. In the latter, however,

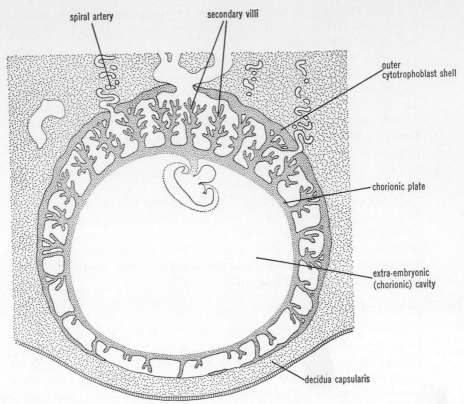

spiral artery   secondary villi

outer
cytotrophoblast shell

chorionic plate

extra-embryonic
(chorionic) cavity

decidua capsularis

Figure 5-2. *Schematic representation of the human embryo at the beginning of the second month of development. At the embryonic pole the villi are numerous and well formed; at the abembryonic pole they are few in number and poorly developed (modified after von Ortmann).*

blood vessels remain in the center of the connective tissue core, as they do not participate in the exchange between the two circulations (fig. 5-3B).

Although in the early weeks of development the villi cover the entire surface of the chorion, as pregnancy advances this situation changes. Those villi found over the embryonic pole continue to grow and expand, thus giving rise to the *chorion frondosum* (bushy chorion); those on the abembryonic pole start to degenerate, and by the third month this side of the chorion is smooth and known as the *chorion laeve* (fig. 5-4A).

This difference in the embryonic and abembryonic poles of the chorion is also reflected in the structure of the decidua. The decidual layer located over the chorion frondosum, the *decidua basalis*, consists of the compact layer which is tightly connected to the chorion and the

General Embryology

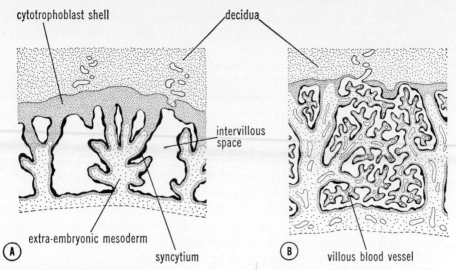

Figure 5-3. *Schematic drawing of the structure of the villi at various stages of development. A, During the fourth week. Note how the extra-embryonic mesoderm penetrates the secondary stem villi in the direction of the decidual plate. B, During the fourth month. In many small villi the wall of the capillaries is in direct contact with the syncytium (modified after Starck).*

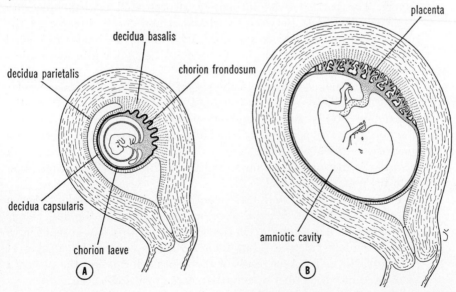

Figure 5-4. *Schematic drawing showing the relation of the fetal membranes and the wall of the uterus. A, End of the second month. Note the yolk sac in the chorionic cavity between the amnion and chorion. At the abembryonic pole the villi have disappeared (chorion laeve). B, End of the third month. The amnion and chorion have fused and the uterine cavity is obliterated by fusion of the chorion laeve and the decidua parietalis.*

Third to Tenth Months of Development

spongy layer containing the spiral arteries and the dilated glands. The compact layer containing the decidual cells is often referred to as the *decidual plate*.

The decidual layer over the abembryonic pole and bordering the uterine lumen is known as the *decidua capsularis*. At first this layer is similar to the decidua basalis, but with increase in the size of the chorionic vesicle, it projects deep into the uterine cavity, becomes stretched, and, probably under the influence of a diminished blood supply, begins to degenerate by the third month (fig. 5-4B). The chorion laeve, consisting mainly of cytotrophoblastic cells, then comes in contact with the epithelium of the *decidua parietalis* on the opposite side of the uterus. When the decidua parietalis loses the epithelial surface, its endometrial stroma fuses with the chorion laeve and most of the uterine cavity is obliterated (fig. 5-4B). Hence, the only functional portion of the chorion is the chorion frondosum which, together with the decidua basalis, makes up the *placenta*.

The placenta has two components: (1) a *fetal portion* formed by the chorion frondosum, and (2) a *maternal portion* formed by the decidua basalis. On the fetal side the placenta is bordered by the extra-embryonic mesoderm of the chorion, the *chorionic plate*; on its maternal side by the decidua basalis, composed of the compact and spongy layers. The portion most intimately incorporated into the placenta is the *decidual plate*. Between the chorionic and decidual plates are the intervillous spaces which are filled with maternal blood and lined with syncytium of fetal origin. The villous trees grow into these intervillous chorionic blood lakes.

With continuous increase in the size of the uterus, the placenta also enlarges. Its increase in surface area roughly parallels that of the expanding uterus and throughout pregnancy amounts to approximately 25 to 30 per cent of the internal surface of the uterus. Its increase in thickness results from a lengthening of the existing villi and the formation of new ones, and is not due to further penetration into the maternal tissues.[2]

During the fourth and fifth months the decidua basalis forms a number of septa, the *decidual septa*, which project into the intervillous spaces but do not reach the chorionic plate (fig. 5-5). These septa have a core of maternal tissue, but their surface is covered by a layer of trophoblastic cells.[3] As a result of this septum formation the placenta is divided into a number of compartments or *cotyledons* (fig. 5-5).

The manner in which these cotyledons receive their blood supply has long been a subject of much discussion. Originally it was suggested that the spiral arteries entered the intervillous spaces of a cotyledon by way of the maternal septa and that the venous blood passed from one intervillous space to another and finally drained into a marginal

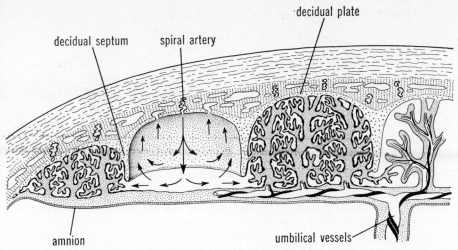

decidual septum   spiral artery   decidual plate

amnion   umbilical vessels

Figure 5-5. *Composite drawing of the placenta in the second half of pregnancy. The cotyledons are partially separated from each other by the decidual (maternal) septa. Note that most of the intervillous blood returns to the maternal circulation by way of the endometrial veins in the decidual plate. A small portion enters neighboring cotyledons. The intervillous spaces are lined by syncytium (modified after Ramsey; and Hamilton and Boyd).*

sinus at the periphery of the placenta.[4, 5] It is now generally accepted that the spiral arteries pierce the decidual plate and enter the intervillous spaces at more or less regular intervals.[6, 7] The pressure in these arteries forces the blood well into the intervillous spaces and bathes the numerous small villi of the villous tree in oxygenated blood.[8-10] Venous openings draining the intervillous spaces are found over the entire surface of the decidual plate, and the blood from the intervillous lakes drains back into the maternal circulation through these openings (fig. 5-5).

Under normal conditions the intervillous spaces contain approximately 150 cc. of blood, which is replenished about three or four times per minute.[11] This blood moves along the chorionic villi the surface area of which, according to various sources, varies from 4 to 14 sq. meters. It must be remembered, however, that placental exchange does not take place in all villi but only in those in which the fetal vessels are in intimate contact with the covering syncytial membrane. In these villi the syncytium often has a brush border consisting of numerous microvilli, thus greatly increasing the exchange rate between the two systems.[12]

At full term the placenta has a discoid shape, a diameter of 15 to 25 cm., and is approximately 3 cm. thick. When after birth it is viewed from the decidual side, 15 to 20 slightly bulging areas, the *cotyledons*,

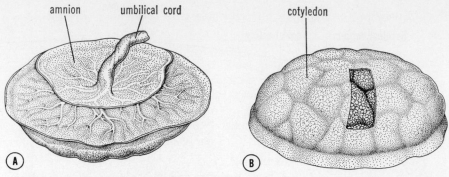

Figure 5-6. *Drawing of a full term placenta. A, As seen from the fetal side. Note that this side is covered by the amnion. B, As seen from the maternal side. Note the cotyledons. In one area the decidua has been removed.*

covered by a thin layer of decidua basalis and cytotrophoblastic shell are clearly recognizable (fig. 5-6B). The grooves between the cotyledons are formed by the decidual septa.

The fetal surface of the placenta is smooth, has no cotyledon structure, and is covered entirely by the chorionic plate. In the mesoderm of this plate are a number of large arteries and veins, the *chorionic vessels*, which converge toward the umbilical cord (fig. 5-6A). The vascular mesoderm of the chorion in turn is covered by the amnion. The attachment of the umbilical cord is usually eccentric and occasionally even marginal. Rarely, however, does it insert into the chorionic membrane outside the placenta.

Function of the Placenta

The main function of the placenta is the exchange of metabolic and gaseous products between the maternal and fetal blood streams, with no mixing of the two. The dividing membrane, often referred to as the *placental barrier*, is composed exclusively of fetal tissue. In the early stages it consists of four layers: (1) the endothelial lining of the fetal vessels; (2) the connective tissue in the core of the villi; (3) the cytotrophoblastic layer; and (4) the covering syncytium (fig. 5-2).

From the fourth month on, however, the placental barrier becomes much thinner, since most of the villi lose their cytotrophoblastic layer, and the connective tissue surrounding the fetal capillaries gradually disappears. The endothelial lining of the capillaries then comes into intimate contact with the syncytial membrane, thus greatly increasing the rate of exchange.[13] In the final stages of pregnancy the small villi show an extremely thin, double-layered membrane separating maternal and fetal blood. These layers, however, persist at all times. Since the maternal blood in the intervillous spaces is separated from the fetal blood by the placental barrier, a chorionic derivative, the human placenta is considered to be of the *hemochorial* type.

In addition to the exchange of gaseous products, electrolytes, amino-acids, carbohydrates, fats, and other metabolic products, with or without the support of enzymatic systems, the placenta has an important function with regard to the transmission of antibodies and the production of hormones.

It was initially thought that high molecular weight substances such as proteins and particularly maternal gamma-globulins could pass through the placental barrier only in the case of actual breaks. Recently, however, it has been suggested that many antibodies are taken up by the fetus by pinocytosis. Whatever the precise mechanism, the passage of antibodies from the maternal blood stream to the fetus has been demonstrated repeatedly.[14, 15] In this manner the fetus acquires some of the antibodies which the mother has produced against infectious diseases such as diphtheria, scarlet fever, smallpox, measles, and others.

By the end of the fourth month the placenta produces progesterone in sufficient amounts to maintain pregnancy. Hence, when this occurs the corpus luteum is no longer needed and it begins to degenerate. In addition to progesterone, the placenta produces increasing amounts of estrogenic hormones until just before the end of pregnancy, when a maximum level is reached. This is thought to be one of the factors responsible for the beginning of parturition. Furthermore, the placenta produces gonadotropins which have an effect very similar to that of the luteinizing hormones of the anterior lobe of the pituitary. The gonadotropic hormones are excreted in the urine and, especially in the early stages of gestation, their presence in the urine is used as an indicator in a number of pregnancy tests. When the urine of a pregnant woman is injected into an immature mouse, corpora lutea will be formed (Ascheim-Zondek test).

Amnion and Umbilical Cord

During the second week of development, when the amnion is formed, it consists of a single layer of flat epithelial cells, the *amnioblasts*, which are in close contact with the cytotrophoblast and continue peripherally into the columnar cells of the ectodermal germ layer (figs. 3-1 and 3-2). Soon the mono-layered amnion loses its connection with the trophoblast and its outer surface becomes covered with extra-embryonic somatopleuric mesoderm. It maintains its connection with the ectoderm at the so-called *amnio-ectodermal junction* (figs. 3-3 and 3-4).

As the embryonic disc folds in cephalocaudal direction, the amnio-ectodermal junction becomes located on the ventral aspect of the embryo (fig. 4-6), and its line of reflexion becomes oval-shaped and

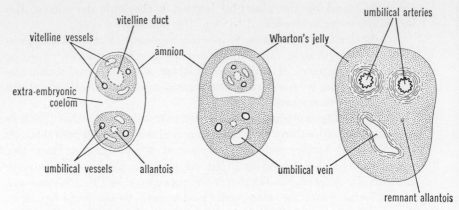

Figure 5-7. *Transverse sections through the umbilical cord at various stages of development. Note the extra-embryonic coelom in the umbilical cord at the early stage of development. The intestinal loops herniate into this space during the second month.*

known as the *primitive umbilical ring.* Through this ring extend: (1) the connecting stalk with the allantois and umbilical vessels; (2) the yolk sac stalk and vitelline vessels; and (3) the canals connecting the intra- and extra-embryonic coelomic cavities which temporarily contain some of the intestinal loops (fig. 5-7A). By the fifth week the umbilical ring constricts, crowding its contents and thus forming the *primitive umbilical cord,* which is entirely surrounded by the amnion. Although the long and slender yolk sac stalk is taken up into the primitive umbilical cord, the yolk sac itself remains in the extra-embryonic coelom between the amnion and chorion (fig. 5-4A). Shortly thereafter, the intestinal loops withdraw from the cord into the abdominal cavity and the coelom in the cord is obliterated. When in addition the allantois, vitelline duct and vessels are obliterated, all that remains are the umbilical vessels surrounded by the *jelly of Wharton,* a mucous differentiation product of mesoderm protecting the blood vessels (fig. 5-7B, C).

The amniotic cavity surrounding the embryo enlarges rapidly at the expense of the extra-embryonic coelom. Finally the amnion covered by extra-embryonic somatopleuric mesoderm comes in contact with the chorion, thereby obliterating the extra-embryonic coelom or chorionic cavity (fig. 5-4B). At the end of intra-uterine life the two membranes are usually firmly united, and it is often difficult to separate them.

The amniotic cavity is filled with a clear, watery fluid produced by the amniotic cells. During the early months of pregnancy the embryo is suspended by its umbilical cord in this fluid, which serves as a protective cushion. The fluid absorbs jolts, prevents the adherence of the embryo to the amnion, and allows for fetal movements. Probably from the beginning of the fifth month, the fetus swallows its own amniotic fluid. Evidence for this is seen in the fact that fetuses unable to swallow, either because of esophageal atresia or through lack of nervous control of the swallowing mechanism, as in anencephaly, are usually surrounded by large amounts of amniotic fluid (hydramnios). Under normal conditions the amniotic fluid is absorbed through the gut into the blood stream and passes into the maternal blood by way of the placenta. At the end of pregnancy and during childbirth, the amnion and chorion combined form a hydrostatic wedge which helps to dilate the cervical canal.

At birth the umbilical cord is approximately 2 cm. in diameter and 50 to 60 cm. long. It is tortuous, which may result in the so-called *false knots*. An extremely long cord may encircle the neck of the fetus, whereas a short one may cause difficulties during delivery by pulling the placenta from its attachment.

References

1. Scammon, R. E., and Calkins, H. A. *Development and Growth of the External Dimensions of the Human Body in the Foetal Period.* University of Minnesota Press, Minneapolis, 1929.
2. Stieve, H. Die Entwicklung und der Bau der menschlichen Placenta, Zotten, Trophoblastinseln und der Scheidewand in der ersten Hälfte der Schwangerschaft. Z. Mikroskopischanat. Forsch., **48**: 287, 1940.
3. Serr, D. M., Sadowsky, A., and Kohn, G. The placental septa. J. Obstet. Gynaec. Brit. Emp., **65**: 774, 1958.
4. Bumm, E. Über die Entwicklung des mutterlichen Blutkreislaufes in der menschlichen Placenta. Arch. Gynaek., **43**: 181, 1893.
5. Spanner, R. Mutterlicher und kindlicher Kreislauf der menschlichen Placenta und seine Strombahnen. Z. Anat. Entwicklungsgesch., **105**: 163, 1935.
6. Hamilton, W. J., and Boyd, J. D. Development of the human placenta in the first three months of gestation. J. Anat., **94**: 297, 1960.
7. Ramsey, E. M. Distribution of arteries and veins in the mammalian placenta. In *Gestation* (Transactions of the Second Conference on Gestation), edited by C. A. Villee, p. 299. Josiah Macy, Jr., Foundation, New York, 1956.
8. Ramsey, E. M. Vascular patterns in the endometrium and the placenta. Angiology, **6**: 321, 1955.
9. Ramsey, E. M. Vascular adaptations of the uterus to pregnancy. Ann. N. Y. Acad. Sci., **75**: 726, 1959.
10. Borell, U., Fernstrom, I., and Westman, A. Eine arteriographische Studie des Plazentarkreislaufs. Geburtsh. Frauenheilk., **18**: 1, 1958.
11. Assali, N. S., Rauramo, L., and Peltonen, T. Measurement of uterine blood flow and uterine metabolism. VIII. Uterine and foetal blood flow and oxygen consumption in early human pregnancy. Amer. J. Obstet. Gynec., **79**: 86, 1960.
12. Wislocki, G. B., and Dempsey, G. W. Electron microscopy of the human placenta. Anat. Rec., **123**: 133, 1955.
13. Flexner, L. B., Cowie, D. B., Hellman, L. M., Wilde, W. S., and Vos-

BURGH, G. J. Permeability of human placenta to sodium in normal and abnormal pregnancies and supply of sodium to human fetus as determined with radioactive sodium. Amer. J. Obstet. Gynec., 55: 469, 1948.

14. MALMNÄS, C. *Immunity in Pregnancy*. Almquist and Wiksells, Stockholm, 1958.

15. HAGERMAN, D. D., AND VILLEE, C. A. Transport functions of the placenta. Physiol. Rev., 40: 313, 1960.

CHAPTER 6

Congenital Malformations and Their Causes

INCIDENCE

ETIOLOGY OF MALFORMATIONS
- ENVIRONMENTAL FACTORS
  Infectious agents: rubella; Asian influenza and other viral infections; toxoplasmosis; syphilis
  Radiation
  Chemical agents: drugs
  Hormones: progestins; cortisone; maternal diabetes
  Antibodies
  Nutritional deficiencies
  Hypoxia
- CHROMOSOMAL AND GENIC FACTORS
  Autosome abnormalities: trisomy 21; trisomy 17–18 and 13–15
  Sex chromosome abnormalities: Klinefelter's syndrome; Turner's syndrome; triple-X syndrome
  Abnormalities of the genes: autosomal dominant inheritance; sex-linked inheritance; autosomal recessive inheritance; sporadic cases

GENERAL CONSIDERATIONS ON THE ACTION OF TERATOGENS

Congenital malformations are defined as "gross structural defects" present at birth.[1] Although several abnormalities at the cellular and even at the molecular level are also known to be congenital in nature, they are not usually included in the above definition but rather referred to as "congenital anomalies."

Incidence

The figures on the incidence of congenital malformations vary greatly. In studies of civic birth records, the percentage of children with abnormalities varied from 0.75 to 1.98 per cent.[2-6] These estimates were found to be rather low when compared with data from hospital birth records in which a variation of 1.43 to 3.3 per cent was noted.[7-9] Although the latter figures are probably the more accurate, they differ considerably among themselves. This may be due to actual differences in frequency in different countries or to the types of malformations considered. The racial make-up of the sample may also influence the incidence figures, since the frequency and types of malformations vary from race to race.[9] When the figure is based on examination of infants at 6 and 12 months of age, as well as at birth, the percentage often doubles, and an incidence of 7.5 per cent has been reported.[10]

Summarizing, it is probable that 2 to 3 per cent of all liveborn infants show one or more significant congenital malformations at birth, and that at the end of 1 year this figure is doubled by discovery of malformations indiscernible at birth.

Etiology of Malformations

The human embryo is well protected from outside mechanical injury by the uterus, fetal membranes, and amniotic fluid, and from damaging agents present inside the maternal organism by the placenta, long considered an almost impregnable barrier. Hence, until the early 1940's, it was assumed that congenital defects were caused mainly by hereditary factors. With the discovery by Gregg[11] that German measles affecting a mother during early pregnancy caused abnormalities in the embryo, it suddenly became evident that congenital malformations in man could also be caused by environmental factors. The pioneering work of Warkany,[1, 12] who showed that a specific maternal dietary deficiency during pregnancy was teratogenic in rats, has since stimulated a great many investigations and led to the discovery of a large number of environmental factors teratogenic for the developing mammalian embryo. (For significant contributions in this field, see Warkany and Kalter,[1, 12] Wilson,[13] Fraser,[14, 15] and Giroud and Tuchmann-Duplessis.[16])

Despite this rapid development our knowledge of congenital malformations in humans has increased relatively little. At present it is estimated that approximately 10 per cent of all known human malformations are due to environmental factors and another 10 per cent to genetic and chromosomal factors; the remaining 80 per cent are presumably caused by the intricate interplay of several genetic and environmental factors.

Environmental Factors

Infectious Agents

RUBELLA OR GERMAN MEASLES. Gregg[11] in 1941 was the first to suggest that German measles affecting pregnant women in the early stages of gestation could lead to congenital malformations in the off-spring. At present it is well established that rubella virus can cause malformations of the eye (cataract and microphthalmia); internal ear (congenital deafness due to destruction of the organ of Corti); heart (persistence of the ductus arteriosus as well as atrial and ventricular septal defects); and occasionally of the teeth (enamel layer).[17-19] The virus may also be responsible for some cases of brain abnormalities and mental retardation.[20, 21]

The type of malformation is determined by the stage of embryonic development at which infection occurs.[22] For example, cataracts result from infection during the sixth week of pregnancy, and deafness from infection during the ninth week. Cardiac defects follow infection in the fifth to 10th weeks, and dental deformities between the sixth and ninth weeks.[23-26]

It is extremely difficult to determine the exact incidence of malforma-tions in the offspring of infected mothers, since German measles may be mild and thus escape detection, or may be accompanied by unusual clinical features and remain unrecognized. Furthermore, as pointed out above, some birth defects are not recognized until the child reaches 2 to 4 years of age. On the other hand, rashes caused by other viruses may be incorrectly attributed to rubella. Initial figures indicated a malformation risk of about 75 per cent when the disease occurred during the first 4 months of pregnancy. These figures have since been found to be greatly exaggerated.[27-29] In a recent prospective study, the risk of malformations in infants examined immediately after birth was estimated at 47 per cent when the infection occurred during the first 4 weeks of pregnancy; 22 per cent following infection in the fifth to eighth weeks; 7 per cent in the ninth to 12th weeks; and 6 per cent in the 13th to 16th weeks.[30] Prematurity and fetal death may also follow infection in the first 8 weeks.[31]

If abnormalities such as mental retardation and dental defects, which do not become evident until later in life, were to be considered it is likely that the above percentages would be higher (65 per cent of congenital deafness due to rubella is not discovered until the fourth year).[32]

ASIAN INFLUENZA. Reports on the possible teratogenic effects of Asian influenza have been rather controversial.[33, 34] Some investiga-tors find no indication of such effects, others report that the frequency of anencephaly is higher in offspring of mothers infected with this virus during early pregnancy than in a control population.[35] It has been concluded, therefore, that anencephaly may occur occasionally as a result of maternal infection but the risk appears low.[36]

OTHER VIRAL INFECTIONS. Malformations following maternal infec-tion with measles, mumps, hepatitis, poliomyelitis, chickenpox, and ECHO viruses have been described.[37] Recent prospective studies, however, indicate that probably none of them causes malformations.[38] With regard to measles some results were negative and some suggestive.[39]

TOXOPLASMOSIS. Maternal infection with the protozoon parasite, *Toxoplasma gondii*, has been shown to produce congenital malformations. The affected child may have cerebral calcification, hydrocephalus, or mental retardation; chorioretinitis, microphthalmus, and other ocular defects have been reported as well.[40, 41] It is impossible to give precise figures on the incidence of malformations caused by toxoplasmosis since the disease is usually unrecognized.

SYPHILIS. Formerly, it was thought that syphilis was a major cause of malformations. This has since proved to be ill-founded. When syphilis was widespread, congenital malformations such as cleft lip and palate, spina bifida, and others were often attributed to this disease. However, when the disease became rarer, the association between the disease and congenital malformations also became rarer. Yet, there is no doubt that syphilis may lead to congenital deafness and mental retardation in the offspring.

Radiation

The teratogenic effect of x-radiation has been known for many years, and it is well recognized that microcephaly, skull defects, spina bifida, blindness, cleft palate, and defects of the extremities may result from treating pregnant women with large doses of roentgen rays or radium. Although the maximum safe dose for humans is not known, in mice the fetus can be damaged with a dose as small as 5 r.[42] It must be realized that the nature of the malformation depends on the dose and stage of development at which radiation is given.[43, 44]

Studies on the offspring of Japanese women pregnant at the time of the atomic bomb explosions over Hiroshima and Nagasaki revealed that among the survivors, 28 per cent aborted, 25 per cent gave birth to children who died in their first year of life, and 25 per cent of the surviving children had abnormalities of the central nervous system such as microcephaly and mental retardation.[45, 46]

In addition to the effect of direct radiation on the embryo, indirect effects on the germ cells must be considered. Indeed, relatively small doses of radiation have been shown to cause mutations which subsequently led to the occurrence of congenital malformations in succeeding generations.[47]

Although some investigations have shown that radiation caused no abnormalities in children of exposed parents, others have suggested that an accumulated dose of radiation of between 30 to 80 r per generation may double the spontaneous incidence of mutation in man.[48-50]

General Embryology

Despite the fragmentary and often controversial findings, one must be aware of the possible dangers of radiation in man.

Chemical Agents

DRUGS. The role of drugs in the production of developmental abnormalities in man is difficult to assess, because studies carried out in this field are of necessity retrospective. Few of the many drugs used during pregnancy have been positively identified as being teratogenic for the child. The most recent example is *thalidomide*, an anti-nauseant and sleeping pill. During the last few years it was noted in West Germany that the frequency of *amelia* and *phocomelia* (total or partial absence of the extremities), heretofore considered a rare hereditary abnormality, had suddenly increased. This led to the examination of the prenatal histories of the affected children, resulting in the discovery that many of the mothers had taken thalidomide early in pregnancy. In the case of some women who could not recall having taken the drug, pharmacy records revealed that it had been prescribed. The causal relationship between thalidomide and phocomelia was discovered only because the drug produced such an unusual type of abnormality. If the defect had been of a more common type, the association with the drug might easily have been overlooked.

The defects produced by thalidomide are: absence or gross deformities of the long bones, intestinal atresia, and cardiac anomalies.[51-53] Although it is too early to estimate the incidence of malformations resulting from taking this drug, the probability is thought to be about 20 per cent.

An older drug, long suspected as being teratogenic, is *quinine*. In high doses it has frequently been used as a means of abortion and, as such, is believed to produce congenital deafness.[54] Although animal experiments seem to support this belief, there is no positive evidence for it as far as humans are concerned.[55]

A more dangerous drug, likewise used to produce abortion, is *aminopterin*. This compound belongs to the antimetabolites and is an antagonist of folic acid. Experimental studies have shown that it is a very potent teratogen.[56-58] Since, in doses somewhat higher than the teratogenic level, the drug will terminate pregnancy, it has been used during early pregnancy to induce therapeutic abortion in women suffering from tuberculosis.[59] In four cases in which abortion did not occur, malformed offspring were found. The defects noted were anencephaly, meningocele, hydrocephalus, and cleft lip and palate. In two cases in which the drug had been used unsuccessfully to attempt illegal abortion, malformed children were born.[60] However, since this drug has been used in a number of cases during pregnancy without producing teratogenic effects, its teratogenicity in man cannot yet be considered to have been demonstrated satisfactorily.

Two other drugs, *busulfan* and *tolbutamide*, used to treat leukemia and diabetes, respectively, have recently been suggested as teratogenic.[61-63] Further information, however, is needed.

Hormones

PROGESTINS. Synthetic progestins are frequently used during pregnancy to avert abortion. Occasionally, however, progestin treatment has been associated with the production of congenital malformations, and recently 70 cases of masculinization of the genitalia in female embryos have been reported.[64] The abnormalities produced consisted of an enlarged clitoris associated with varying degrees of fusion of the labioscrotal folds. Comparable results have been obtained experimentally by treating pregnant rats with progestin.[65]

CORTISONE. Experimental work has repeatedly shown that cortisone injected into mice and rabbits at certain stages of pregnancy may cause a high percentage of cleft palates in the offspring.[66, 67] Although some investigations indicate that cortisone given to pregnant women during early gestation may cause cleft palate in the child, a number of cases have recently been reported in which the mother received cortisone throughout pregnancy, yet the baby was normal.[68, 69] So far, it has been impossible to implicate cortisone as an environmental factor causing cleft palate in man.

MATERNAL DIABETES. Disturbances in carbohydrate metabolism due to maternal diabetes or prediabetic stages in pregnancy cause a high incidence of stillbirths, neonatal deaths, and abnormally large infants. According to some workers, an increased incidence of congenital malformations has been noted. Critical analysis of the data available, however, showed that the incidence of congenital malformations in diabetic and prediabetic women is approximately the same as in the general population.[70]

Recently, it was reported that when women with previous histories of congenital defects and an indication of a disturbed carbohydrate metabolism were treated with insulin or thyroid, or both, subsequent pregnancies resulted in fewer miscarriages, stillbirths, and infants with congenital malformations.[71] Unfortunately, however, there is no proof that these women would not have produced normal children without treatment.

Antibodies

A completely new teratogenic mechanism is now under consideration as a possible cause of congenital malformations. It was found that the serum of several mothers who had given birth to athyrotic cretins contained antithyroid antibodies and a thyrotoxic factor. This suggested a causal relationship between cretinism and maternal auto-immunization to thyroid tissue.[72, 73] Some support for this theory can be found in recent experimental work in which it was shown that congenital malformations may be induced by actively immunizing pregnant mice to tissue extracts.[74] Much work remains to be done in this field, however, particularly as to the manner in which maternal antibodies pass through the placenta, how they leave the fetal circulation, and how an antigen-antibody reaction inside the embryo occurs.

Nutritional Deficiencies

Although many nutritional deficiencies, particularly vitamin deficiencies, have been proved to be teratogenic in experimental work, there is no definite evidence that they are teratogenic in humans. With the exception of endemic cretinism, which is related to maternal iodine deficiency, no analogies to the animal experiments have been found in humans.[75] (For an extensive review on nutritional deficiencies and their effect on the production of congenital malformations in experimental animals, see Kalter and Warkany,[12] and Giroud and Tuchmann-Duplessis.[16])

Hypoxia

Hypoxia induces congenital malformations in a great variety of experimental animals.[76] Whether the same is valid for humans remains to be seen. Although children born at relatively high altitudes are usually lighter in weight and smaller than those born near or at sea level, an increase in the incidence of congenital malformations has not been noted.[77] In addition, women with cyanotic cardiovascular diseases often give birth to small infants, but usually without gross congenital malformations.

Chromosomal and Genic Factors

Tissue culture techniques have recently made it possible to analyze precisely the chromosomal pattern of the human cell.[78, 79] It was thus found that the normal somatic cell contains 46 chromosomes, of which 44 are autosomes and two are sex chromosomes.[80, 81] In figure 6-1, they are arranged in 23 pairs which are identified by number according to their total length, the position of the centromere, and the length of the arms on each side of the centromere.[82] In the female the sex chromosomes are represented by two X chromosomes, which resemble the autosomes of the 6–12 group; in the male by an X chromosome and a much shorter Y chromosome which resembles somewhat the autosomes of the 21–22 group.

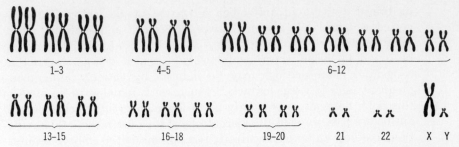

Figure 6-1. *Karyotype of the chromosomes as seen during mitosis of a normal somatic cell. The pairs are numbered according to the Denver system. Note the X and Y sex chromosomes.*

Once the normal chromosomal pattern was established, it soon became evident that some patients had an abnormal number or configuration of chromosomes.[83] Some of these abnormalities involved the autosomes, usually an extra chromosome; others, the sex chromosomes, usually the X chromosome. If an additional chromosome is present, making three chromosomes instead of the usual pair, the individual is said to be trisomic for this chromosome and the condition is known as *trisomy*. Four such conditions are now well established: (1) trisomy 21; (2) trisomy 17–18; (3) trisomy 13–15; and (4) trisomy X.

Autosome Abnormalities

TRISOMY 21. This condition is found in the somatic cells of the majority of mongoloid defectives.[84, 85] During meiosis the two homologs of a chromosome pair normally separate so that each daughter cell contains only half as many chromosomes as the mother cell (see Chapter 1). If instead of separating, both members of a pair move into one cell (*nondisjunction*), this cell will contain 24 instead of the normal 23 chromosomes. When at fertilization another set of 23 chromosomes is added to the abnormal gamete, the result will be 47 chromosomes, of which three will be identical (trisomy). Since the frequency of mongolism increases with advancing maternal age, it is thought that nondisjunction occurs during oogenesis rather than during spermatogenesis.[86, 87]

In a few cases of mongolism, the extra chromosome 21 is not free but is found attached to another chromosome, usually to one of the 13–15 or 21–22 group. This is the result of a phenomenon known as *translocation*.[88-90] The resulting mongoloid will have 46 chromosomes, but one of them will be unusually large, since in effect it consists of two chromosomes.

In some cases a translocation of chromosome 21 can be seen in the parent of a mongoloid child. This parent then has 45 chromosomes, but

General Embryology

is clinically normal inasmuch as all the normal chromosomal material is present. The bearers of this chromosomal pattern are referred to as *carriers*.[88, 91] The pairing and separation of the translocated chromosome and the two single normal homologs (21 and 13–15) during meiosis determines the chromosomal complement of the germ cells.[92] Although many of the possible combinations are thought to be lethal to the developing embryo, it is known that when a normal gamete with a chromosomal combination 13–15 plus 21 combines with a translocated chromosome 13–15–21, plus a free 21, the result will be trisomy 21, a pattern characteristic of mongolism (Down's syndrome).

The chromosomal studies in mongolism have considerable importance. If the parents of a mongoloid have normal chromosomes, the chance of a second child being mongoloid is 1 to 2 per cent. If, however, one of the parents is a carrier of a translocated chromosome 21, the chances of a second mongoloid child being born to them are greatly increased and are thought to be about one in three.[93]

TRISOMY 17–18. Patients with this chromosomal arrangement show the following features suggesting a distinct clinical entity: mental retardation, congenital heart defects, low-set ears, and flexion of fingers and hands.[94, 95] In addition, these patients frequently show micrognathia, renal anomalies, syndactyly, and malformations of the skeletal system.

TRISOMY 13–15. The main abnormalities of this syndrome are mental retardation, congenital heart defects, deafness, cleft lip and palate, and eye defects such as microphthalmia, anophthalmia, and coloboma.[96]

Sex Chromosome Abnormalities

An important stimulus to the study of sex chromosome abnormalities was provided by the work of Barr *et al.*,[97, 98] who observed a difference in the morphology of the cell nuclei. In about 40 to 80 per cent of the cells of a normal female, a small, darkly staining body was found, located almost always against the nuclear membrane. This body was rarely, if ever, found in normal male cells. The female cells are therefore called chromatin-positive, and the male ones, chromatin-negative. Although the nature of this sex chromatin body was long controversial, it has recently become certain that it represents one of the two X chromosomes of the female cell.[99]

Application of the nuclear sexing technique together with chromosome analysis has shown that some cases of infertility are characterized by an abnormal sex chromosome complement. As in the case of autosomal abnormalities, it is likely that these are also caused by nondisjunction of the chromosomes. If, during meiosis, the two homologous X chromosomes fail to separate and move into one daughter cell, the resultant oocyte has either two X chromosomes or none. If an oocyte with two X chromosomes combines with a Y-containing sperm, the result will be an individual with an XXY sex chromosomal complement. In case it combines with an X-containing sperm, the result is an XXX individual. Similarly, if the oocyte without sex chromosomes is fertilized with an X sperm, the resultant individual will be characterized by an XO sex chromosomal make-up. Fertilization with a Y sperm will produce a YO zygote. Alternatively, nondisjunction during spermatogenesis can give rise to sperms without a sex chromosome, or with both an X and Y. Fertilization of a normal oocyte will result in an XO or XXY sex chromosomal complement. A number of patients with these abnormal sex chromosomal complements have been observed.

KLINEFELTER'S SYNDROME. The clinical features of this syndrome found only in males are sterility, testicular atrophy, hyalinization of the seminiferous tubules, and gynecomastia.[100] The cells have 47 chromosomes with a sex chromosomal complement of the XXY type, and a sex chromatin body is found in 80 per cent of cases.[101] The incidence of Klinefelter's syndrome in the normal population is about 1 in 500 males, but among mentally defective subjects the incidence may be as high as 1 in 100 males.[102] On the basis of statistical evidence it is believed that nondisjunction of the XX homologs is the most common causative event.

Occasionally patients with Klinefelter's syndrome have 48 chromosomes, that is, 44 autosomes and 4 sex chromosomes (XXXY).[103] This sex chromosome complement is thought to be caused either by nondisjunction of the sex chromosomes in the gametes of both parents or, and this is more likely, by a nondisjunction of the X chromosomes in the female gamete in both first and second meiotic divisions.

In some patients it was found that the tissues examined contained a mixture of cells; some with a normal chromosomal pattern, and others with an abnormal configuration. Some cases showed a variety of abnormal sex chromosomal complements.[104] This phenomenon, known as *mosaicism*, is thought to be caused by nondisjunction of the sex chromosomes during the mitotic cleavage divisions.

TURNER'S SYNDROME. This condition, found in women with an unmistakably female appearance, is characterized by the absence of the ovaries (gonadal dysgenesis). Despite the female appearance of these patients, almost all of their cells are sex chromatin-negative. In addition their cells have only 45 chromosomes with an XO chromosomal complement.[105] Genetic analysis has shown that this syndrome is usually caused by nondisjunction in the male gamete during meiosis. As in patients with Klinefelter's syndrome, patients with Turner's syndrome occasionally show mosaicism (XO/XX; XO/XY; or XO/XYY combinations are seen).

General Embryology

TRIPLE-X SYNDROME. Patients with triple-X syndrome are infantile, with scanty menses and some degree of mental retardation.[106] They have two sex chromatin bodies in their cells and are therefore sometimes called "superfemale." The triple-X syndrome results from fertilization of an XX oocyte and an X-containing sperm.

Abnormalities of the Genes

It has long been known that many congenital malformations in man are inherited and that some show a clear Mendelian pattern of inheritance. In many cases the abnormality is directly attributable to a change in a single gene, hence the name *single gene mutation.* It is estimated that this type of defect makes up approximately 10 per cent of human malformations.[106-109]

AUTOSOMAL DOMINANT INHERITANCE. In such conditions the affected gene will cause malformations whether the gene comes from only one parent (heterozygous) or from both (homozygous). Usually, the abnormality is of heterozygous origin, since it would be rare, indeed, if both parents were to carry similarly affected genes.

In malformations with autosomal dominant inheritance the child of the affected (heterozygous) individual has a 50 per cent chance of being affected. The following malformations are examples of such conditions: achondroplasia; cleidocranial dysostosis; lobster claw defects of hands and feet; osteogenesis imperfecta.

SEX-LINKED INHERITANCE. In these conditions the abnormal genes are carried by the X chromosome (diseases caused by genes carried by the Y chromosome have not yet been found).[110] Congenital malformations showing sex-linked dominant inheritance have not been reported in man. If the affected gene on the X chromosome is recessive it will not express itself in heterozygous females but only in males. In such cases the abnormality is transmitted through the female and appears in half the sons. Such conditions include: one form of hydrocephalus, one form of gargoylism, and the testicular feminization syndrome.

AUTOSOMAL RECESSIVE INHERITANCE. A recessive gene expresses itself only when homozygous, that is, when inherited from both father and mother. Malformations caused by recessive genes are seen infrequently, and affected children almost always come from unaffected heterozygous parents. Each sibling of an affected child has one chance in four of being affected. Parents of children with recessive diseases have a higher frequency of consanguinity than is found in the general population. Examples of recessively inherited malformations include: chondro-ectodermal dystrophy; some cases of microcephaly; chondro-dystrophia calcificans congenita.

SPORADIC CASES. Malformations which suddenly appear in families in which there are no other affected relatives with congenital defects are usually regarded as sporadic cases. As these patients are often referred to the physician for genetic advice, a brief summary of the possibilities to be considered is given:

Recessive Genes. As discussed above, a child of a parent carrying a recessive gene has one chance in four of being affected. This, combined with the relatively small size of the modern family, means that most cases of recessively inherited malformations often appear to be sporadic. In the case of achondroplasia this may produce difficulties since both a dominant and a recessive type of this malformation exist.

Mutation. A mutation is a sudden and persistent change in the expression of a gene. If this mutation is dominant, the offspring of the affected person will have a 50 per cent chance of being affected.

Reduced penetrance. Normally, a dominant gene expresses itself similarly in individuals who are either homozygous or heterozygous for that gene. If, however, the effects of a dominant gene do not appear in some individuals, the gene is said to have reduced penetrance. Similarly a recessive gene shows reduced penetrance when it fails to manifest itself in the homozygous individual. In the case of dominant genes with reduced penetrance, the disease appears to "skip" generations. Reduced penetrance can sometimes be explained by the fact that one of the individuals affected died before the disease became apparent.

Phenocopies. If a genetically normal individual is exposed to a specific environmental change at a particular stage of development it may acquire an abnormal phenotype. For example, a cataract resulting from a prenatal infection with rubella may be regarded as a phenocopy of a clinically similar cataract caused by a gene. If in a sporadically occurring abnormality a genetic change is involved, the probability of recurrence of the malformation within the same family may be quite high; if, however, the malformation is a phenocopy, the chance of recurrence is low. Unless a prenatal factor such as rubella can be identified, it is often impossible to distinguish this from other reasons for a negative family history. (For a discussion of the genetic factors in human malformations, see Stern.[110b])

General Considerations on the Action of Teratogens

From data available on the action of teratogenic factors in mammals, a few basic principles have emerged.[111] Although it is too early to list these as "laws," they must be kept in mind when considering the probability of children being affected by specific teratogenic factors.

1. The stage of embryonic development determines the susceptibility to teratogenic factors. Mammalian development starts with a rapid multiplication of cells which show little, if any, differentiation. This period is followed by implantation during which the cells begin to show distinct morphological differences presumably resulting from changes at the chemical level (chemodifferentiation).

Several teratogenic factors, such as hypervitaminosis A and radiation, which in later stages of development are known to be highly teratogenic were found to have no effect on the embryo in the first phase of development.[112-114] It is now thought that when a teratogen acts during early development it either damages all or a majority of the cells of the embryo, resulting in its death; or it injures only a few cells, in which case the regulative potentialities of the embryo will compensate for the loss and no abnormalities will be apparent.[115]

During the second phase, that is, the stage of intensive differentiation, most teratogenic agents are highly effective and produce numerous malformations. The type of malformation produced, however, depends on which organ is most susceptible at the time of injury. Each organ seems to go through its most susceptible stage early in its differentiation, and the various body organs become susceptible one after the other. This was clearly demonstrated by giving rats a pteroylglutamic acid-deficient diet.[58] It was thus found that abnormalities of the central nervous system and heart can be produced from day 7 to day 9; skeletal, urinary, and other cardiovascular abnormalities from day 9 to day 11; and skeletal anomalies from day 11 to day 14.

During the third period of development, characterized by growth of the organs, susceptibility to teratogenic agents rapidly decreases and is negligible. The only noticeable effect may be inhibited growth or degeneration of existing tissues.

2. The effect of a teratogenic factor depends on the genotype. A number of experiments seem to indicate that a teratogenic agent accentuates the incidence of those defects which occur sporadically without treatment and that the malformations appear as they do because of underlying genetic instabilities. When a strain of mice that regularly produces approximately 2 per cent of offspring with skeletal abnormalities was starved for 24 hours, the result was a 22 per cent increase in skeletal defects.[116]

Another example of the importance of the genotype is seen in the fact that not only different species but also different strains and substrains react differently to similar teratogenic agents.[117] These differences were mainly quantitative with variations of up to 70 per cent.

When an appropriate dose of cortisone was injected into pregnant mice of strains A and C57, it caused cleft palate in all the offspring of strain A and in 19 per cent of strain C57. When a strain C57 male was bred with a strain A female, 43 per cent of the young had cleft palate. However, when a strain C57 mother was crossed with a strain A father, the incidence dropped to 4 per cent; this showed that the genes of the mother as well as those of the embryo may influence the susceptibility to a teratogen.[118]

3. A teratogenic agent acts in a specific way on a particular aspect of cell metabolism. Many teratogenic agents produce a characteristic pattern of malformations when applied to a certain species at a specific stage of development. If the malformations produced by two teratogenic factors are completely different, they most likely act on entirely different biochemical phases of the embryonic metabolic pattern. When malformations caused by two different agents overlap, it is likely that both factors act partially on similar phases of development and differ in others. When the pattern produced by two agents is the same or similar, their action is likely to be the same, though not necessarily so.

A teratogenic agent does not necessarily act on one specific metabolic process but may interfere with different biochemical processes at completely different times of development. For example, the teratogenic action of insulin on the chick embryo early in development was counteracted by pyruvic acid. At a later stage of development, however, only nicotinamide could prevent the teratogenic effects produced by the insulin.[119]

References

1. WARKANY, J., AND KALTER, H. Congenital malformations. New Engl. J. Med., **265:** 993, 1961.
2. GENTRY, J. T., PARKHURST, E., AND BULIN, G. V. Epidemiological study on congenital malformations in New York State. Amer. J. Public Health, **49:** 497, 1959.
3. IVY, R. H. Congenital anomalies, as recorded on birth certificates in Division of Vital Statistics of Pennsylvania Department of Health for period 1951–1955, inclusive. Plast. Reconstr. Surg., **20:** 400, 1957.
4. WALLACE, H. M., AND BAUMGARTNER, L. Congenital malformations and birth injuries in New York City. Pediatrics, **12:** 525, 1953.
5. NEEL, J. V. Study on major congenital defects in Japanese infants. Amer. J. Hum. Genet., **10:** 398, 1958.
6. McKEOWN, T., AND RECORD, R. G. Malformations in population observed for five years after birth. In *Ciba Foundation Symposium on Congenital Malformations,* edited by G. E. W. Wolstenholme and E. M. O'Connor, p. 2. Little, Brown and Company, Boston, 1960.
7. SCHENK, H. Über die Missbildungen in den Jahren 1938–41 an der Universitäts-Frauenklinik, Berlin. Zbl. Gynaek., **46:** 2078, 1942.
8. BÖÖK, J. A., AND FRACCARO, M. Research on congenital malformations. Études néo-natales, **5:** 39, 1956.
9. STEVENSON, S. S., WORCESTER, J., AND RICE, R. G. Six hundred and seventy-seven congenitally malformed infants and associated gestational characteristics. I. General considerations. Pediatrics, **6:** 37, 1950.
10. McINTOSH, R., ET AL. Incidence of congenital malformations; a study of 5964 pregnancies. Pediatrics, **14:** 505, 1954.

General Embryology

11. GREGG, N. M. Congenital cataract following German measles in mothers. Trans. Ophthal. Soc. Aust., **3**: 35, 1941.

12. KALTER, H., AND WARKANY, J. Experimental production of congenital malformations in mammals by metabolic procedure. Physiol. Rev., **39**: 69, 1959.

13. WILSON, J. G. General principles in experimental teratology. In *Proceedings of the First International Conference on Congenital Malformations*, p. 187. J. B. Lippincott Co., Philadelphia, 1961.

14. FRASER, F. C. The use of teratogens in the analysis of abnormal developmental mechanisms. In *Proceedings of the First International Conference on Congenital Malformations*, p. 179. J. B. Lippincott Co., Philadelphia, 1961.

15. FRASER, F. C. Methodology of experimental mammalian teratology. In *Methodology in Mammalian Genetics*, edited by W. J. Bundette, p. 233. Hold and Day, San Francisco, 1962.

16. GIROUD, A., AND TUCHMANN-DUPLESSIS, H. Malformations congénitales. Role des facteurs exogènes. Path. Biol. (Par.), **10**: 119, 1962.

17. LOGAN, W. P. D. Effects of virus infections in pregnancy. Medicine (Illus.), **8**: 502, 1954.

18. RHODES, A. J. Virus infections and congenital malformations. In *Proceedings of the First International Conference on Congenital Malformations*. J. B. Lippincott Co., Philadelphia, 1961.

19. TÖNDURY, G. Zur Kenntnis der Embryopathica rubeolica, nebst Bemerkungen über die Wirkung anderer Viren auf den Keimling. Geburtsh. Frauenheilk., **12**: 865, 1952.

20. ARIENS KAPPERS, J. Developmental disturbance of the brain induced by German measles in an embryo of the 7th week. Acta Anat., **31**: 1, 1957.

21. LACOMME, M. Le point de vue de l'obstétricien sur les malformations congénitales. Maternité, **6**: 231, 1954.

22. INGALLS, T. H. The study of congenital anomalies by the epidemiologic method. New Engl. J. Med., **243**: 67, 1950.

23. BASS, M. H. Diseases of pregnant women affecting the offspring. Advance. Intern. Med., **5**: 15, 1952.

24. TEDESCHI, C. G., HELFERN, M. M., AND INGALLS, T. H. Pathological manifestations in an infant after maternal rubella in the sixteenth week of gestation. New Engl. J. Med., **249**: 439, 1953.

25. JACKSON, H. D. M., AND FISH, L. Deafness following maternal rubella; results of a prospective investigation. Lancet, **2**: 1241, 1958.

26. KEITH, J. K., ROWE, R. D., AND VLAD, P. *Heart Disease in Infancy and Childhood*. The Macmillan Company, New York, 1958.

27. AYCOCK, L. W., AND INGALLS, T. H. Maternal disease as principle in epidemiology of congenital anomalies; with review of rubella. Amer. J. Med. Sci., **212**: 366, 1946.

28. INGALLS, T. H., AND PURSHOTTOM, N. Fetal risks from rubella during pregnancy. New Engl. J. Med., **249**: 454, 1953.

29. OXORN, H. Rubella and pregnancy. Amer. J. Obstet. Gynec., **77**: 628, 1959.

30. MICHAELS, R. H., AND MELLIN, G. W. Prospective experience with maternal rubella and associated congenital malformations. Pediatrics, **26**: 200, 1960.

31. SIEGEL, M., AND GRÜNBERG, M. Fetal death, malformation and prematurity after maternal rubella; results of a prospective study, 1949–1958. New Engl. J. Med., **262**: 389, 1960.

32. JACKSON, A. D. M., AND FISH, L. Deafness following maternal rubella; results of prospective study. Lancet, **2**: 1241, 1958.

33. WALKER, W. M., AND MCKEE, A. P. Asian influenza in pregnancy. Obstet. Gynec. (N. Y.), **13**: 394, 1959.
34. WILSON, M. G., HEINS, H. L., IMAGAWA, D. T., AND ADAMS, J. M. Teratogenic effects of Asian Influenza. J. A. M. A., **171**: 638, 1959.
35. COFFEY, V. P., AND JESSOP, W. J. E. Maternal influenza and congenital deformities. Lancet, **2**: 935, 1959.
36. DOLL, R., HILL, A. B., AND SAKULA, J. Asian influenza in pregnancy and congenital defects. Brit. J. Prev. Soc. Med., **14**: 167, 1960.
37. WESSELHOEFT, C. Acute infectious diseases in pregnancy. Ann. Intern. Med., **42**: 555, 1955.
38. MANSON, M. M., LOGAN, W. P. D., AND LOY, R. M. *Rubella and Other Virus Infections during Pregnancy* (Great Britain Ministry of Health Reports on Public Health and Medical Subjects, Publication No. 101). Her Majesty's Stationery Office, London, 1960.
39. DUMONT, M. Viroses inapparentes et malformations foetales. Presse Med., **68**: 1087, 1960.
40. FELDMAN, H. A. Toxoplasmosis. Pediatrics, **22**: 559, 1958.
41. LELONG, M. Rapport sur la prophylaxie de la toxoplasmose du nouveau-né et de la femma enceinte. Rev. Hyg. Med. Soc., **7**: 71, 1959.
42. RUGH, R., AND GRUPP, E. Congenital defects following low level X-irradiation. Anat. Rec., **138**: 380, 1960.
43. WILSON, J. G. Differentiation and the reaction of rat embryos to radiation. J. Cell. Comp. Physiol., **43**: 11, 1954.
44. HICKS, S. P. The effects of ionizing radiation, certain hormones and radiometric drugs on the developing nervous system. J. Cell. Comp. Physiol., **43**: 151, 1954.
45. PLUMMER, G. Anomalies occurring in children exposed in utero to atomic bomb in Hiroshima. Pediatrics, **10**: 687, 1952.
46. YAMASAKI, J. N., WRIGHT, S. W., AND WRIGHT, P. M. Outcome of pregnancy in women exposed to atomic bomb in Nagasaki. A. M. A. J. Dis. Child., **87**: 448, 1954.
47. CARTER, T. C., LYON, M. F., AND PHILLIPS, R. J. S. Genetic hazard of ionizing radiations. Nature (Lond.), **182**: 409, 1958.
48. CROW, J. F. Comparison of fetal and infant death rates in progeny of radiologists and pathologists. Amer. J. Roentgenol., **73**: 467, 1955.
49. SCHULL, W. J., AND NEEL, J. V. Radiation and sex ratio in man. Science, **128**: 343, 1958.
50. *Biological Effects of Atomic Radiation* (summary of reports from a study by the National Academy of Sciences, National Research Council). U. S. Government Printing Office, Washington, D. C., 1956.
51. LENZ, W. Thalidomide and congenital abnormalities. Lancet, **1**: 1219, 1962.
52. SOMERS, G. F. Thalidomide and congenital abnormalities. Lancet, **1**: 912, 1962.
53. WEICKER, H., AND HUNGERLAND, H. Thalidomid-embryopathie. I. Vorkommen inner und ausserhalb Deutschlands. Deutsch. Med. Wschr., **87**: 992, 1962.
54. WHITEHOUSE, D. B., AND MCKEOWN, T. Note on significance of attempted abortion in aetiology of congenital abnormalities. J. Obstet. Gynaec. Brit. Emp., **63**: 224, 1956.
55. WINKEL, C. F. W. Quinine and congenital injuries of ear and eye of foetus. J. Trop. Med., **51**: 2, 1948.
56. GIROUD, A., AND LEFEBRVES-BOISSELOT, J. Influence tératogène de la carence en acide folique. C. R. Soc. Biol. (Par.), **145**: 526, 1951.

57. NELSON, M. M., ASLING, C. W., AND EVANS, H. M. Production of multiple congenital malformations in young by maternal pteroyl-glutamic acid deficiency during gestation. J. Nutr., 48: 61, 1952.

58. NELSON, M. M., WRIGHT, H. V., ASLING, C. W., AND EVANS, H. M. Multiple congenital abnormalities resulting from transitory deficiency of pteroylglutamic acid during gestation in rats. J. Nutr., 56: 349, 1955.

59. THIERSCH, J. B. The effects of antimetabolites on the fetus and litter of the rat in utero. In *Proceedings of the Sixth International Conference on Planned Parenthood*, p. 156. International Planned Parenthood Federation, New Delhi, India, 1959.

60. WARKANY, J., BEAUDRY, P. H., AND HORNSTEIN, S. Attempted abortion with aminopterin: malformations of the child. A. M. A. J. Dis. Child., 97: 274, 1959.

61. DIAMOND, T., ANDERSON, M. M., AND McCREADIE, S. R. Transplacental transmission of busulfan in mother with leukemia (production of fetal malformation and cytomegaly). Pediatrics, 25: 85, 1960.

62. CAMPBELL, G. D. Possible teratogenic effect of tolbutamide in pregnancy. Lancet, 1: 891, 1961.

63. TUCHMANN-DUPLESSIS, H., AND MERCIER-PAROT, L. Sur l'action teratogène d'un sulfamide hypoglycémiant: étude expérimentale chez la ratte. J. Physiol. Path. Gen., 51: 65, 1959.

64. WILKINS, L., JONES, H. W., JR., HOLMAN, G. H., AND STEMPFEL, R. S., JR. Masculinization of the female fetus associated with administration of oral and intramuscular progestins during gestation; nonadrenal female pseudohermaphroditism. J. Clin. Endocr., 18: 559, 1958.

65. REVESZ, C., CHAPPEL, C. I., AND GANDRY, R. Masculinization of female fetuses in rat by progestational compounds. Endocrinology, 66: 140, 1960.

66. FRASER, F. C., KALTER, H., WALKER, B. E., AND FAINSTAT, T. D., Experimental production of cleft palate with cortisone and other hormones. J. Cell Comp. Physiol. (Suppl. 1), 43: 237, 1954.

67. FAINSTAT, T. D. Cortisone-induced congenital cleft palate in rabbits. Endocrinology, 55: 502, 1954.

68. HARRIS, J. W. S., AND ROSS, I. P. Cortisone therapy in early pregnancy; relation to cleft palate. Lancet, 1: 1045, 1956.

69. PREISLER, O. Is prolonged cortisone treatment in pregnancy damaging to the infant? Zbl. Gynaek., 18: 675, 1960.

70. RUBIN, A., AND MURPHY, D. P. Studies in human reproduction. III. Frequency of congenital malformations in offspring of non-diabetic and diabetic individuals. J. Pediat., 53: 579, 1958.

71. HOET, J. P., GOMMERS, A., AND HOET, J. J. Causes of congenital malformations; role of prediabetes and hypothyroidism. In *Ciba Foundation Symposium on Congenital Malformations*. Little, Brown & Co., Boston, 1960.

72. BLIZZARD, R. M., CHANDLER, R. W., LANDING, B. H., PETTIT, H. D., AND WEST, C. D. Maternal auto-immunization to thyroid as a probable cause of athyrotic cretinism. New Engl. J. Med., 263: 327, 1960.

73. SUTHERLAND, J. M., ESSELBORN, V. M., BURKET, R. L., SKILLMAN, T. B., AND BENSON, J. T. Familial nongoitrous cretinism apparently due to maternal antithyroid antibody. New Engl. J. Med., 263: 336, 1960.

74. GLUECKSOHN-WAELSCH, S. The effect of maternal immunization against organ tissues on embryonic differentiation in the mouse. J. Embryol. Exp. Morph., 5: 83, 1957.

75. EGGENBERGER, H. Kropf und Kretinismus. In *Handbuch der inneren Sekretion*, Vol. 3, p. 684. Kabitzsch, Leipzig, 1928.

76. INGALLS, T. H., CURLEY, F. J., AND PRINDLE, R. A. Experimental production of congenital abnormalities; timing and degree of anoxia as factors causing fetal deaths and congenital abnormalities in mouse. New Engl. J. Med., 247: 758, 1952.

77. LICHTY, J. A., TING, R. Y., BRUNS, P. D., AND DYAR, E. Studies on babies born at high altitudes. I. Relation of altitude to birth and weight. A. M. A. J. Dis. Child., 93: 666, 1957.

78. HSU, T. C. Mammalian chromosomes *in vitro*; the karyotype in man. J. Hered., 43: 167, 1952.

79. FORD, C. E., JACOBS, P. A., AND LAJTHA, L. G. Human somatic chromosomes. Nature (Lond.), 181: 1565, 1958.

80. TJIO, J. H., AND LEVAN, A. The chromosome number of man. Hereditas, 42: 1, 1956.

81. FORD, C. E., AND HAMERTON, J. L. The chromosomes of man. Nature (Lond.), 178: 1020, 1956.

82. A proposed standard system of nomenclature of human mitotic chromosomes. Lancet, 1: 1063, 1960.

83. HIRSCHORN, K., AND COOPER, M. L. Chromosomal aberrations in human disease. Amer. J. Med., 31: 442, 1961.

84. LEJEUNE, J., GAUTIER, M., AND TURPIN, R. Les chromosomes humains en culture de tissus. C. R. Acad. Sci. (Par.), 248: 602, 1959.

85. JACOBS, P. A., BAIKIE, A. G., COURT BROWN, W. M., AND STRONG, J. A. The somatic chromosomes in mongolism. Lancet, 1: 710, 1959.

86. PENROSE, L. S. Relative aetiological importance of birth order and maternal age in mongolism. Proc. Roy. Soc. (Biol.), 115: 431, 1934.

87. PENROSE, L. S. Mongolism. Brit. Med. Bull., 17: 184, 1961.

88. CARR, D. M. The chromosome abnormality in mongolism. Canad. Med. Assn. J., 87: 490, 1962.

89. CARTER, C. O., ET AL. Chromosome translocation as a cause of familial mongolism. Lancet, 2: 678, 1960.

90. FRACCARO, M., KAIJSER, K., AND LINDSTEN, J. Chromosomal abnormalities in father and Mongol child. Lancet, 1: 724, 1960.

91. SERGOVICH, F. R., SOLTAN, H. C., AND CARR, D. H. A 13–15/21 translocation chromosome in carrier father and mongol son. Canad. Med. Assn. J., 87: 852, 1962.

92. GERMAN, J. L., DEMAYO, A. P., AND BEARN, A. G. Inheritance of an abnormal chromosome in Down's syndrome (mongolism) with leukemia. Amer. J. Hum. Genet., 14: 31, 1962.

93. HAMERTON, J. L., ET AL. Differential transmission of Down's syndrome (mongolism) through male and female translocation. Lancet, 2: 956, 1961.

94. KOENIG, E., LUBS, M., AND BRANDT, T. Congenital malformations and autosomal abnormalities. Yale J. Biol. Med., 35: 189, 1962.

95. EDWARDS, J. H., HARNDEN, D. G., CAMERON, A. H., CROSSE, J. M., AND WOLFF, O. W. A new trisomic syndrome. Lancet, 1: 787, 1960.

96. PATAU, K., SMITH, W. D., THERMAN, E., AND INHORN, S. L. Multiple congenital anomalies caused by an extra autosome. Lancet, 1: 790, 1960.

97. BARR, M. L., BERTRAM, L. F., AND LINDSAY, H. A. The morphology of the nerve cell nucleus according to sex. Anat. Rec., 107: 283, 1950.

98. MOORE, K. L., AND BARR, M. L. Nuclear morphology, according to sex in human tissues. Acta Anat., 21: 197, 1954.

99. BARR, M. L., AND CARR, D. H. Correlations between sex chromatin and sex chromosomes. Acta Cytol., 6: 34, 1962.

100. KLINEFELTER, H. F., REIFENSTEIN, F. C., AND ALBRIGHT, F. Syndrome

characterized by gynecomastia, aspermatogenesis without a-leydigism and increased excretion of FSH. J. Clin. Endocr., **2**: 615, 1942.

101. JACOBS, P. A., AND STRONG, J. A. A case of human intersexuality having a possible XXY sex determining mechanism. Nature (Lond.), **183**: 302, 1959.
102. FERGUSON-SMITH, M. A. The prepubertal lesion in chromatin-positive Klinefelter's syndrome as seen in mentally handicapped children. Lancet, **1**: 219, 1959.
103. CARR, D. H., BARR, M. L., PLUNKETT, E. R., GRUMBACH, M. M., MORISHIMA, A., AND CHU, E. H. Y. An XXXY sex chromosome complex in Klinefelter subjects with duplicated sex chromatin. J. Clin. Endocr., **21**: 491, 1961.
104. BARR, M. L., ET AL. An XY/XXXY sex chromosome mosaicism in a mentally defective male patient. J. Ment. Defic. Res., **6**: 65, 1962.
105. FORD, C. E., JONES, K. W., POLANI, P. E., DE ALMEIDA, J. C., AND BIGGS, J. H. A sex chromosome anomaly in a case of gonadal dysgenesis (Turner's syndrome). Lancet, **1**: 711, 1959.
106. JACOBS, P. A., BAIKIE, A. G., COURT BROWN, W. M., MACGREGOR, T. N., AND MACLEAN, N. Evidence for the existence of the human "superfemale." Lancet, **2**: 423, 1959.
107. FRASER, F. C. Genetics and congenital malformations. In *Progress in Medical Genetics*, edited by A. G. Steinberg, p. 38. Grune and Stratton, Inc., New York, 1961.
108. STEVENSON, A. C. The load of hereditary defects in human populations. Radiat. Res. (Suppl.), **1**: 306, 1959.
109. FRANCOIS, J. *L'Hérédité en Ophthalmologie*. Masson et Cie., Paris, 1958.
110a. STERN, C. The problem of complete Y-linkage in man. Amer. J. Hum. Genet., **9**: 147, 1957.
110b. STERN, C. *Principles of Human Genetics*, Ed. 2, Freeman, San Francisco, 1960.
111. WILSON, G. W. Experimental studies on congenital malformations. J. Chron. Dis., **10**: 111, 1959.
112. GIROUD, A., AND MARTINET, M. Action tératogène de l'hypervitaminose A chez la souris en fonction du stade embryonaire. C. R. Soc. Biol. (Par.) **154**: 1353, 1960.
113. HICKS, S. P. The effects of ionizing radiation, certain hormones and radiometric drugs on the developing nervous system. J. Cell. Comp. Physiol., **43**: 151, 1954.
114. CHANG, M. C., AND HUNT, D. M. Effects of *in vitro* radio-cobalt irradiation of rabbit ova on subsequent development *in vivo*, with special reference to the irradiation of maternal organism. Anat. Rec., **137**: 511, 1960.
115. RUGH, R. X-irradiation effects on the human fetus. J. Pediat., **52**: 531, 1958.
116. RUNNER, M. N. Inheritance of susceptibility to congenital deformity. Metabolic clues provided by experiments with teratogenic agents. Pediatrics, **23**: 245, 1959.
117. FRASER, F. C., AND FAINSTAT, T. D. Production of congenital defects in offspring of pregnant mice treated with cortisone. Pediatrics, **8**: 527, 1951.
118. KALTER, H. The inheritance of susceptibility to the teratogenic action of cortisone in mice (abstract). Genetics, **39**: 185, 1954.
119. LANDAUER, W. On the chemical production of developmental abnormalities and of phenocopies in chicken embryos. J. Cell. Comp. Physiol., **43**: 261, 1954.

PART II

SPECIAL EMBRYOLOGY

CHAPTER 7

Formation and Differentiation of the Somite

When the embryo is 17 days old (approximately 1.4 mm.) the intra-embryonic mesoderm forms a thin sheet of loosely woven tissue on each, side of the notochord between the ectodermal and entodermal germ layers (fig. 7-1*A*). Shortly thereafter, when the neural groove becomes clearly visible, the tissue lateral to the midline starts to proliferate and forms the so-called *paraxial mesoderm* (fig. 7-1*B*). These thickened masses of mesoderm gradually thin out toward the periphery, where they continue in the *lateral plates* which, following the appearance and subsequent coalescence of numerous intercellular cavities, are split up into two layers (figs. 7-1*B* and 7-2*A*). These layers, the *somatic* (parietal) and *splanchnic* (visceral) *mesoderm layers* line the *right* and *left intra-embryonic coeloms* and are continuous with the *extra-embryonic mesoderm* covering the wall of the amnion and yolk sac, respectively (fig. 7-2*A*) (see "Coelomic Cavity and Mesenteries," Chapter 13). Although the lateral plates at first are connected to the paraxial tissue

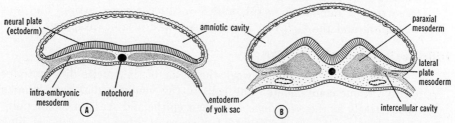

Figure 7-1. *A, Schematic representation of a transverse section through an embryo of approximately 17 days. The mesoderm forms a thin sheet of tissue between the ectodermal and entodermal germ layers on each side of the notochord. B, Similar section through a 19-day embryo, showing the paraxial mesoderm and the lateral plate mesoderm. Note the intercellular cavities in the lateral plate.*

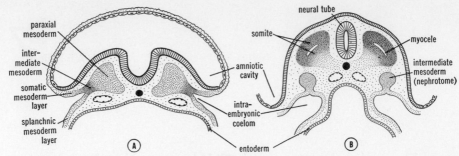

Figure 7-2. *A, Transverse section through a 20-day embryo, showing the paraxial and intermediate mesoderm. The lateral plate is split into the somatic (parietal) and splanchnic (visceral) mesoderm layers which line the intra-embryonic coelomic cavity. B, Similar section through a 21-day embryo. The intermediate mesoderm has lost its contact with the somite and will soon develop into a nephrotome.*

by the *intermediate mesoderm*, this contact is soon lost (fig. 7-2*A*, *B*). The intermediate mesoderm then begins to proliferate and forms the excretory units of the urinary system, known as the *nephrotomes* (fig. 7-2*B*) (see "Urogenital System," Chapter 10).

Formation of the Somite

At the end of the third week the paraxial mesoderm, which initially forms a longitudinal strip of solid tissue on each side of the neural tube, becomes segmented into blocks of epithelioid cells, the *somites* (fig. 7-3*A*, *B*). These initially contain a small central cavity, which with time is obliterated by proliferation of the surrounding cells (fig. 7-2*B*).

The first pair of somites develops immediately caudal to the cepahlic tip of the notochord. From here the succeeding ones arise in cranio-caudal direction until, at the end of the fifth week, 42 to 44 pairs of somites are present (fig. 7-3*A*, *B*). These are 4 occipital, 8 cervical, 12 thoracic, 5 lumbar, 5 sacral, and 8 to 10 coccygeal pairs. The first occipital and the last 5 to 7 coccygeal somites later disappear.

Differentiation of the Somite

At the end of the fourth week the tissue of the somite differentiates into various components. The cells in the ventromedial part, known collectively as the *sclerotome*, lose their epithelioid shape, become polymorphous, and establish contact with each other by means of long cellular processes. The spaces between the cells are gradually filled with a jelly-like substance, which in all likelihood is secreted by the cells. The tissue so formed is known as *mesenchyme*, or young connective tissue, and forms a kind of packing tissue between organs.

       Special Embryology

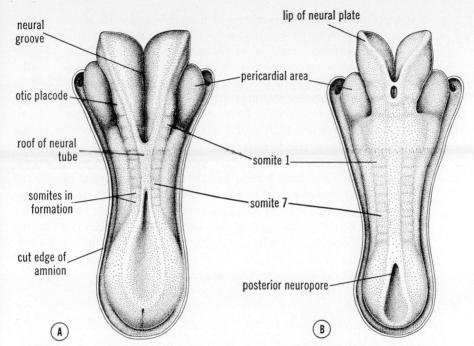

Figure 7-3. *Dorsal view of human embryo, showing the formation of the somites. A, Approximately 22 days old (modified after Payne); B, approximately 23 days old (modified after Corner). The somites on each side of the neural tube are clearly visible through the transparent overlying ectoderm.*

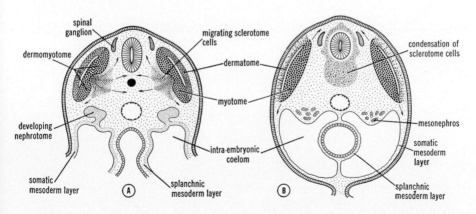

Figure 7-4. *A, Schematic representation of a transverse section through a 26-day embryo. The cells of the sclerotome migrate toward the midline, while the remaining cells of the somite form the dermomyotome. Note the developing nephrotome. B, Similar section through a 28-day embryo. The sclerotome cells condense around the neural tube to form the axial skeleton. The arrows indicate the direction in which the cells of the myotome and dermatome migrate.*

Formation of the Somite

One of the main characteristics of mesenchymal cells is their capacity to develop in many different ways.[1-3] They may become fibroblasts, associated with the formation of the reticular, collagenous, and elastic fibers as seen in connective tissue; chondroblasts, involved in the formation of cartilage; or osteoblasts, associated with bone formation (see "Skeletal System," Chapter 8).

After the sclerotome cells have split off from the somite and migrated medially (figs. 7-2B and 7-4A), the remaining portion of the somite is known as the *dermomyotome* (fig. 7-4A, B). The cells of the medial part of the dermomyotome subsequently proliferate, become spindle-shaped, and form young muscle cells or *myoblasts*. Hence, the tissue so composed is known as the *myotome*, and provides the musculature of its own segment (see "Muscular System," Chapter 9).

The cells of the lateral part of the somite, known collectively as the *dermatome*, become mesenchymatous and spread out under the overlying ectoderm. Here they form the dermis and subcutaneous tissue of the skin (see "Integumentary System," Chapter 18).

References

1. BLOOM, W. Cellular differentiation and tissue culture. Physiol. Rev., 17: 589, 1937.
2. FISHER, F. *Biology of Tissue Cells*. Cambridge University Press, London, 1946.
3. WILLIER, B. H., WEISS, P. A., AND HAMBURGER, V. *Analysis of Development.* W. B. Saunders Co., Philadelphia, 1955.

Special Embryology

CHAPTER 8

Skeletal System

NORMAL DEVELOPMENT
- CHONDROGENESIS
- OSTEOGENESIS: *membranous ossification; endochondral ossification*
- AXIAL SKELETON: *vertebral column*
- SKULL: *neurocranium; viscerocranium*
- JOINTS: *diarthroses; synarthroses*

CONGENITAL MALFORMATIONS
- VERTEBRAL COLUMN: *spina bifida*
- RIBS
- CLAVICLES: *cleidodysostosis*
- STERNUM
- SKULL: *microcephalus; acrocephalus*
- APPENDICULAR SKELETON: *amelia; phocomelia; micromelia; sympodia; syndactyly; lobster claw*

Normal Development

Chondrogenesis

The first sign of cartilage formation can be noted in embryos approximately 5 weeks old. In those areas where cartilage is to be formed the mesenchyme cells then begin to proliferate actively, acquire a round shape (*chondroblasts*), and form a compact, cell-rich tissue known as *precartilage*. The intercellular spaces of this tissue contain collagenous fibers embedded in a homogeneous basophilic substance, the so-called ground substance. With further development, this intercellular material, the *cartilage matrix*, becomes so voluminous that the cells are pushed apart. According to the type of matrix, three different kinds of cartilage are finally distinguishable: (1) *hyaline cartilage*, found on the articular surfaces of bones in the synovial joints, contains an intercellular substance with fine white collagenous fibrils embedded in a large amount of ground substance; (2) *fibrous cartilage*, found in the intervertebral discs, contains many heavy white fibers embedded in a lesser amount of ground substance; and (3) *elastic cartilage* which, in addition to collagenous fibers and ground substance, contains branching yellow elastic fibers.

Osteogenesis

Membranous Ossification

In those areas where membranous bone tissue is formed, the cells of the mesenchyme begin to proliferate actively and gradually change shape. The newly formed cells, the *osteoblasts*, have a basophilic cytoplasm, whereas their nuclei are located in an eccentric position (fig. 8-1A).[1]

The osteoblasts, initially arranged in irregular fashion, later arrange themselves in regular rows and secrete a collagenous material known as *prebone* or *osteoid*. This material gives the tissue a membranous appearance, hence this type of ossification is called *membranous ossification*. At some distance from the osteoblasts, the first-formed prebone

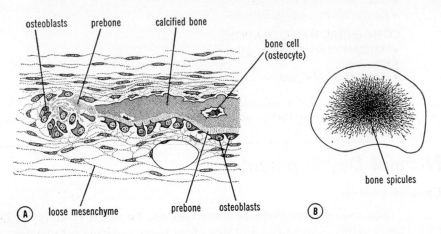

Figure 8-1. *A, Schematic drawing to show the membranous ossification. On the left side the mesenchyme cells are transformed into irregularly arranged osteoblasts which deposit the prebone. Toward the right, the osteoblasts are arranged in regular rows, where they continue to secrete prebone or osteoid. At some distance from the osteoblasts the prebone is transformed into a bone matrix, which calcifies. The newly formed bone always remains separated from the osteoblasts by a thin layer of prebone. Note how a few osteoblasts are trapped in the calcified bone to become bone cells or osteocytes. B, Schematic representation of a membranous bone of the skull approximately 3 months old (drawn after a cleared preparation stained with alizarin). It shows the spread of the bone spicules from the ossification center toward the periphery.*

Special Embryology

is transformed into bone matrix which subsequently calcifies. This calcification is believed to result from the release by the osteoblasts of the enzyme, phosphatase.[2] The newly formed bone is always separated from the osteoblasts by a thin layer of prebone. A few of the osteoblasts, however, become trapped in the bone itself to form the bone cells or *osteocytes* (fig. 8-1*A*). In this manner, a number of needle-like *bone spicules* are formed which, with time, progressively radiate from the primary ossification centers toward the periphery, thereby giving rise to trabecular bone (fig. 8-1*B*). In the meantime, a great number of capillaries have penetrated between the bone spicules of the ossification centers, thus forming highly vascularized primary bone.

When ossification of the primary center is well on its way, the entire primordium is surrounded by dense vascular mesenchyme which forms the *periosteum*. On the inner surface of this layer the mesenchymal cells differentiate into osteoblasts, which deposit parallel bony plates on the surface of the primary ossification center. These parallel plates of bone formed by the periost are known as *periosteal* or *compact bone*.

With each new layer of bone added to the surface, some osteoblasts are trapped to become the bone cells or osteocytes. These cells are located in small lacunae and are in contact with similar neighboring cells by means of small canals, the *canaliculi*. The osteoblasts so lost are continuously replaced by new ones formed by the periosteum.

In postnatal life membranous bones, as found in the skull, enlarge by apposition of new layers on the surface and in the sutures, and by simultaneous osteoclastic resorption from the inside.[3]

Endochondral Ossification

By the seventh week of development the long bones of the extremities are represented by hyaline cartilage "models" (fig. 8-2*A*). On their surface, these cartilage models are covered with dense vascular mesenchyme, which initially forms the perichondrium, but later develops into the *periosteum*.

Soon a vascular bud accompanied by large mesenchymal cells invades the center of the cartilage shaft, and around the erosion sites the cells respond in such a manner that eventually four zones, each representing a specific stage in the formation of the endochondral bone tissue, can be recognized (fig. 8-2*B*): (1) a zone in which the cartilage cells show abundant mitoses; (2) a zone of cell hypertrophy; (3) a zone where the cells die and the intercellular matrix becomes impregnated with calcium salts; and (4) a zone of actively growing capillaries which occupy the lacunae left by the dead cells.

Accompanying the invading capillaries are specialized mesenchymal cells, the *osteoclasts*, which break down the calcified cartilage matrix, thus causing the initial small lacunae to fuse. Other specialized mesen-

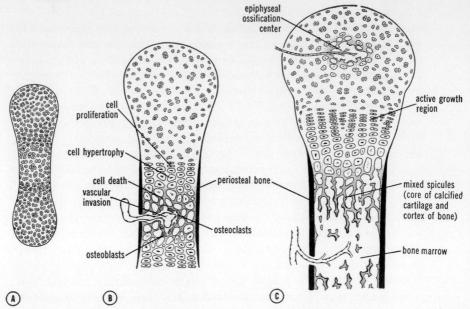

Figure 8-2. *Schematic representation of the endochondral ossification. A, Hyaline cartilage model. B, Around the erosion site, where a vascular bud invades the center of the shaft, can be recognized: (1) zone of cell proliferation, (2) zone of cell hypertrophy, (3) zone of cell death where the matrix is impregnated with calcium salts, (4) lacunar zone with osteoclasts and osteoblasts. Note the deposition of periosteal bone along the periphery of the shaft. C, The central bone spicules disappear while the lateral ones reinforce the wall of the bone. Note the ossification proceeding in the epiphysis in a manner similar to that in the primary center.*

chyme cells, the *osteoblasts*, then arrange themselves along the walls of the newly formed large lacunae and deposit bone along the remaining cartilaginous spicules (fig. 8-2B, C). This process, known as *endochondral ossification*, gives rise to bone-coated cartilage spicules (*mixed spicules*).

Shortly after their formation, a great number of the centrally located bone spicules are broken down by osteoclasts, leaving only the lateral ones intact to reinforce the walls of the bone. As a result of this resorption a broad marrow cavity appears in the center of the bone (fig. 8-2C).

From the primary ossification center in the shaft or diaphysis of the bone, the endochondral ossification progresses gradually toward the ends of the cartilaginous "model." Although the cartilage cells close to the marrow cavity are swollen, those farther away are small and crowded, and multiply actively, thus forming a region of active growth at each end of the marrow cavity (fig. 8-2C).

At birth, the diaphysis of the bone is usually completely ossified but the two extremities, known as the *epiphyses*, are still cartilaginous. Shortly thereafter, however, ossification centers arise in these epiphyses, and endochondral ossification proceeds here in a manner similar to that of the diaphysis of the bone (fig. 8-2C). Finally, the epiphyses are composed of spongy bone covered by a cartilaginous shell.

A cartilage plate remains temporarily between the diaphyseal and epiphyseal ossification centers. This plate, known as the *epiphyseal plate*, plays an important role in the growth in length of the bone (fig. 8-3). On either surface endochondral ossification proceeds, rapidly on the diaphyseal side and very slowly on the epiphyseal side. When the

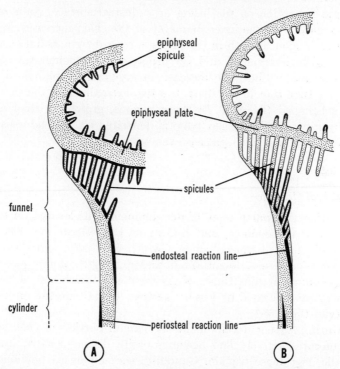

Figure 8-3. *A, Diagram representing part of the head and shaft of a long bone in a young, growing rat killed a few hours after subcutaneous injection of radiophosphorus (P^{32}). (Phosphorus is incorporated at the sites of active bone deposition.) The heavy black lines indicate the surfaces where the reactive material is deposited, that is, on each side of the epiphyseal plate, the spicules of the metaphysis and epiphysis, the endosteal surface of the funnel-shaped portion, and the periosteal surface of the cylindrical portion of the shaft. B, Diagram showing the distribution of radiophosphorus several days after the injection. The reactive material is now found in the spicules well below and above the epiphyseal plate, and in the interior of the compacta of the shaft. The reactive line found on the endosteal surface of the funnel soon after injection is now deeply embedded in the bone along most of the length of the funnel and is even resorbed by osteoclastic activity at the wider end (slightly modified after Leblond and Greulich).*

bone has acquired its full length the epiphyseal plates disappear and the epiphyses unite with the shaft of the bone.

In the long bones an epiphyseal plate is found on each extremity; in the smaller ones, such as the phalanges, an epiphyseal plate is present only at one extremity; and in irregular bones, such as the vertebrae, one or more primary centers of ossification, and usually several secondary centers, are found.[4]

Whereas growth in length takes place at the epiphyseal plates, growth in thickness is more complicated. In the straight part of the shaft, the so-called *cylinder*, the bone grows by deposition of new layers of periosteal bone on the outer surface, and by simultaneous osteoclastic resorption on the inside or endosteal surface. As a result, the outer as well as the inner diameter of the shaft increases. In the epiphyseal region, growth in thickness is caused by a radial expansion of the cartilaginous shell and by progressive endochondral ossification on the inside. Since the increase in size in the epiphyseal region is greater than that in the shaft, the two extremities of the shaft become funnel-shaped (fig. 8-3). In these regions, growth in thickness is entirely different. Here, new bone is deposited on the endosteal surface, while resorption takes place on the outer surface.[5]

Axial Skeleton

Vertebral Column

During the fourth week of development cells located on the medial aspect of the somites, and known as the sclerotome cells, migrate medially toward the notochord, which gradually comes to lie in the center of a dense, longitudinal mesenchymal column (see fig. 7-4). This column retains traces of its segmental origin as the sclerotomic blocks are separated by less dense areas containing the intersegmental arteries (fig. 8-4A).

During further development the caudal portion of each sclerotome proliferates actively and becomes easily distinguishable from its cephalic, less dense portion. Caudally, the condensed portion joins the cephalic part of the underlying sclerotome, and the intersegmental tissue is thus incorporated into the *precartilaginous vertebral body* (fig. 8-4B). Hence, the body of the vertebra is intersegmental in origin.[6]

Cells originating in the cephalic part of the underlying vertebral body fill the space between two precartilaginous vertebral bodies and so contribute to the formation of the *intervertebral disc*.[7] While the notochord regresses entirely in the region of the vertebral bodies, it persists and enlarges in the region of the intervertebral discs. Here it undergoes mucoid degeneration and forms the *nucleus pulposus*, which is later surrounded by the circular fibers of the *annulus fibrosis* (fig. 8-4B).[8] Combined, these two structures form the *intervertebral disc*.

Special Embryology

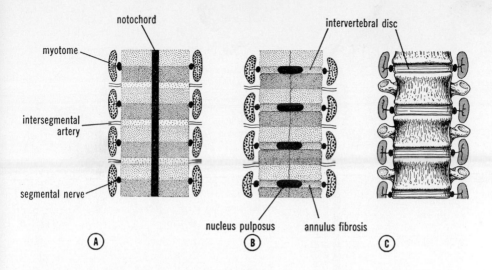

myotome

notochord

intervertebral disc

intersegmental artery

segmental nerve

nucleus pulposus   annulus fibrosis

(A)   (B)   (C)

Figure 8-4. *Scheme to show the formation of the vertebral column at various stages of development. A, At the fourth week of development the sclerotomes surrounding the notochord show a dense caudal and a less dense cephalic portion. Note the position of the myotomes, intersegmental arteries, and segmental nerves. B, The precartilaginous vertebral bodies are formed by the upper and lower halves of two successive sclerotomes and the intersegmental tissue. The notochord degenerates except in the region of the intervertebral disc, where it forms the nucleus pulposus. C, The vertebral column in the adult. The myotomes overbridge the intervertebral discs.*

The rearrangement of the sclerotomes into the definitive vertebrae causes the myotomes to bridge the intervertebral discs, and this alteration gives them the opportunity of moving the spine (fig. 8-4*B*, *C*). For the same reason, the intersegmental arteries, at first located between the sclerotomes, now pass midway over the vertebral bodies. The spinal nerves, however, segmental in origin, come to lie near the intervertebral discs and leave the vertebral column through the intervertebral foramina.

Skull

The skull can be divided into two parts: the *neurocranium*, which forms a protective case around the brain, and the *viscerocranium*, which gives rise to the skeleton of the face. Both portions are initially formed by dense mesenchyme; later some parts are converted into membranous bone, and others into cartilage. The latter, in turn, may persist throughout life or undergo endochondral ossification.

Neurocranium

The neurocranium is, from a developmental standpoint, most conveniently divided into two portions: (1) the *base of the skull*, or *chondro-*

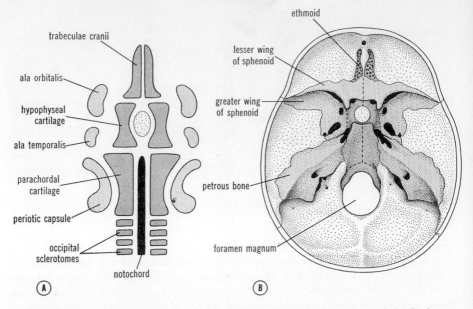

Figure 8-5. *A, Diagram showing the different components that play a role in the formation of the base of the skull or chondrocranium (modified after Clara). B, Schematized dorsal view of the chondrocranium in the adult, showing the derivatives of the various components represented in A.*

cranium, which undergoes endochondral ossification; and (2) the *flat bones,* which undergo membranous ossification.

An important role in the formation of the base of the skull is played by the notochord, which initially extends to the buccopharyngeal membrane but which, with development of the hypophysis, terminates directly behind the sella turcica. Chondrification of the mesenchyme surrounding the cephalic portion of the notochord results in the formation of the unpaired *parachordal cartilage* or *basal plate* (fig. 8-5). This plate extends in the midplane from a point caudal to the sella turcica to the occipital somites which during early embryonic life form four fairly typical sclerotomes. The most cephalic of these sclerotomes disappears completely,[9] but the remaining three persist and form an unsegmented cartilage, fusing with the basal plate. Hence, the base of the occipital bone is formed by the parachordal cartilage and the bodies of the occipital sclerotomes (fig. 8-5). Later, this part extends dorsally around the neural tube to form the *occipital tectum.* Although the original segmentation of the occipital sclerotomes is lost, some evidence of it is retained in the structure of the hypoglossal canal. Occasionally, the hypoglossal nerve leaves the skull through a canal which is divided by a bony bridge into two separate compartments.

Special Embryology

Rostral to the parachordal plate are found the *hypophyseal* or *polar cartilages* flanking the hypophysis and the *trabeculae cranii* (fig. 8-5). These cartilages soon fuse to form the body of the sphenoid and ethmoid, respectively. In this manner an elongated median plate of cartilage, extending from the nasal region to the anterior border of the foramen magnum, is formed.

A number of other mesenchymal condensations arise on either side of this median plate. The most rostral of these, the *ala orbitalis* or *orbitosphenoid*, forms the lesser wing of the sphenoid bone. Caudally, it is followed by the *ala temporalis* or *alisphenoid*, which gives rise to the greater wing of the sphenoid. These components later fuse with the median plate and with each other, except for the openings through which the second, third, fourth, and sixth cranial nerves, as well as the first two divisions of the fifth, leave the skull (fig. 8-5*B*).

A third component, which lies lateral to the parachordal plate and posterior to the ala temporalis, is formed by the *periotic capsule*.[10] This capsule, surrounding the otic vesicle, gives rise to the petrous and mastoid parts of the temporal bone. Later, this portion fuses with the ala temporalis and the parachordal plate except for the large *jugular foramen* through which pass the internal jugular vein and the ninth, 10th, and 11th cranial nerves. The periotic capsule itself is medially pierced by an opening for the seventh and eighth cranial nerves.

The base of the skull is thus formed by cartilage which subsequently is transformed into bone by endochondral ossification.

In contrast to the base of the skull, the lateral sides and roof, formed by the frontals, parietals, squamous temporals, and part of the occipitals, undergo membranous ossification.

At birth the flat bones of the skull are separated from each other by narrow seams of connective tissue, the *sutures*. At points where more than two bones meet, the sutures are wide and known as the *fontanelles* (fig. 8-6). The most prominent of these is the anterior fontanelle, found at the point where the two parietals and two frontals meet. In the first few years after birth, palpation of this fontanelle may give valuable information as to whether ossification is proceeding normally.

Viscerocranium

The viscerocranium is formed by the cartilaginous bars of the first two pharyngeal arches, which are later supplemented and partly replaced by membranous bones. The first or mandibular arch gives rise to a dorsal portion, the *maxillary process*, extending forward beneath the region of the eye, and a ventral portion, known as *Meckel's cartilage*. The dorsal tip of the mandibular process, along with that of the second pharyngeal arch (*Reichert's cartilage*), later articulate with the posterior

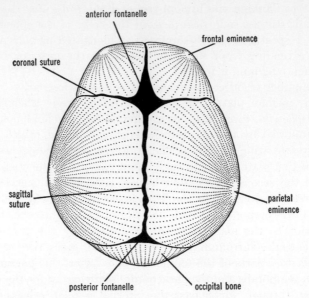

Figure 8-6. *Skull of a newborn, seen from above. Note the anterior and posterior fontanelles and the sutures.*

portion of the maxillary process, the *pterygoquadrate bar*. With further development this bar develops into the *incus*, while the dorsal portions of Meckel's and Reichert's cartilage give rise to the *malleus* and *stapes*, respectively. Ossification of the cartilaginous malleus, incus, and stapes begins in the fourth month, thus making these the first bones to become fully ossified (see also Chap. 12, pp 203–205, and Chap 16).

Joints

Diarthroses or Synovial Joints

The first indication of the skeletal elements in the extremities appears in the fifth week of development as mesodermal condensations within the core of the limb buds. These condensations subsequently show a number of chondrification centers, one for each skeletal element, and the mesenchyme that remains between two or more chondrifying elements forms a homogeneous tissue known as the *interzone* (fig. 8-7A). In the synovial joints the interzone is three-layered: two chondrogenic layers continuous with the perichondria of the future skeletal elements, and an intermediate avascular layer (fig. 8-7B).[11] Toward the periphery this avascular layer is continuous with the surrounding mesenchyme, the *synovial mesenchyme*, which is bounded by the future *fibrous capsule* (fig. 8-7B).[12] At about the sixth week small cavities appear in the

Special Embryology

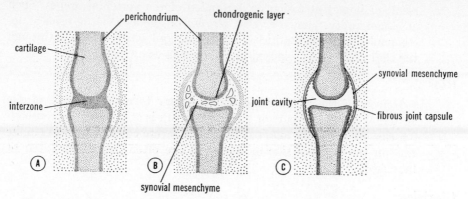

Figure 8-7. *Schematic representation of three stages in the development of a synovial joint.*

synovial mesenchyme and intermediate layer. After coalescence of these clefts the joint cavity is formed.

The mesenchymal cells lining the inside of the joint cavity differentiate into flattened mesothelial cells, which form the *synovial membrane*, while the dense tissue on the outside of the joint gives rise to the fibrous capsule (fig. 8-7C). Intra-articular structures, such as menisci and discs, arise as condensations in the synovial mesenchyme before cavitation occurs.[13-15]

Synarthroses

In the more simple joints, such as those between the bones of the skull, the mesenchyme persists and does not show any cavitation. Such joints, the *synarthroses*, are divided into three types: (1) *syndesmoses*, in which the mesenchymal tissue of the interzone is converted into fibrous tissue; (2) *synchondroses*, in which the interzone becomes chondrified; and (3) *synostoses*, in which the tissue between the bones becomes ossified.

Congenital Malformations

Vertebral Column

Spina Bifida

The formation and subsequent rearrangement of the segmental sclerotomes into the definitive vertebrae is a complicated process and it is therefore not uncommon that two successive vertebrae fuse asymmetrically or that half a vertebra is missing. Likewise, it is not infrequently noted that the regular number of vertebrae is increased or decreased. One of the most serious vertebral defects, however, is the result of imperfect fusion or non-union of the vertebral arches. Such an abnormality, known as *cleft vertebra* or *spina bifida*, is usually accompanied by abnormalities of the spinal cord which herniates through the cleft and is thus exposed to the outside (see Chapter 14).

Ribs

Defects of the ribs are mostly secondary to malformations of the vertebral column. If part or all of a vertebra is absent, the corresponding ribs are generally missing. In case of severe congenital scoliosis the ribs on the concave side of the chest are often irregularly fused or branched.

Clavicles

Cleidodysostosis

Absence of all or part of the clavicle is known as *cleidodysostosis*. In such a defect, which is usually bilateral, the shoulders can be drawn forward to meet under the chin. This abnormality is often associated with skull defects and is then known as *cleidocranial dysostosis*.

Sternum

Clefts of the sternum are seen as isolated anomalies but are usually associated with severe malformations of the chest.

Skull

Microcephalus; Acrocephalus

Abnormalities of the skull are manifold and either all or part of the skull is involved. They are frequently associated with brain defects, which in turn are often incompatible with life (see Chapter 14). When the sutures between the various flat bones of the skull close prematurely, the result may be *microcephalus* or *acrocephalus*.

Appendicular Skeleton

Amelia; Phocomelia; Micromelia; Sympodia; Syndactyly; Lobster Claw

The abnormalities of the extremities vary greatly. In the most extreme form, all four extremities may be absent (*amelia*), or represented only by hands and feet attached to the trunk by a small, irregularly shaped bone, a defect known as *phocomelia*. Sometimes all segments of the extremities are present, but abnormally short (*micromelia*).

In addition to complete or partial absence of the extremities, occasionally the lower limbs may be fused (*sympodia* or *sirenomelia*), a defect always associated with a profound disturbance in the formation of the pelvis. The single lower extremity then most commonly contains a single femur, two or three bones below the knee, and five or six digits attached to the foot. Sometimes abnormal fusion involves only the fingers of one hand, a condition known as *syndactyly*.

Abnormalities consisting of absence of a bone or part of a bone usually involve only one extremity, whereas those in which an excessive number of bones is present are mostly bilateral. For example, absence of a thumb is usually unilateral, whereas duplication is often bilateral.

A *lobster claw* deformity consists of an abnormal cleft between the central metacarpal bones and soft tissues, dividing the hand into two parts. The third metacarpal and phalangeal bones are almost always absent.

Although abnormalities of the limbs such as phocomelia and amelia were considered hereditary, recently it was revealed dramatically that they likewise can be produced by environmental teratogenic factors. During the last couple of years in West Germany, the high frequency of children born with phocomelia led to a review of the prenatal histories of the affected children.[16] It was thus noted that many of the mothers reported having taken thalidomide, a new drug widely used as a sleeping pill and anti-nauseant. It is interesting to know that in several cases neither the physician nor the mother could remember any exposure to the drug, but examination of the druggist's records showed that it had indeed been prescribed.[17] It is now well accepted that thalidomide, when taken in the early stages of pregnancy, can cause a characteristic syndrome of malformations, consisting of absence or gross deformities of the long bones, intestinal atresias, and cardiac anomalies[18-20] (see Chapter 6).

Production of similar defects in offspring of pregnant rabbits given thalidomide removed all doubts about the causal association.[21] Although it is too early to estimate precisely the frequency with which malformations occur as a result of taking the drug, the probability is roughly estimated at about 20 per cent.[22]

The teratogenic action of thalidomide was discovered only because it produced malformations of a very unusual kind. It is therefore not unreasonable to wonder how many malformations of more common nature are being produced by the new drugs appearing on the market. It is good to keep in mind that many new drugs are being given during early pregnancy and there is not an adequate amount of evidence to show that these are completely nontoxic to the embryo.

References

1. PRITCHARD, J. J. The osteoblast. In *The Biochemistry and Physiology of Bone*, edited by G. H. Bourne. Academic Press, Inc., New York, 1956.
2. BOURNE, G. H. (editor). Phosphatase and bone. In *The Biochemistry and Physiology of Bone*. Academic Press, Inc., New York, 1956.

3. HANCOX, N. M. The osteoclast. In *The Biochemistry and Physiology of Bone*, edited by G. H. Bourne. Academic Press, Inc., New York, 1956.
4. GARDNER, E. Osteogenesis in the human embryo and fetus. In *The Biochemistry and Physiology of Bone*, edited by G. H. Bourne. Academic Press, Inc., New York, 1956.
5. LEBLOND, C. P., AND GREULICH, R. C. Autoradiographic studies of bone formation and growth. In *The Biochemistry and Physiology of Bone*, edited by G. H. Bourne. Academic Press, Inc., New York, 1956.
6. SENSENIG, E. C. The early development of the human vertebral column. Contrib. Embryol., **33**: 21, 1949.
7. PRADER, A. Die frühembryonal Entwicklung der menschlichen Zwischenwirbelscheibe. Acta Anat. (Basel), **3**: 68, 1947.
8. PEACOCK, A. Observations on the prenatal development of the intervertebral disc in man. J. Anat., **85**: 260, 1951.
9. AREY, H. B. The history of the first somite in human embryos. Contrib. Embryol., **27**: 235, 1938.
10. BAST, T. H., AND ANSON, B. J. *The Temporal Bone and the Ear*. Charles C Thomas, Springfield, Ill., 1949.
11. HAINES, R. W. The development of joints. J. Anat., **81**: 33, 1947.
12. BARNETT, C. H., DAVIES, D. V., AND MACCONAILL, M. A. *Synovial Joints. Their Structure and Mechanics*. Longmans, Green & Co., Inc., London, 1961.
13. GARDNER, E., AND GRAY, D. J. Prenatal development of the human hipjoint. Amer. J. Anat., **87**: 163, 1950.
14. GARDNER, E., AND GRAY, D. J. Prenatal development of the human shoulder and acromioclavicular joints. Amer. J. Anat., **92**: 219, 1953.
15. GRAY, D. J., GARDNER, E., AND O'RAHILLY, R. The prenatal development of the skeleton and joints of the human hand. Amer. J. Anat., **101**: 169, 1957.
16. LENZ, W. Thalidomide and congenital abnormalities. Lancet, **1**: 1219, 1962.
17. SPEIRS, H. L. Thalidomide and congenital abnormalities. Lancet, **1**: 303, 1962.
18. WEICKER, H., AND HUNGERLAND, H. Thalidomid-embryopathie. I. Vorkommen inner und ausserhalb Deutschlands. Deutsch. Med. Wschr., **87**: 992, 1962.
19. VICKERS, T. H. Congenital abnormalities and thalidomide. Med. J. Aust., **1**: 649, 1962.
20. DEVITT, R. E. F., AND KENNY, S. Thalidomide and congenital abnormalities. Lancet, **1**: 430, 1962.
21. SOMERS, G. F. Thalidomide and congenital abnormalities. Lancet, **1**: 912, 1962.
22. McBRIDE, W. G. Thalidomide and congenital abnormalities. Lancet, **2**: 1358, 1961.

CHAPTER 9

Muscular System

Cross-striated Musculature

Myotome

After the cells of the sclerotome and dermatome have migrated from the somite, the remaining tissue is known as the myotome (fig. 9-1*A*, *B*). The cells composing this tissue are at first epithelioid, but soon

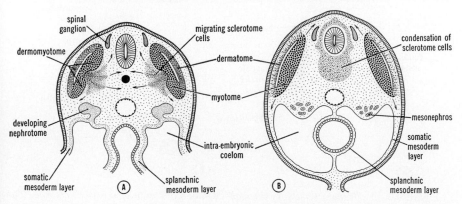

Figure 9-1. *A, Diagrammatic transverse section through a 4-week embryo, showing the migration of the sclerotome cells. The cells of the myotome form the ventromedial portion of the remaining tissue. B, Similar section as in A, showing the condensation of the sclerotome cells in the midline and the migration of the cells of the dermatome. The cells of the myotome migrate in a dorsal and ventral direction as indicated by arrows.*

become elongated and spindle-shaped, with round nuclei, thus forming the primitive muscle cells or *myoblasts*. Although formation of the myotome is essentially the same in all segments from the second occipital to the third or fourth coccygeal, the most typical development occurs in the thoracic segments. Here, the myotome enlarges rapidly and the myoblasts migrate dorsally, flanking the neural tube, and ventrally, extending into the somatic mesoderm layer (figs. 9-1*B* and 9-2*A*). At the end of the fifth week the myotome is divided into a small dorsal portion, the *epimere*, and a larger ventral part, the *hypomere* (fig. 9-2*A*). The two portions remain connected to each other by a plate of mesenchyme, known as the *intermuscular septum*, which is later attached cranially and caudally to the transverse processes of two successive vertebrae. Similarly, the nerve innervating the myotome is divided into a *dorsal primary ramus* for the epimere, and a *ventral primary ramus* for the hypomere (fig. 9-2*A*).

The dorsal portions of the myotomes finally give rise to the extensor muscles of the vertebral column, while the ventrolateral portions form the lateral and ventral flexor musculature (fig. 9-2*B*). The latter, however, splits into three layers which, in the thorax, are represented by the *external intercostal*, *internal intercostal*, and a deep *intracostal* or *transverse thoracic muscle*. In the abdominal wall these three muscle

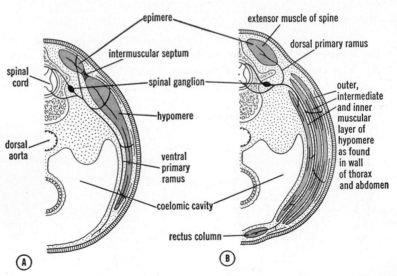

Figure 9-2. *A*, *Transverse section through the thoracic region of a 5-week embryo. The dorsal portion of the myotome (epimere) is connected to the ventral portion (hypomere) by a mesenchymatous intermuscular septum. The innervating nerve is divided into a dorsal primary ramus for the epimere, and a ventral primary ramus for the hypomere. B, Similar section as in A, though at a later stage of development. The hypomere has formed three separate muscle layers and a ventral longitudinal muscle (modified after Clara).*

layers consist of the *external oblique, internal oblique,* and *transverse abdominis muscles.* The muscles in the wall of the thorax maintain their segmental character, owing to the ribs, whereas in the abdominal wall the myotomes of the various segments combine to form large sheets of muscle tissue.

In addition to the above three layers, the ventral tips of the hypomeres form buds which grow along the ventral aspect of the body, where they unite to give rise to a longitudinal muscular column (fig. 9-2B). In the abdominal region this column is represented by the *rectus abdominis* muscle, and in the cervical region by the *infrahyoid musculature.* In the thoracic region this longitudinal muscle normally disappears but is occasionally represented by the *sternalis muscle.*

Occipital and Preotic Myotomes

In the head region the development of the myotomes is not so clear. Initially, four pairs of occipital somites can be distinguished, but the most cephalic of these disappears soon after its formation.[1] It is generally believed that the myoblasts of the three remaining occipital myotomes migrate forward and finally form the extrinsic and intrinsic musculature of the tongue (fig. 9-3A).[2, 3]

Although the origin of the extrinsic muscles of the eye has not been traced in mammalian embryos, it has been suggested that these muscles originate from mesoderm surrounding the prochordal plate[4] (see

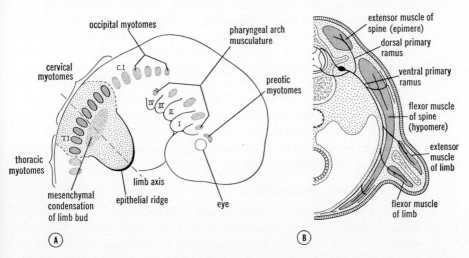

Figure 9-3. *A, Schematic representation of the myotomes in the head, neck, and thorax region of a 7-week embryo. The superior limb bud is attached opposite the lower six cervical and upper two thoracic segments. Note the localization of the preotic and occipital myotomes and the condensation of mesenchyme at the base of the limb bud. B, Transverse section through the region of attachment of the limb bud. Each segment forms both a dorsal (extensor) and a ventral (flexor) muscular component in the limb bud.*

Chapter 3). This mesoderm is thought to form three myotomes known as the *preotic myotomes* (fig. 9-3A). The eye muscles derived from these myotomes are later innervated by the third, fourth, and sixth cranial nerves.

Limb Musculature

In the lower cervical and upper thoracic regions as well as in the lumbar and sacral regions the migration of the hypomeres is complicated by the development of the limb buds. These flattened buds appear in the sixth week of development and have a craniocaudal attachment to the body (fig. 9-3A). The upper limb buds lie opposite the lower six cervical and upper two thoracic segments; the lower limb buds, opposite the lower four lumbar and upper three sacral segments.

The first indication of the limb musculature is found in the seventh week of development as a condensation of mesenchyme near the base of the buds (fig. 9-3A). Whether in the human embryo this mesenchyme is derived from the somatic mesoderm layer or the neighboring somites, as has been shown in some lower vertebrates, is unknown.[5] Taking into account the segmental innervation of the limb musculature as seen in the adult, it would seem that this musculature is of segmental origin in man also.

With elongation of the limb buds the segmented muscular tissue, as yet undifferentiated, penetrates the buds, thereby splitting up into ventral (flexor) and dorsal (extensor) components (fig. 9-3B). With time, the muscles lose their segmental character and are then composed of muscle tissue derived from several segments. The innervating nerves follow a similar pattern. At first they enter the limb bud with isolated dorsal and ventral branches, but soon these branches unite to form large dorsal and ventral nerves. Thus the radial nerve which supplies the extensor musculature is formed by combination of the dorsal segmental branches, whereas the ulnar and median nerves, which supply the flexor musculature, are formed by combination of the ventral branches of the segmental nerves.

Pharyngeal Arch Musculature

Not all cross-striated muscles are derived from the myotomes; some develop from the mesoderm of the pharyngeal arches. When the embryo is approximately 7 weeks old the mesodermal cells located in the dorsal end of the arches differentiate into myoblasts, which subsequently migrate in various directions. Despite their extensive migration their origin can always be traced, as they remain innervated by the nerve of the arch of origin (see Chapter 12, pages 203–205).

Postnatal growth of the cross-striated muscle fibers is almost entirely due to enlargement of preexisting fibers, but is associated with

Special Embryology

an increase in the number of nuclei.[6] In case of injury to a few muscle fibers, regeneration is complete; if, however, damage is extensive, the injured muscle fibers are replaced by fibrous tissue.[7, 8]

Smooth Musculature

Smooth muscle tissue develops mainly from the splanchnic mesoderm layer surrounding the gastrointestinal tract and its derivatives. Here the mesodermal cells form the muscle coat of the gut, trachea, and bronchi, as well as that of the vessels found in the mesenteries. The vessels which develop in the limb buds, head, and body wall obtain their muscular coat from local mesenchyme. In fact, mesenchyme anywhere in the body is a potential source of smooth muscle tissue.

The smooth muscles of the iris form an exception. These muscles, the *sphincter* and *dilatator pupillae*, are thought to differentiate from the ectoderm of the optic cup[9, 10] (see Chapter 15).

References

1. AREY, H. B. The history of the first somite in human embryos. Contrib. Embryol., **27**: 235, 1938.
2. BATES, M. N. The early development of the hypoglossal musculature of the cat. Amer. J. Anat., **83**: 329, 1948.
3. DEUCHAR, E. M. Experimental demonstration of tongue muscle origin in chick embryos. J. Embryol. Exp. Morph., **6**: 527, 1958.
4. GILBERT, P.W. Origin and development of head cavities in the human embryo. J. Morph., **90**: 149, 1952.
5. GLÜCKSMANN, A. Über die Entwicklung der Amniotenextremitäten und ihre Homologie mit den Flossen. Z. Anat. Entwicklungsgesch., **102**: 498, 1934.
6. ENESCO, M. Increase in the number of nuclei in various striated muscles of the growing rat. Anat. Rec., **139**: 225, 1961.
7. GODMAN, J. C. On the regeneration and redifferentiation of mammalian striated muscle. J. Morph., **100**: 27, 1957.
8. WALKER, B. E. The origin of myoblasts in normal and dystrophic mice. Anat. Rec., **142**: 289, 1962.
9. COLLIN, R. Recherches sur le développement du muscle sphincter de l'iris. Bibliographie Anat., **11**: 183, 1902.
10. NUSSBAUM, M. Die Entwicklung der Binnenmuskeln des Auges der Wirbeltiere. Arch. Mikroskop. Anat. Entwicklungsmech., **58B**: 199, 1901.

CHAPTER 10

Urogenital System

Functionally, the urogenital system can be divided into two entirely different components: the *urinary system*, which excretes waste products and excess water by means of an intricate tubular system in the kidneys; and the *genital system*, which assures continuation of the human race by production of the germ cells.

Embryologically and anatomically, however, both systems are interwoven. Both develop from a common ridge formed by proliferation of mesoderm along the posterior wall of the abdominal cavity, and the excretory ducts of both systems initially enter a common cavity, the cloaca.

With further development, the overlapping of the two systems is particularly evident in the male. Here, the primitive excretory duct first functions as a urinary duct, but later is transformed into the definitive genital duct. Moreover, in the adult, the urinary as well as the genital organs discharge their products to the outside through a common duct.

Another example of the intimate relationship of the two systems is seen in the development of the ureter, the definitive urinary duct extending from the kidney to the bladder. This duct arises as an outbudding of the primitive urinary duct, which in the male becomes the outflow duct of the testis, but in the female regresses almost entirely.

Despite the close association of the two systems with regard to development and adult anatomical relationship, for purposes of description it is thought necessary to discuss the two systems separately.

URINARY SYSTEM

NORMAL DEVELOPMENT
- PRONEPHROS
- MESONEPHROS
- METANEPHROS: *collecting system; excretory system*
- BLADDER AND URETHRA

CONGENITAL MALFORMATIONS
- *Polycystic kidney; pelvic and horseshoe kidney; renal agenesis; double ureter; urachal cyst and fistula*

Normal Development

In the third week of development, the intra-embryonic mesoderm differentiates into three distinct parts: (1) the *paraxial portion* which forms the somites; (2) the *lateral plate* which splits into the somatic and splanchnic layers lining the intra-embryonic coelom; and (3) the *intermediate mesoderm* which temporarily connects the paraxial tissue and the lateral plate (fig. 10-1A) (see "Formation and Differentiation of the Somite," Chapter 7). In the cervical region the intermediate mesoderm is segmented, in the thoracic region it gradually loses this segmentation, and in the caudal part of the embryo it forms a solid, unsegmented mass of tissue, the *nephrogenic cord* (fig. 10-2A). From

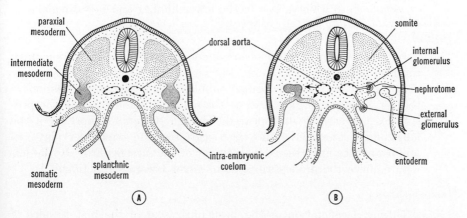

Figure 10-1. *Schematic transverse sections through the cervical region of the embryo to show various stages in the development of an excretory tubule of the pronephric system. A, At 21 days; B, 25 days. Note the formation of the external and internal glomeruli, and the open connection between the coelomic cavity and the excretory tubule (modified after Heuser).*

this partly segmented, partly unsegmented, intermediate mesoderm the excretory units of the urinary system arise.

In the cervical and upper thoracic regions, the intermediate mesoderm forms segmentally arranged cell clusters which soon elongate and obtain a lumen, thus forming a tubule known as the *nephrotome*. Medially, the nephrotome opens into the intra-embryonic coelom, while its opposite extremity grows first in a lateral and then in a caudal direction (fig. 10-1*B*). During this caudal growth the tubules of the succeeding segments unite and form a longitudinal duct on each side of the embryo (fig. 10-2*B*).

While this occurs, small branches of the dorsal aorta cause invaginations in the wall of the nephrotome and in that of the coelomic cavity, thereby forming the *internal* and *external glomeruli*, respectively (fig. 10-1*B*). Each cervical segment is characterized by the formation of one excretory tubule and one internal and external glomerulus. In the thoracic, lumbar, and sacral regions, however, a segment may have two, three, or even more excretory tubules and several internal glomeruli. The external glomeruli are absent, since the nephrotomes in these regions lose their contact with the coelomic cavity.

Though the structure of the nephrotomes from the cervical to the sacral region is basically the same, three different, slightly overlapping, kidney systems are formed during intra-uterine life.[1, 2] The earliest and simplest of these is the *pronephros*, a vestigial structure found in the cervical region. It is replaced by a more advanced system, the *mesonephros*, which extends from the lower cervical to the upper lumbar segments. This system in turn is replaced by the *permanent kidney* or *metanephros*, which arises in the lower lumbar and sacral regions.

Pronephros

In man, the pronephric system consists of 7 to 10 rudimentary tubules and a collecting tube, known as the *longitudinal pronephric duct* (fig. 10-2). The first formed tubules of this system regress before the last ones are formed, and at the end of the fourth week the pronephros has entirely disappeared. Though the cranial portion of the longitudinal pronephric duct also regresses, the remainder plays an important role in further development of the mesonephros. In the human embryo the pronephric system never becomes functional.

Mesonephros

During degeneration of the pronephric system the first tubules of the mesonephros begin to appear. These tubules, which lack a connection with the coelomic cavity, lengthen rapidly and acquire an internal glomerulus at their medial extremity (fig. 10-3*A*). At their opposite end they enter the longitudinal pronephric duct, now known as the *mesonephric* or *Wolffian duct* (figs. 10-2 and 10-3*A*). While the upper

Special Embryology

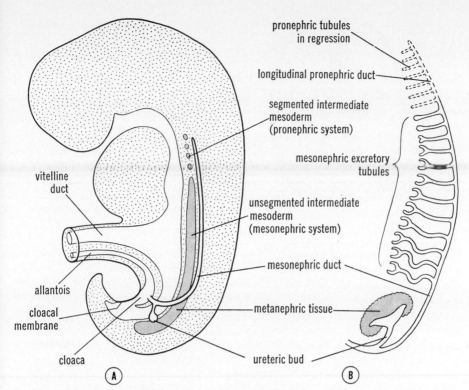

Figure 10-2. *A, Schematic diagram showing the relation of the intermediate mesoderm of the pronephric, mesonephric, and metanephric systems. In the cervical and upper thoracic regions the intermediate mesoderm is segmented; in the lower thoracic, lumbar, and sacral regions it forms a solid, unsegmented mass of tissue, the nephrogenic cord. Note the longitudinal collecting duct, initially formed by the pronephros but later taken over by the mesonephros. B, Schematic representation of the excretory tubules of the pronephric and mesonephric systems in a 6-week-old embryo. The ureteric bud penetrates the metanephric tissue (adapted from several sources).*

thoracic segments each give rise to one excretory tubule and one glomerulus, the lower thoracic and lumbar segments may give rise to two, three, or even four tubules, each with several glomeruli.

In the middle of the second month the mesonephros forms a large, ovoid organ on each side of the midline, projecting from the posterior abdominal wall into the coelomic cavity. Soon, however, the cranial tubules begin to degenerate, and by the end of the second month the majority of the excretory tubules and glomeruli of the mesonephric system have disappeared.[3] Only a few of the tubules persist, and these are later found near the testis and the ovary. The fate of the longitudinal mesonephric duct differs with the sex of the embryo. In the male it persists as the ductus deferens, but in the female it disappears almost entirely (see "Genital System").

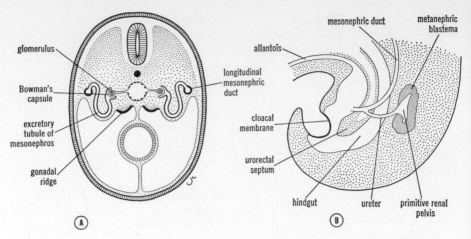

Figure 10-3. *A, Transverse section through the lower thoracic region of a 5-week embryo, showing an early stage in the formation of a mesonephric excretory tubule. Note the appearance of the gonadal ridge. B, Schematic representation of the caudal end of a 6-week embryo, showing the mesonephric duct entering into the developing primitive urogenital sinus and the ureteric bud penetrating the metanephric blastema.*

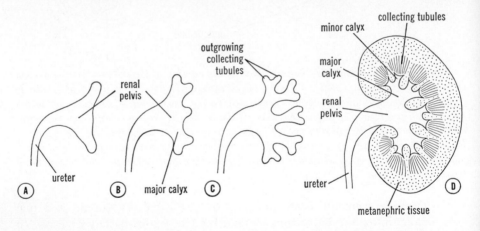

Figure 10-4. *Diagram showing the development of the collecting duct system of the metanephros. A, At 6 weeks; B, end of sixth week; C, 7 weeks; D, newborn.*

Though functional activity of the mesonephric system has been shown to exist in embryos of the cat, rabbit, and pig,[4] such activity has not been demonstrated in the human embryo.

Metanephros

During regression of the mesonephric system, a third urinary organ known as the *metanephros* or *permanent kidney* appears. Its excretory units develop from the intermediate mesoderm, which forms a solid

Special Embryology

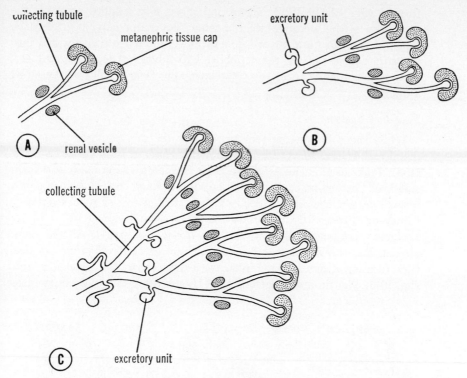

Figure 10-5. *Schematic representation of the development of the collecting duct system of the metanephros in relation to the metanephric tissue caps. Note the formation of the renal vesicle and the excretory units. A, B, and C show various stages of development (modified after Huber).*

mass of tissue known as the *metanephric blastema*. The development of its collecting ducts, however, differs from the pronephric and mesonephric systems in that it is formed by an outbudding of the mesonephric duct.

Collecting System

The development of the collecting tubules of the permanent kidney begins in the fourth week with the formation of the *ureteric bud*, an outgrowth of the dorsomedial wall of the mesonephric duct close to its entrance into the cloaca (figs. 10-2 and 10-3B). This bud grows dorsocranially, thereby penetrating the metanephric blastema, which forms a cap over its distal end (fig. 10-3B). This end subsequently enlarges and splits into a cranial and caudal portion, the future *major calyces* (fig. 10-4). Each calyx, while penetrating the metanephric tissue, gives rise to two new subdivisions, and the newly formed buds or ducts continue to subdivide until 13 or more generations of ducts have been formed (fig. 10-4).[5] While more and more new tubules arise on the periphery of the metanephric blastema, the major calyces absorb the ducts of the third and fourth generations, which are transformed into the *minor calyces* of the renal pelvis. The tubules of the fifth and succeeding generations form the definitive collecting tubules of the adult kidney.

Excretory System

While the collecting system penetrates the metanephric tissue, the distal end of each newly formed tubule is covered by a tissue cap (fig. 10-5). Parts of this cap separate from the main tissue mass and form small cell clusters on each side of the tubule. Each cluster develops into a small vesicle, the *renal vesicle*, which in turn gives rise to an excretory tubule or *nephron* (fig. 10-6). While the proximal end of the nephron becomes invaginated and forms the *Bowman's capsule* of the renal glomerulus, the distal end opens into one of the collecting tubules, thus forming a passageway from the excretory to the collecting unit (fig. 10-6). Continuous lengthening of the excretory tubules exaggerates

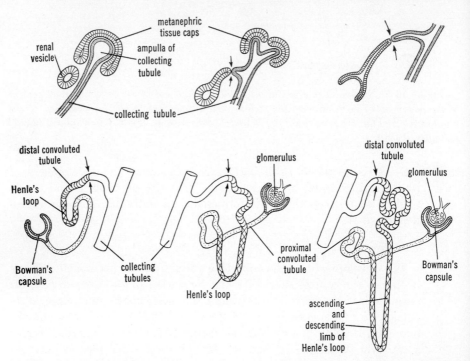

Figure 10-6. *Schematic representation of the development of a metanephric excretory unit. Arrows indicate the place where the excretory tubule comes in open communication with the collecting tubule, thus allowing for the flow of urine from the glomerulus into the collecting ducts.*

Special Embryology

the existing curvatures and results in the *proximal convoluted tubule,* the *loop of Henle,* and the *distal convoluted tubule.* The excretory units belonging to the second, third, and fourth generations of collecting tubules are vestigial and disappear when these tubules are incorporated into the pelvis of the kidney, forming the minor calyces.[6]

The metanephros, initially located in the lower lumbar and sacral regions, later shifts to a more cranial position. This so-called *ascent of the kidney* is thought to be caused by a diminution of the body curvature as well as by the continuous cranial growth of the ureteric bud.[7] The metanephros becomes functional at the end of pregnancy.[4, 8]

Bladder and Urethra

During the fourth to seventh weeks of development, the terminal part of the hindgut, the *cloaca,* is subdivided posteriorly into the *anorectal canal,* and anteriorly into the *primitive urogenital sinus* (fig. 10-7*A*) (see Chapter 12). This is accomplished by the descent of the *urorectal septum,* which arises in the angle between the allantois and the hindgut and grows caudad until it fuses with the *cloacal membrane.* The latter is then divided by the septum into the *urogenital membrane,* anteriorly, and the *anal membrane,* posteriorly (fig. 10-7C).

Two portions of the primitive urogenital sinus can be distinguished: one above the entrance openings of the mesonephric ducts, the *vesico-urethral canal,* and one below this level, the *definitive urogenital sinus* (fig. 10-7*B*). With further development, the position of the mesonephric orifices changes considerably because of the gradual absorption of the ducts into the wall of the sinus. As a result of this incorporation the ureters, initially outbuddings of the mesonephric ducts, enter the blad-

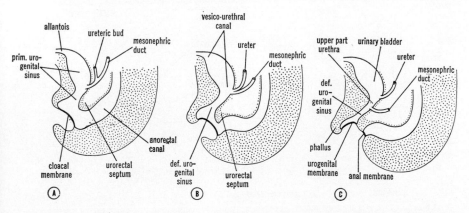

Figure 10-7. *Diagrams showing the development of the urinary bladder and the definitive urogenital sinus. The mesonephric duct is gradually absorbed into the wall of the urogenital sinus and the ureter enters separately. A, End of fifth week; B, 7 weeks; C, 8 weeks.*

der separately (fig. 10-7*B, C*). Later, the orifices of the ureters move further cranially and laterally, while the mesonephric ducts enter the upper part of the urethra.[9] Since the mesonephric ducts as well as the ureters are mesodermal structures, the mucosa of the bladder, formed by incorporation of these ducts, is likewise of mesodermal origin. With time, this mesodermal lining is replaced by entodermal epithelium, so that finally the wall of the urinary bladder is completely lined with epithelium of entodermal origin.[10]

The vesico-urethral canal thus gives rise to the urinary bladder and the upper portion of the urethra (fig. 10-7*C*). In the adult, the bladder is connected to the umbilicus by the *median umbilical ligament*. This ligament is formed by obliteration of the lumen of the *urachus*, an intra-embryonic canal which initially connects the cloaca with the allantois.[11]

The development of the definitive urogenital sinus differs greatly between the two sexes. In the male, two distinct parts can be distinguished (fig. 10-8): (1) a small pelvic portion which forms the lower part of the prostatic urethra and the membranous urethra; and (2) a long phallic portion which later forms the penile urethra. In the female, the definitive urogenital sinus forms a small portion of the urethra, the lower one-fifth of the vagina, and the vestibule (fig. 10-9) (see "Genital System").

At the end of the third month the epithelium of the cranial portion of the urethra begins to proliferate and forms a number of outbuddings which penetrate the surrounding mesenchyme. In the male these buds

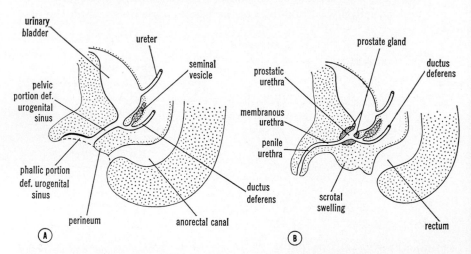

Figure 10-8. *Formation of the urethra in the male. The definitive urogenital sinus forms a pelvic and phallic portion, which in turn develop into the lower prostatic, membranous, and penile urethra, respectively. A and B show successive stages of development.*

Special Embryology

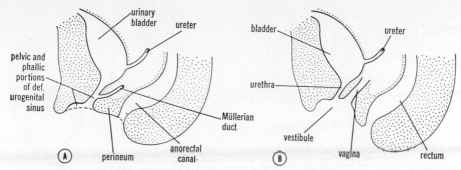

Figure 10-9. *Formation of the urethra in the female. The definitive urogenital sinus forms the lower portion of the urethra, a small portion of the vagina, and the vestibule. A and B show successive stages of development. The Müllerian duct gives rise to the uterus and part of the vagina.*

form the *prostatic gland* (fig. 10-8), whereas in the female they give rise to the *urethral* and *para-urethral glands* (fig. 10-9).

Congenital Malformations

Polycystic Kidney

Under normal conditions the collecting tubules formed by the ureteric bud unite with the excretory units of the metanephric blastema, thus allowing for the flow of urine from the glomeruli to the renal pelvis (fig. 10-6). Occasionally, however, the collecting and excretory tubules fail to join. Despite this, the excretory units develop in a normal manner and may even form functional glomeruli. Accumulation of urine in the convoluted tubules causes them to dilate and gradually to form cysts lined with cuboidal epithelium. These cysts, usually found in the cortex of the kidney, may be so numerous that insufficient active renal tissue remains.

Sometimes, one or more cysts are found close to the renal pelvis. These cysts are thought to be remnants of the nephrons of the second, third, and fourth order which usually disappear shortly after their formation.[12]

Pelvic and Horseshoe Kidney

From their initial position in the pelvis the kidneys normally ascend to the lumbar region. During this ascent they pass through the arterial fork formed by the umbilical arteries, but occasionally one of the kidneys fails to do so. It then remains in the pelvis close to the common iliac artery and is known as a *pelvic kidney* (fig. 10-10A). Sometimes both kidneys are pushed so close together during their passage through the arterial fork that their lower poles fuse. This results in the forma-

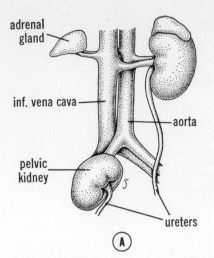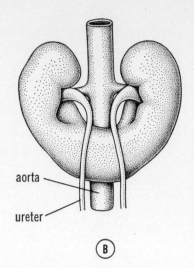

adrenal gland

inf. vena cava

aorta

pelvic kidney

ureters

A

aorta

ureter

B

Figure 10-10. *A, Unilateral pelvic kidney. Note the position of the adrenal gland on the affected side. B, Horseshoe kidney, ventral view.*

tion of a *horseshoe kidney* (fig. 10-10*B*).[13] This type of abnormal kidney is usually located at the lower lumbar level, since its ascent is prevented by the root of the inferior mesenteric artery.

Renal Agenesis

Bilateral or unilateral renal agenesis is presumably due either to failure of the mesonephric ducts to descend to the area where the ureteric bud arises, or to an early degeneration of the ureteric bud itself. If the agenesis occurs in the female, the Müllerian ducts which lie between the mesonephric ducts are also affected. This results in the absence of the uterus and a major portion of the vagina. The newborn with total renal agenesis will die shortly after birth.[14]

Double Ureter

Early splitting of the ureteric bud into two parts may result in partial or complete duplication of the ureter (fig. 10-11*A*, *B*). The metanephric blastema may then be divided into two parts, each with its own renal pelvis and ureter. More frequently, however, the two parts have a number of lobes in common, as a result of the intermingling of the collecting tubules. In rare cases one ureter opens into the bladder, while the other enters the vagina, urethra, or vestibule.

Urachal Cyst and Fistula

When the lumen of the urachus persists over its entire length urine may drain from the umbilicus, and this abnormality is known as a

Special Embryology

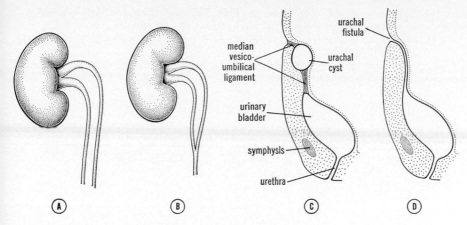

Figure 10-11. *A and B, Complete and partial double ureter; C, urachal cyst; D, urachal fistula connecting the urinary bladder with the umbilicus.*

urachal fistula (fig. 10-11*D*).[15] If only a localized area of the urachus retains its lumen, secretory activity of its lining results in a cystic dilatation, the *urachal cyst* (fig. 10-11*C*). These cysts are not malignant, but in later life may become enlarged and filled with fluid.

References—Urinary System

1. FRASER, E. A. The development of the vertebrate excretory system. Biol. Rev., 25: 159, 1950.
2. TORREY, R. W. The early development of the human nephros. Contrib. Embryol., 35: 175, 1954.
3. ALTSCHULE, M. D. The changes in the mesonephric tubules of human embryos ten to twelve weeks old. Anat. Rec., 46: 81, 1930.
4. GERSH, I. The correlation of structure and function in developing mesonephros and metanephros. Contrib. Embryol., 26: 33, 1937.
5. HUBER, G. C. Renal tubules. In *Special Cytology*, edited by E. V. Cowdry, Vol. 2. Paul B. Hoeber, Inc., New York, 1932.
6. KAMPMEYER, O. F. The metanephros or so-called permanent kidney in part provisional and vestigial. Anat. Rec., 33: 115, 1926.
7. GRUENWALD, P. The normal changes in the position of the embryonic kidney. Anat. Rec., 85: 163, 1943.
8. WELLS, L. J., AND BELL, E. T. Functioning of the fetal kidney as reflected by still-born infants with hydroureter and hydronephrosis. Arch. Path., 42: 274, 1946.
9. FRAZER, J. E. The terminal part of the Wolffian duct. J. Anat., 69: 455, 1935.
10. GYLLENSTEN, L. Contributions to embryology of the urinary bladder; development of definitive relations between openings of the Wolffian ducts and ureters. Acta Anat., 7: 305, 1949.
11. BEGG, R. C. The urachus; its anatomy, histology and development. J. Anat., 64: 170, 1930.
12. McKENNA, C. M., AND KAMPMEIER, O. F. Consideration of development of polycystic kidney. Trans. Amer. Assn. Genitourin. Surg., 26: 373, 1933.

13. GORDON-TAYLOR, G. On horseshoes and horseshoe kidneys, concave downwards. Brit. J. Urol., 8: 112, 1936.
14. DAVIDSON, W. M., AND ROSS, G. I. M. Bilateral absence of kidneys and related congenital anomalies. J. Path. Bact., 68: 459, 1954.
15. MAHONEY, P. J., AND ENNIS, D. Congenital patent urachus. New Engl. J. Med., 215: 193, 1936.

GENITAL SYSTEM

Normal Development

Gonads

Although the sex of the embryo is determined at the time of fertilization, the gonads do not acquire their male or female morphological characteristics until the seventh week of development.

Gonadal Ridge

The first indication of the gonads appears in a 4-week embryo as a pair of longitudinal ridges, the *gonadal* or *genital ridges*, located on each side of the midline between the mesonephros and the dorsal mesentery (fig. 10-12A). They are formed by proliferation of the coelomic epi-

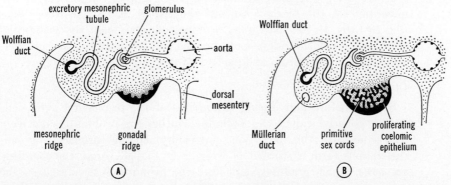

Figure 10-12. *A, Diagrammatic transverse section through the lumbar region of a 4-week embryo, showing the gonadal ridge, located between the dorsal mesentery and the mesonephros. B, Similar section, as in A, of a 6-week embryo, showing the indifferent gonad with the primitive sex cords (modified after Giroud).*

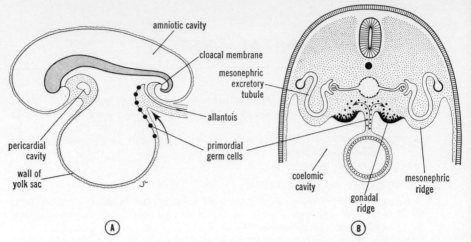

Figure 10-13. *A, Diagram of early somite embryo, showing the primordial germ cells in the wall of the yolk sac, close to the attachment of the allantois. Arrow indicates the direction in which the germ cells migrate. B, Transverse section through the lumbar region of the embryo at the end of the fifth week of development. The primordial germ cells located in the dorsal mesentery of the gut begin to migrate into the gonadal ridges.*

thelium and condensation of the underlying mesenchyme. There are no germ cells in the gonadal ridges until the sixth week of development.[1, 2]

Primordial Germ Cells

In mammalian and human embryos the primordial germ cells appear at an early stage of development (human embryo, 21 days), and are initially located in the wall of the yolk sac close to the allantois (fig. 10-13A).[3-8] From here they migrate actively along the dorsal mesentery of the hindgut toward the region of the gonadal ridges (fig. 10-13B). In the sixth week of human development the primordial germ cells enter the ridges and are then located partly in the proliferating surface epithelium and partly in the underlying mesenchyme.

Indifferent Gonad

Shortly before and during the arrival of the primordial germ cells in the gonadal ridge, the coelomic epithelium proliferates actively and penetrates the underlying mesenchyme. The proliferating epithelial cells form a number of irregularly shaped cords, the *primitive sex cords*, which gradually surround the primordial germ cells in the mesenchyme (fig. 10-12B). In both male and female embryos these cords remain connected to the surface epithelium, and at this stage of development it is impossible to differentiate between the male and female gonad. Hence, the gonad is known as the *indifferent gonad*.

Special Embryology

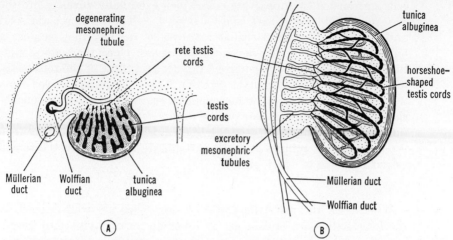

Figure 10-14. *A, Diagrammatic transverse section through the testis in the eighth week of development. Note the tunica albuginea, the testis cords, and the rete testis. The glomerulus and Bowman's capsule of the mesonephric excretory tubule are in regression. B, Schematic representation of the testis and the genital ducts in the fourth month of development. The horseshoe-shaped testis cords are continuous with the rete testis cords. Note the vasa efferentia (excretory mesonephric tubules) which enter the Wolffian duct (modified after Giroud).*

Testis

If the embryo is genetically male, the indifferent gonad undergoes a number of typical morphological changes during the sixth to eighth weeks of development (crown-rump length, 15 to 25 mm.)

During this period the primitive sex cords continue to proliferate and penetrate the medulla of the gland, thereby forming a series of well defined cell cords, anastomosing with one another and known as the *testis cords* (fig. 10-14A). Toward the hilus of the gland the cords break up into a network of tiny cell strands which later give rise to the tubules of the *rete testis* (fig. 10-14A).

As this growth and organization continues the testis cords lose contact with the surface epithelium, and by the end of the seventh week are separated from it by a dense layer of fibrous connective tissue, the *tunica albuginea*. The epithelium on the surface of the gonad then flattens and disappears, while the tunica albuginea forms the capsule of the testis.

In the fourth month of development the testis cords become more or less horseshoe-shaped, and their extremities are continuous with the cell strands of the rete testis (fig. 10-14B).[9, 10] Later, the two extremities of the testis cord narrow to form the *tubuli recti*, while the arch becomes convoluted and is known as the *tubulus contortus*.

During fetal life the testis cords are composed of primitive germ cells surrounded by supporting cells which eventually develop into the *sustentacular cells of Sertoli* (see Chapter 1).[11] The cords remain solid until puberty, but when sexual maturity is reached they acquire a lumen, thus forming the *seminiferous tubules*. Once the seminiferous tubules are canalized, their lumina rapidly join those of the rete testis, which in turn enter the *vasa efferentia*. These ductules, derived from the excretory tubules of the mesonephric system, enter the mesonephric duct, known in the male as the *ductus deferens* (fig. 10-14*B*). The *interstitial cells of Leydig* develop from mesenchyme located between the seminiferous tubules and are particularly abundant in the fourth to sixth months of development.

Ovary

Whereas in the male the primitive sex cords are well defined, in the female they are broken up by invading mesenchyme into irregular cell clusters (fig. 10-15*A*). These clusters, containing groups of primitive germ cells, are located in the medullary part of the ovary, and are later replaced by vascular stroma which forms the *ovarian medulla*.

The surface epithelium of the female gonad, unlike that of the male, remains thick and continues to proliferate. It thus gives rise to a second generation of cords, the *cortical cords*, which penetrate the underlying mesenchyme but remain close to the surface of the gland (fig. 10-15*A*). These cords are also split into isolated cell clusters, each con-

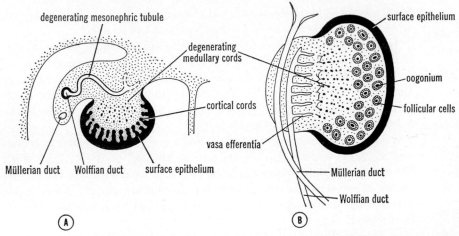

Figure 10-15. *A*, *Transverse section through the ovary at the seventh week of development, showing the degeneration of the primitive (medullary) sex cords and the formation of the cortical cords. B, Schematic drawing of the ovary and genital ducts in the fifth month of development. Note the degeneration of the medullary cords. The excretory mesonephric tubules do not communicate with the rete. The cortical zone of the ovary contains groups of oogonia surrounded by follicular cells.*

Special Embryology

taining one or more primitive germ cells (fig. 10-15B). These cells subsequently develop into the *oogonia*, while the surrounding epithelial cells, descendants of the surface epithelium, form the *follicular cells* (see Chapter 1). It is generally accepted that the primary medullary cords are a distinctly male feature, whereas the secondary cortical cords are characteristic of the female gonad.[1, 12]

Genital Ducts

Indifferent Stage

In the sixth week of development, both male and female embryos have two pairs of genital ducts: (1) the *mesonephric* or *Wolffian duct* extending from the mesonephros to the cloaca; and (2) the *paramesonephric* or *Müllerian duct*, a newly formed duct parallel to the former and likewise entering the cloaca (fig. 10-16A, B).

The paramesonephric duct arises as a longitudinal invagination of the coelomic epithelium, and is cranially in open connection with the

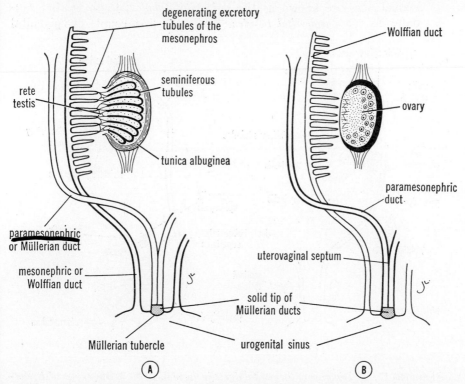

Figure 10-16. *Diagram of the genital ducts in the sixth week of development in the male (A), and in the female (B). The Wolffian and Müllerian ducts are present in both male and female.*

coelomic cavity. From here, the newly formed duct runs lateral to the mesonephric duct, but then crosses it ventrally, and grows in caudo-medial direction, joining its fellow from the opposite side. The two Müllerian ducts are initially separated by a septum but later fuse to form the *uterovaginal canal* (fig. 10-18*A*). The solid caudal tip of the combined duct continues to grow caudad until it reaches the posterior wall of the urogenital sinus between the orifices of the Wolffian ducts (fig. 10-16). On the inside of the urogenital sinus, the Müllerian ducts cause a small swelling, the *Müllerian tubercle* (fig. 10-19*A*).

Depending upon the sex of the embryo, either the Wolffian or the Müllerian duct completes its development. If the embryo is male the Wolffian duct forms the main genital duct; if the embryo is female the Müllerian duct develops.

Male Genital Ducts

As the mesonephros regresses, its excretory tubules disappear except for those in the region of the gonad. Of these, the first 5 to 12 cranial ones are known as the *epigenital tubules*; those located caudally, as the *paragenital tubules*. While the first couple of epigenital

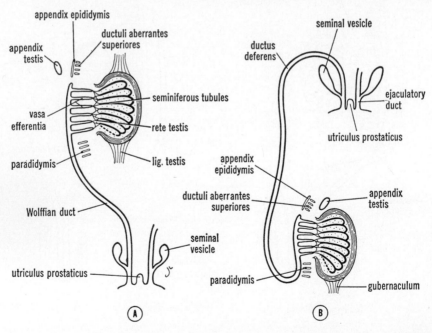

Figure 10-17. *A, Diagram of the genital ducts in the male in the fourth month of development. The Müllerian duct has degenerated except for the appendix testis and utriculus prostaticus. B, The genital ducts after descent of the testis. Note the gubernaculum testis (modified after Starck).*

Special Embryology

tubules become isolated (the *ductuli aberrantes superiores*), the remaining ones become connected to the rete testis and develop into the *vasa efferentia of the testis* (fig. 10-17). The paragenital tubules do not join the rete testis; moreover, they lose contact with the Wolffian duct (fig. 10-17*A*). They are known collectively as the *paradidymis*.

Despite the regression of a major part of the mesonephros, the Wolff-ian duct persists (except for its most cranial portion, the *appendix epididymis*), and forms the main genital duct. Immediately below the entrance of the vasa efferentia it elongates greatly and becomes highly convoluted, thus forming the *epididymis*. From the tail of the epididymis to the outbudding of the seminal vesicle, the Wolffian duct obtains a thick muscular coat and is known as the *ductus deferens*. Its most distal portion, extending from the seminal vesicle to the entrance into the urogenital sinus, forms the *ejaculatory duct* (fig. 10-17*B*).

By the end of the eighth week the paramesonephric or Müllerian duct in the male has degenerated entirely, except for a small portion at its cranial end which persists as the *appendix testis*. The fate of its caudal part is not precisely known. According to some authors it develops into the *utriculus prostaticus*, but others believe that the utricu-

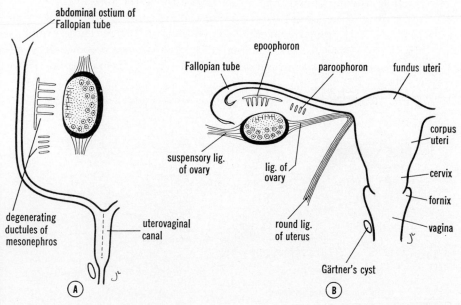

Figure 10-18. *A, Diagram of the genital ducts in the female in the fourth month of development. Note the epoophoron, paroophoron, and Gärtner's cyst, as remnants of the mesonephric system. B, The genital ducts after descent of the ovary. Note the suspensory ligament of the ovary, the ligament of the ovary proper, and the round ligament of the uterus (modified after Starck).*

lus prostaticus is formed by an outpocketing of the urogenital sinus (fig. 10-17A, B).[13]

Female Genital Ducts

The Müllerian duct develops into the main genital duct of the female. It may be divided into three parts: (1) a cranial vertical portion which opens into the coelomic cavity; (2) a horizontal part which crosses the Wolffian duct; and (3) a caudal vertical part which fuses with its partner from the opposite side (fig. 10-18A). The first two parts develop into the *oviduct* or *Fallopian tube*, and the coelomic opening is then known as the *abdominal ostium of the Fallopian tube* or *oviduct*. The site where the tubes from right and left meet marks the location of the fundus of the uterus. From here to the entrance into the urogenital sinus the two ducts gradually fuse to become the *uterovaginal canal*. The septum initially separating the two ducts disappears entirely by the end of the third month.

The blind-ending caudal tip of the uterovaginal canal proliferates actively and forms a solid tissue bar extending toward the posterior wall of the urogenital sinus (figs. 10-19 and 10-20A, B). During further development this bar lengthens considerably, in part because of its own further caudad growth and in part because of the outgrowth of two solid evaginations from the posterior wall of the urogenital sinus, or as some believe, from the Wolffian ducts (fig. 10-19B).[14] These evaginations, the *sinovaginal bulbs*, temporarily increase the distance between the lumen of the uterovaginal canal and that of the urogenital sinus

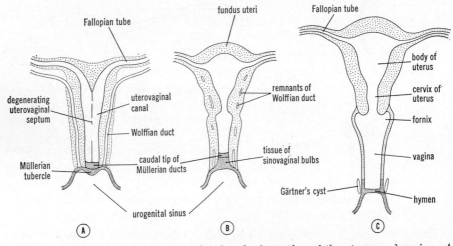

Figure 10-19. *Schematic drawing showing the formation of the uterus and vagina. A At 9 weeks. Note the fusion of the two Müllerian ducts. B, At 11 weeks. Note the solid tissue bar between the lumen of the uterovaginal canal and that of the urogenital sinus. C, Newborn. The vagina is formed by the uterovaginal canal and the sinovaginal bulbs.*

Special Embryology

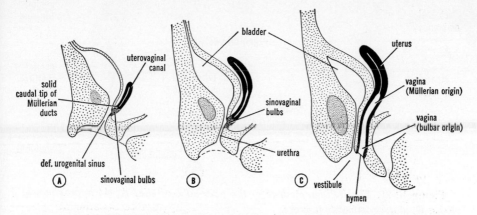

Figure 10-20. *Schematic longitudinal sections showing the formation of the uterus and vagina at various stages of development. The upper four-fifths of the vagina is formed by the uterovaginal canal, while the lower one-fifth develops from the sinovaginal bulbs. The uterovaginal canal first enters the urethra, but with further development descends until it opens into the vestibule.*

(fig. 10-20A, B). Soon, however, the tissue bar is canalized from cranial to caudal, thus increasing the length of the uterovaginal canal.

The musculature of the uterovaginal canal is derived from the surrounding mesenchyme. In the cranial portion, which develops into the *corpus and cervix of the uterus*, this mesenchyme forms a thick muscular coat, the *myometrium*. In the caudal portion of the canal, the future upper four-fifths of the vagina, it forms only a few muscle fibers. The lower one-fifth of the vagina, formed by canalization of the sinovaginal bulbs, likewise contains only a thin muscular layer.[15, 16]

The lumen of the vagina remains separated from that of the urogenital sinus by a thin tissue plate, known as the *hymen* (figs. 10-19C and 10-20C). The hymen consists of the epithelial lining of the vaginal canal, the epithelial lining of the sinus, and a thin intermediate layer of mesoderm.[14]

Although in the female the main genital duct is formed by the paramesonephric or Müllerian duct, some parts of the mesonephric system persist. Remnants of the cranial excretory tubules and a small portion of the mesonephric duct itself may be found in the mesovarium, where they form the *epoophoron* (fig. 10-18A, B). The more caudally located tubules form a remnant known as the *paroophoron*. The Wolffian duct disappears entirely except for a small cranial portion found in the epoophoron, and occasionally a small caudal portion, which may then form a cyst, *Gärtner's cyst*, in the wall of the lower part of the vagina (fig. 10-18B).

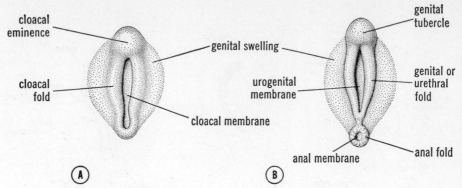

Figure 10-21. *The indifferent stage of the external genitalia. A, At approximately 4 weeks; B, at approximately 6 weeks.*

External Genitalia

Indifferent Stage

In the third week of development the cloacal membrane is gradually surrounded by mesenchyme derived from the primitive streak. This mesenchyme forms a pair of slightly elevated folds, the *cloacal folds*, which fuse with each other directly in front of the cloacal membrane to form the *cloacal eminence* (fig. 10-21*A*). When, in the sixth week, the cloacal membrane is subdivided into the *urogenital* and *anal membranes*, the cloacal swellings are likewise split into the *genital* or *urethral folds* anteriorly, and into the *anal folds* posteriorly (fig. 10-21*B*). In the meantime, the cloacal eminence has lengthened and is now known as the *genital turbercle*.

In addition to the above-mentioned swellings, another pair of elevations, the *genital swellings*, become visible on each side of the genital folds (fig. 10-21). In the male these swellings later differentiate into the *scrotal swellings*, and in the female, into the *labia majora*. Thus far, the development of the external genitalia is identical in male and female, and it is impossible to distinguish between the two sexes.

External Genitalia in the Male

Further development of the external genitalia is characterized by the rapid elongation of the genital tubercle, known as the *phallus* (fig. 10-22*A*). During this elongation the phallus pulls the genital or urethral folds forward so that they form the lateral walls of the deep *urogenital* or *urethral groove*. This groove, formed after the disappearance of the urogenital membrane, extends along the caudal aspect of the elongated phallus.[17] The entoderm at the bottom of this groove proliferates and forms the *urethral plate* (fig. 10-22*B*).

　　　　　　　　　　　　　　Special Embryology

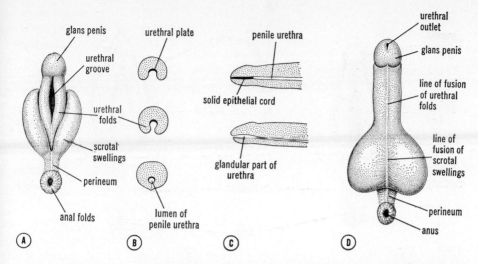

Figure 10-22. *A, Development of the external genitalia in the male at 10 weeks. Note the deep urethral groove flanked by the urethral folds. B, Transverse sections through phallus during the formation of the penile urethra. The urogenital groove is bridged over by the two urethral folds. C, Development of the glandular portion of the penile urethra. D, In the newborn.*

At the end of the third month the two urethral folds close over the urethral plate, thus forming the *urethral canal of the penis* (fig. 10-22B, C).[18] This canal does not initially extend to the tip of the phallus and temporarily lacks an outlet to the surface (fig. 10-22C). During the fourth month, however, ectodermal cells from the proximal tip of the penis penetrate inward and form a solid epithelial cord extending toward the lumen of the urethra in the shaft of the penis. This cord later canalizes and develops into the *glandular portion of the penile urethra* (fig. 10-22C).

The genital swellings known in the male as the scrotal swellings are initially located in the inguinal region. With further development they move caudally, and each swelling then makes up a half of the scrotum, separated from its partner by the scrotal septum (fig. 10-22D).[19]

External Genitalia in the Female

The changes in the external genitalia of the female are less profound than those in the male. The genital tubercle elongates only slightly and forms the *clitoris* (fig. 10-23A, B); the genital folds do not fuse as in the male, but develop into the *labia minora*; and the genital swellings enlarge greatly and form the *labia majora*. The urogenital groove is open to the surface and forms the *vestibule* (fig. 10-23B).

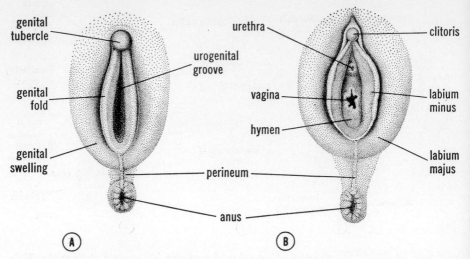

Figure 10-23. *Development of the external genitalia in the female at 5 months (A), and in the newborn (B).*

Descent of the Testis

The mesonephros and the nearby gonad gradually bulge into the peritoneal cavity, thereby causing the peritoneum to fold over them in mesentery-like fashion. This peritoneal fold extends cranially from the upper pole of the mesonephros toward the diaphragm; caudally, from the lower pole of the mesonephros to the inguinal region. With regression of the mesonephros and concomitant increase in size of the testis, these ligaments are gradually taken over by the testis. The initial caudal mesonephric ligament then becomes the *ligamentum testis*, while the cranial ligament regresses (fig. 10-17).

In the meantime, the coelomic cavity forms an evagination on each side of the midline into the scrotal swellings, thereby pushing the muscular layers of the abdominal wall ahead of it (fig. 10-26A). The extension of the coelomic cavity into the scrotal swellings is known as the *vaginal process* (figs. 10-24 and 10-26A). The connective tissue surrounding this vaginal process condenses and forms the *scrotal ligament*. This, together with the ligamentum testis, forms the *gubernaculum of the testis*.

By the middle of the third month the testis begins to descend beneath the peritoneum to a more caudal position, and by the end of the fifth month it lies close to the inguinal ring, approximately 10 segments below its level of origin (fig. 10-24A, B). During the seventh month, and sometimes later, the testis continues its descent through the inguinal ring and over the rim of the pubic bone into the scrotal pouch.

Special Embryology

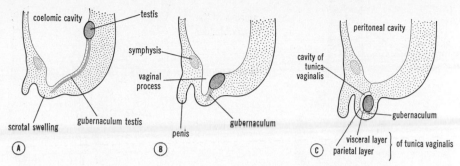

Figure 10-24. *Schematic representation of the descent of the testis. A, Middle of the third month; B, seventh month; C, shortly after birth. The coelomic cavity evaginates into the scrotal pouch, where it forms the cavity of the tunica vaginalis.*

Once arrived in the pouch at about the time of birth, the medial side of the testis is covered by the peritoneal lining of the vaginal process, the *visceral layer of the tunica vaginalis proprius*; the remainder of the wall of the peritoneal sac forms the *parietal layer of the tunica vaginalis proprius* (figs. 10-24C and 10-26A). It must be remembered that the testis always remains outside the vaginal process. The passage initially connecting the vaginal process with the peritoneal cavity is obliterated at birth or shortly thereafter.[20] The descent of the testis is accompanied by a shortening of the gubernaculum, but whether or not this shortening causes the descent of the testis is still controversial.[21, 22] Undoubtedly, however, the descent of the testis is partially controlled by hormones such as gonadotropins and androgens.[23]

The gonad moves considerably less in the female than in the male and is finally located just below the brim of the true pelvis. The cranial mesonephric ligament is thought to form the *suspensory ligament of the ovary*, whereas the caudal mesonephric ligament forms the *ligament of the ovary proper* and the *round ligament of the uterus*, extending into the labia majora (fig. 10-18B).

Congenital Malformations

Hypospadia

Under normal conditions the urethral groove is closed and transformed into the penile urethra by fusion of the urethral or genital folds (fig. 10-22B). Hence, when this fusion is incomplete, abnormal openings of the urethra may be found along the inferior aspect of the penis. Most frequently these abnormal orifices are near the glans, along the shaft, or near the base of the penis (fig. 10-25A). In rare cases the urethral meatus may even be located along the scrotal raphe. When

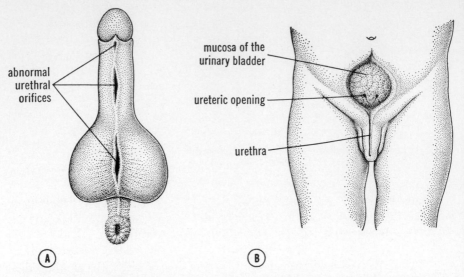

A   **B**

Figure 10-25. *A, Hypospadia. The drawing shows the various locations of abnormal urethral orifices. B, Epispadia combined with ectopia of the bladder. The mucosa of the bladder is exposed to the surface, and the orifices of the ureters can readily be seen. In this case the urethral slit extends along the length of the penis.*

fusion of the urethral folds fails entirely, the urethral meatus forms a sagittal slit along the entire length of the penis. The two scrotal swellings may then closely resemble the labia majora.

Epispadia

This anomaly is characterized by the presence of the urethral meatus on the dorsum of the penis, and in its most extreme form it is associated with an ectopia of the bladder. This malformation is thought to be caused primarily by the abnormal position of the genital tubercle. Instead of having developed at the anterior margin of the cloacal membrane, it seems to have formed at a level opposite the urorectal septum. Hence a portion of the cloacal membrane is found cranial to the genital tubercle, and the outlet of the urogenital sinus then comes to lie on the cranial aspect of the penis (fig. 10-25B).[24] Occasionally, the two sides of the genital tubercle do not fuse at all, and this results in a so-called *divided penis.*

Ectopia or Exstrophy of the Bladder

Ectopia of the bladder, seen frequently in combination with epispadia, is caused by an insufficient migration of mesoderm around the cloacal membrane.[18, 25] Under normal conditions the abdominal wall in front of the bladder is formed by mesoderm derived from the primitive streak, which migrates around the cloacal membrane. When this

                                       Special Embryology

fails to occur the rupture of the cloacal membrane may extend upward further than is normal, thus establishing an *ectopia of the bladder*. The mucosa of the bladder is then exposed to the surface of the body, and the ureters and urethra can be readily seen. At regular intervals urine can be seen escaping from the ureteric orifices[26] (fig. 10-25B).

Cryptorchism

At about the time of birth, but with wide individual variation, the testes normally arrive in the scrotum. In certain cases one or both testes may remain in the pelvic cavity above the inguinal ring until puberty and then descend or remain indefinitely in the pelvic position.[27] This condition is known as *cryptorchism*, and seems to be due to abnormal endocrine conditions and/or failure of the gubernaculum to shorten. An undescended testis is unable to produce mature spermatozoa, most likely because of the high temperature in the abdominal cavity.[28]

Congenital Inguinal Hernia

Failure of the testes to descend into the scrotum is often accompanied by a congenital inguinal hernia. The passage from the coelomic cavity into the scrotal sac normally closes after descent of the testes. If it remains open the intestinal loops usually descend into the scrotum, thus causing a *congenital inguinal hernia* (fig. 10-26B). Sometimes closure of this passage takes place irregularly, leaving small cysts along its course. Later these cysts begin to secrete excess fluid, resulting in the formation of a *hydrocele* (fig. 10-26C).

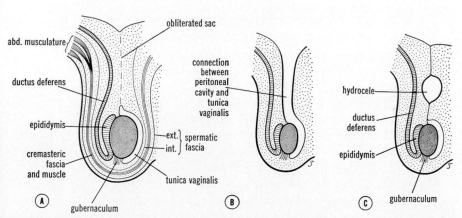

Figure 10-26. *A, Diagrammatic drawing of the testis, epididymis, ductus deferens, and the various layers of the abdominal wall which surround the testis in the scrotum. B, Vaginal process in open communication with the coelomic cavity. In such a case, portions of the intestinal loops often descend toward the scrotum, thus causing an inguinal hernia. C, Hydrocele.*

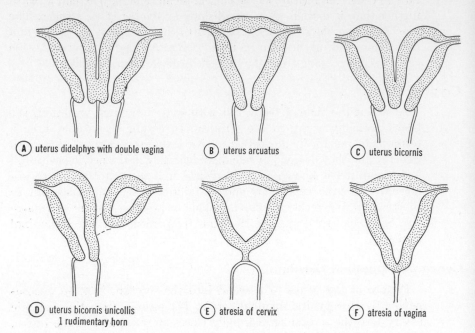

Figure 10-27. *Schematic representation of the main abnormalities of the uterus and vagina, caused by persistence of the uterovaginal septum or obliteration of the lumen of the uterovaginal canal.*

Duplication and Atresia of the Uterovaginal Canal

Under normal conditions the uterus and vagina are formed by fusion of the caudal parts of the Müllerian ducts. Lack of fusion in a localized area or throughout the length of the ducts explains all different types of duplication of the uterus and vagina. In its extreme form the uterus as well as the vagina are completely double (*uterus didelphys with double vagina*) (fig. 10-27*A*). In the least severe form, the uterine fundus is slightly indented in the middle (*uterus arcuatus*) (fig. 10-27*B*). One of the more commonly found anomalies is the *bicornuate uterus*, in which the uterus has two horns entering a common vagina (fig. 10-27*C*). This condition is normal in many of the mammals below the primate.

Another group of malformations is caused by complete or partial atresia of one or both of the Müllerian ducts. If one side only is involved, the rudimentary part lies as an appendage to the well developed side, but since its lumen usually does not communicate with the vagina, complications frequently ensue (*uterus bicornis unicollis with one rudimentary horn*) (fig. 10-27*D*). If the atresia involves both sides partially, an *atresia of the cervix* (fig. 10-27*E*), or *atresia of the vagina* may result (fig. 10-27*F*).[29]

Ovarian Hypoplasia

Ovarian hypoplasia, often associated with hypoplasia of the internal genitalia and hypertrophy of the clitoris, is found in persons showing *Turner's syndrome*. The cells of patients suffering from this syndrome are characterized by 45 chromosomes—44 autosomes and one X chromosome (see Chapter 6).[30]

References—Genital System

1. GRUENWALD, P. The development of the sex cords in the gonads of man and mammals. Amer. J. Anat., **70:** 359, 1942.
2. GILLMAN, J. The development of the gonads in man, with a consideration of the role of fetal endocrines and histogenesis of ovarian tumors. Contrib. Embryol., **32:** 81, 1948.
3. WITSCHI, E. Migrations of germ cells of human embryos from the yolk sac to the primitive gonadal folds. Contrib. Embryol., **32:** 67, 1948.
4. MINTZ, B. Formation and early development of germ cells. In *Symposium on Germ Cells and Development*, pp. 1–24. Institut Internationale d'Embryologie and Fondazione A. Baselli, 1960.
5. MINTZ, B. Embryological phases of mammalian gametogenesis. J. Cell. Comp. Physiol., **56:** 31, 1960.
6. CHIQUOINE, A. D. Identification, origin and migration of the primordial germ cells. Anat. Rec., **110:** 135, 1954.
7. EVERETT, N. B. The present status of the germ cell problem in vertebrates. Biol. Rev., **20:** 45, 1945.
8. McKAY, D. G., HERTIG, A. J., ADAMS, E. C., AND DANZIGER, S. Histochemical observations on the germ cells of human embryos. Anat. Rec., **117:** 201, 1953.
9. CLERMONT, Y., AND HUCKINS, C. Microscopic anatomy of the sex glands and seminiferous tubules in growing adult male albino rats. Amer. J. Anat., **108:** 79, 1961.
10. WILSON, K. W. Origin and development of the rete ovarii and the rete testis in the human embryo. Contrib. Embryol., **17:** 69, 1926.
11. MANCINI, R. E., NARBAITZ, R., AND LAVIERI, J. C. Origin and development of the germinative epithelium and Sertoli cells in the human testis; cytological, cytochemical and quantitative study. Anat. Rec., **136:** 477, 1960.
12. WITSCHI, E. *Development of Vertebrates.* W. B. Saunders Co., Philadelphia, 1956.
13. VILAS, E. Über die Entwicklung des Utriculus prostaticus beim Menschen. Z. Anat. Entwicklungsgesch., **99:** 599, 1933.
14. KOFF, A. K. Development of the vagina in the human fetus. Contrib. Embryol., **24:** 61, 1933.
15. MONIE, S. W., AND SIGURDSON, H. A. A proposed classification for uterine and vaginal anomalies. Amer. J. Obstet. Gynec. **59:** 696, 1950.
16. McKELVEY, J. L., AND BAXTER, J. S. Abnormal development of the vagina and genitourinary tract. Amer. J. Obstet. Gynec., **29:** 267, 1935.
17. SPAULDING, M. M. The development of the external genitalia in the human embryo. Contrib. Embryol., **13:** 67, 1921.
18. GLENISTER, T. W. A correlation of the normal and abnormal development of the penile urethra and of the intra-umbilical abdominal wall. Brit. J. Urol., **30:** 117, 1958.
19. POLITZER, G. Über die Entwicklung des Dammes beim Menschen; nebst Bemerkungen über die Bildung der äusseren Geschlechtsteile und über die

Fehlbildungen der Kloake und des Dammes. Z. Anat. Entwicklungsgesch. 97: 622, 1932.

20. Mitchell, G. A. G. The condition of the peritoneal vaginal process at birth. J. Anat., 73: 658, 1939.

21. Wyndham, N. R. A morphological study of testicular descent. J. Anat., 77: 179, 1943.

22. Backhouse, K. M., and Butler, H. The development of the coverings of the testis and cord. J. Anat., 92: 645, 1958.

23. Wells, L. J. Descent of the testis; anatomical and hormonal considerations. Surgery, 14: 436, 1943.

24. Patten, B. M., and Barry, A. Genesis of exstrophy of the bladder and epispadia. Amer. J. Anat., 90: 35, 1952.

25. Wyburn, G. M. The development of the infra-umbilical portion of the abdominal wall, with remarks on the aetiology of ectopia vesicae. J. Anat., 71: 201, 1937.

26. Uson, A. C., Lattimer, J. K., and Melicow, M. M. Types of exstrophy of the urinary bladder and concomitant malformations. Pediatrics, 23: 927, 1959.

27. Scorer, C. G. Incidence of incomplete descent of the testicle at birth. Arch. Dis. Child., 31: 198, 1956.

28. Moore, K. L., Graham, M. A., and Barr, M. L. Detection of chromosomal sex in hermaphrodites from skin biopsy. Surg. Gynec. Obstet., 96: 641, 1953.

29. Jones, W. S. Obstetric significance of female genital anomalies. Obstet. Gynec. (N. Y.), 10: 113, 1957.

30. Ford, C. E., Jones, K. W., Polani, P. E., de Almeida, J. C., and Briggs, J. H. A sex-chromosome anomaly in a case of gonadal dysgenesis (Turner's syndrome). Lancet, 1: 711, 1959.

CHAPTER 11

Cardiovascular System

NORMAL DEVELOPMENT OF THE HEART

- BLOOD VESSEL FORMATION: *extra-embryonic; intra-embryonic*
- DEVELOPMENT OF THE PRIMITIVE HEART: *endocardial heart tube; cardiac loop; primitive heart chambers*
- DEVELOPMENT OF THE DEFINITIVE HEART
  Sinus venosus: coronary sinus; venous valves
  Septation of the atrium and atrioventricular canal: septum primum; septum secundum
  Atrioventricular valves
  Septation of the bulboventricular region: muscular septum; aorticopulmonary septum; membranous septum
  Semilunar valves

Blood Vessel Formation

Extra-embryonic Blood Vessels

The vascular system of the human embryo appears at the middle of the third week, when the embryo is no longer able to satisfy its nutritional requirements by diffusion alone. At this stage mesenchymal cells in the chorion, the connecting stalk, and the wall of the yolk sac differentiate into primitive blood- and blood vessel-forming cells, the *angioblasts*, which in turn form isolated clusters and cords, the *blood islands* (fig. 11-1).

When subsequently a lumen is formed in the blood islands by the appearance and confluence of intercellular clefts, the central angioblasts are detached and develop into primitive blood cells (fig. 11-2). The

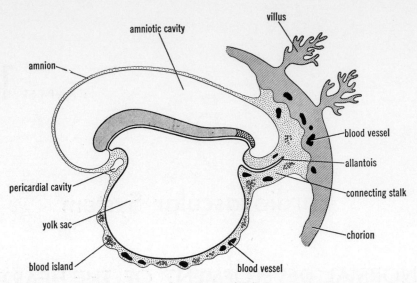

Figure 11-1. *Extra-embryonic blood vessel formation in the chorion, the connecting stalk, and the wall of the yolk sac in a presomite embryo of approximately 19 days (modified from Keibel and Elze).*

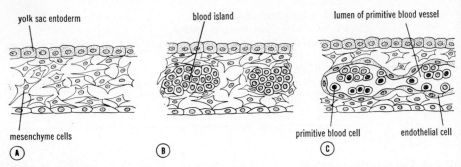

Figure 11-2. *Successive stages of blood vessel formation in the wall of the yolk sac. A, Undifferentiated mesenchyme; B, blood island formation; C, early capillary. Note the differentiation of mesenchymal cells into the primitive blood cells and the endothelial cells.*

peripherally located angioblasts flatten and form the endothelial lining of the lumen.[1, 2] From now on, the blood islands approach each other rapidly by sprouting of the endothelial cells and, after fusion, form a plexiform network. This network in turn is transformed into small blood vessels presumably under the influence of hemodynamic factors.[3]

In this manner the capillary system in the wall of the yolk sac gives rise to the *vitelline vessels*, and that in the chorion to the *umbilical vessels* (fig. 11-3). Through continuous budding these extra-embryonic vessels gradually penetrate the embryo proper.

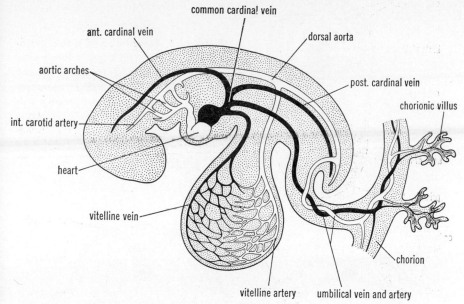

Figure 11-3. *Schematic drawing of the main intra- and extra-embryonic blood vessels in a 4-mm. embryo (end of the fourth week). Only the vessels of the left side of the embryo are represented.*

Intra-embryonic Blood Vessels

Originally the intra-embryonic vessels were thought to be extensions of the ingrowing extra-embryonic vessels.[4] It is now generally accepted that they develop independently from the intra-embryonic mesenchyme in a manner similar to that described above.[5] Contact between the intra- and extra-embryonic vessels is established only secondarily (fig. 11-3).

Development of the Primitive Heart

Formation of the Endocardial Heart Tube

The first sign of heart formation is found at the end of the third week. The embryonic shield is then spread out over the surface of the yolk sac, and the first heart-forming cells appear as irregular clusters and cords in the cephalic portion of the embryo between the entoderm of the yolk sac and the splanchnic mesoderm (fig. 11-4). By the time the first somites appear these cell clusters form solid cell strands across the midline in front of the neural plate and extend down on each side of the embryo.[6, 7]

With the subsequent forward growth of the head end of the embryo, and its folding off from the yolk sac (see Chapter 4), the two cell

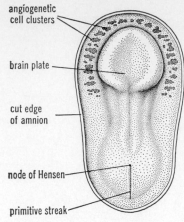

angiogenetic cell clusters

brain plate

cut edge of amnion

node of Hensen

primitive streak

Figure 11-4. *Dorsal view of a late preso-mite embryo (approximately 1.4 mm.) after removal of the amnion. The angiogenetic cell clusters formed in the splanchnic mesoderm in front of the neural plate and on each side of the embryo are visible through the overlying ectoderm and somatic mesoderm layer (mod-ified after Davis (see also fig. 11-5, A)*

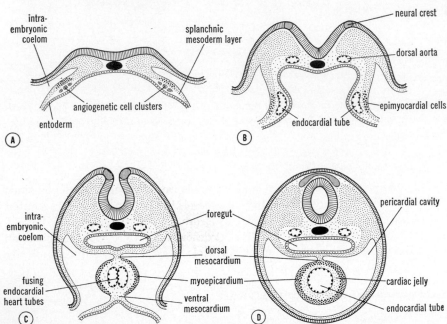

Figure 11-5. *Schematic transverse sections through embryos of different stages of development, showing the formation of the single heart tube from paired primordia. A, Early presomite embryo (approximately 17 days); B, late presomite embryo (approximately 18 days); C, at four somites (approximately 21 days); D, at eight somites (approximately 22 days) (adapted from several sources).*

strands approach each other ventrally and acquire a lumen lined with endothelial cells, thus forming the two *endocardial tubes* where the first contractions occur (fig. 11-5*A*, *B*). The lumen of each of the two tubes gradually extends cranially into the midline cell strands, and finally the two meet. With further lateral folding of the embryo, the fusion of the two endocardial tubes then progresses from the cephalic point in caudal direction, thereby forming a single endocardial tube (fig. 11-5C, D).

While these events occur the mesoderm adjacent to the endocardial tubes (the splanchnic mesoderm) gradually thickens, and by the time the tubes have fused it surrounds them as the *myoepicardial mantle* (fig. 11-5). At first this mantle is separated from the endothelial wall of the tube by a gelatinous substance, the *cardiac jelly*, but later this jelly is invaded by mesenchymal cells, which play an important role in the formation of the valves.[7, 8] Finally, the wall of the heart tube consists of three layers: the *endocardium*, which forms the internal endothelial lining of the heart; the *myocardium* forming the muscular wall; and the *epicardium* or *visceral pericardium* covering the outside of the tube.

Initially the primitive heart tube is connected to the wall of the surrounding pericardial cavity by a *dorsal* and *ventral mesocardium* (fig. 11-5C). Whereas the ventral part disappears immediately after its formation, the dorsal mesocardium persists a little longer (fig. 11-6). Eventually, however, beginning at the cranial end, it also breaks down and has entirely disappeared at the 16-somite stage. The heart tube is then freely suspended in the pericardial cavity and is attached to the surrounding tissues only at its cephalic and caudal ends. The newly formed passage, dorsal to the primitive heart tube, is the future *transverse sinus* of the *pericardial cavity*.

Formation of the Cardiac Loop

During the next period of development (8 to 20 somites, 3 to 4 weeks) the primitive heart tube grows much more rapidly than the pericardial cavity. However, since its two ends are attached to the

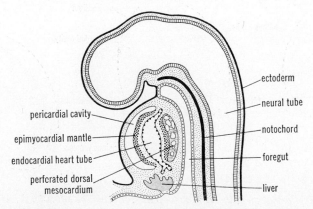

Figure 11-6. *Sagittal section through the cranial end of an eight-somite embryo, showing the various layers of the heart and the perforated areas in the dorsal mesocardium.*

surrounding tissues, elongation of the tube cannot be accomplished in a longitudinal direction and a "buckling" occurs. The cephalic and middle portions of the tube, the first portions to be freed from the dorsal mesocardium, thereby assume a ventral caudal convexity with a slight, right-sided inclination (fig. 11-7 A, B). The *cardiac loop* thus formed consists of a cephalic or ascending limb, which gives rise to the bulbus cordis, and a caudal or descending limb, forming the embryonic ventricle.

The caudal portion of the heart tube, from which the sinus venosus and atrium will develop, remains temporarily embedded in the mesenchymal tissue of the transverse septum and does not initially participate in the formation of the cardiac loop. Only later, when it has been freed from this tissue and has assumed an intrapericardial position, does it move in a cranial and dorsal direction (fig. 11-7C).[9]

Primitive Heart Chambers

Simultaneously with the bending of the heart tube, a number of dilatations separated by grooves become visible. By the end of the fourth week, when the embryo is approximately 5 mm., the following parts can be recognized:

SINUS VENOSUS. This is the most caudal part of the heart and consists of a median portion, the *transverse part*, and a *right* and *left sinus horn* (fig. 11-9A). Into each of these horns enter: (1) the *vitelline vein* from the yolk sac; (2) the *umbilical vein* from the placenta; and (3) the *common cardinal vein* from the body of the embryo proper. The sinus venosus continues into the atrium.

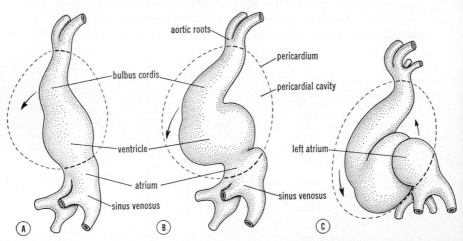

Figure 11-7. *Formation of the cardiac loop as seen from the left side. A, At eight somites; B, 11 somites; C, 16 somites. Broken line indicates parietal pericardium. Note how the atrium gradually assumes an intra-pericardial position (modified from Kramer).*

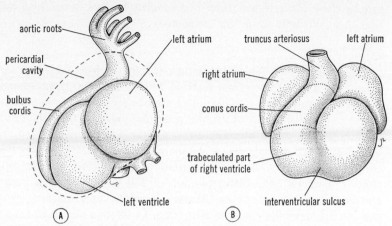

Figure 11-8. *The heart of a 5-mm. embryo (approximately 28 days). A, Seen from the left; B, in frontal view (modified after Kramer).*

ATRIAL REGION. This portion of the heart tube, initially a paired structure located in the transverse septum (fig. 11-7*A*, *B*), at the 5-mm. stage consists of a single chamber located dorsally to the bulboventricular part of the heart (fig. 11-8*A*). It shows two transverse dilatations bulging around the bulbus cordis and forming the *atrial auricles* (fig. 11-8*B*). Ventrally, the atrial cavity continues into the ventricle through the *atrioventricular canal*.

VENTRICULAR REGION. This part is formed by the descending limb of the cardiac loop and is found ventral to the atrial cavity. A shallow groove, the *interventricular sulcus*, separates it from the bulbus cordis.

BULBUS CORDIS. This portion of the heart is formed by the ascending limb of the cardiac loop and continues cranially into the aortic roots. In an embryo of 4 to 5 mm. it is usually divided into three parts (fig. 11-8*B*): (1) the proximal part, which will become the *trabecular part of the right ventricle*; (2) a midportion, the *conus cordis*, which will form the outflow tracts of both ventricles; and (3) a distal part, the *truncus arteriosus*, which will form the roots and proximal portions of of the aorta and pulmonary artery.

Development of the Definitive Heart

At the 5-mm. stage, when the embryo is approximately 4½ weeks old, the heart tube possesses a single lumen through which the blood stream flows from the sinus venosus toward the aortic roots. During the next 4 weeks, however, a number of complicated changes take place, such as the transformation of the sinus venosus into its definitive structure, and the formation of septa in the atrium, the atrioventricular canal, and the bulboventricular region. In the following paragraphs these changes are described separately, but it must be realized that most of them occur simultaneously.

Sinus Venosus

CORONARY SINUS. When the embryo is 3.5 mm. long the sinus venosus consists of a small transverse portion and the left and right sinus horns into which umbilical, vitelline, and common cardinal veins drain (fig. 11-9*A*). With obliteration of the proximal part of the left umbilical vein at 5-mm. stage and the left vitelline vein at 7-mm. stage, the left sinus horn rapidly loses importance (fig. 11-9*B*). When the left common cardinal vein is obliterated at approximately the 60-mm. stage (10 weeks), the distal portion of the left sinus horn forms the *oblique vein of the left atrium* (Marshall), while the remaining proximal portion becomes the *coronary sinus* (fig. 11-9*C*). In the meantime, with the development of a deep *sinu-atrial fold*, the entrance of the sinus venosus into the atrial cavity has gradually shifted to the right and consequently the coronary sinus enters into the right atrium.[10]

While these events occur on the left side, more and more blood from the placental and the intra-embryonic circulation is channeled to the

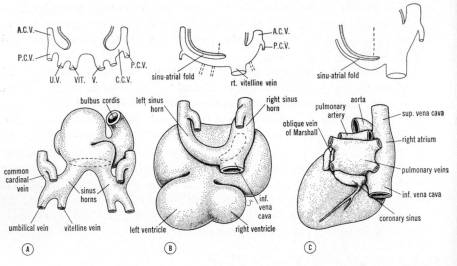

Figure 11-9. *Three stages in the development of the sinus venosus and great veins, seen from dorsal to show the formation of the coronary sinus and the incorporation of the right sinus horn into the wall of the right atrium. Broken line indicates the entrance of the sinus venosus into the atrial cavity. A, At 18 somites (approximately 24 days); B, approximately 35 days; C, in the newborn. Each drawing is accompanied by a scheme to show, in transverse section, the great veins and their relation to the atrial cavity. A.C.V., anterior cardinal vein; P.C.V., posterior cardinal vein; C.C.V., common cardinal vein; U.V., umbilical vein; Vit. V., vitelline vein (modified after several sources).*

Special Embryology

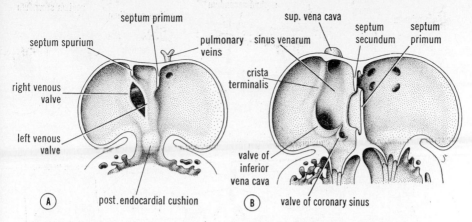

Figure 11-10. *Coronal sections through the heart at the level of the atrioventricular canal seen from ventral to show the development of the venous valves. A, At 7- to 8-mm. stage (5 weeks); B, newborn (modified after His).*

right, resulting in an increase in size of the right sinus horn (fig. 11-9*B*, *C*). With further development (6 to 8 weeks), the right sinus horn is incorporated into the right atrium and finally forms the smooth-walled part of the right atrium known as the *sinus venarum*. This portion is later demarcated from the trabeculated portion of the atrium by the *crista terminalis* (fig. 11-10*A*, *B*).

VENOUS VALVES. Initially, the entrance of the sinus venosus into the atrium is bordered on each side by a valvular fold, the *right and left venous valves*. Dorsocranially, these valves fuse to form a ridge known as the *septum spurium* (fig. 11-10*A*). During incorporation of the right sinus horn into the atrium, the left venous valve undergoes rapid regression and merges with the atrial septum. The cranial portion of the right venous valve largely disappears, while the remainder is divided into two parts: (1) the *valve of the inferior vena cava*, or *Eustachian valve*; and (2) the *valve of the coronary sinus*, or *Thebesian valve* (fig. 11-10*B*).

Septum Formation in the Atrium and Atrioventricular Canal

SEPTUM PRIMUM. The partitioning of the single atrial cavity into a right and left side begins at the 5-mm. stage with the formation of a sickle-shaped septum, the *septum primum*. This septum grows down from the middle of the dorsally located roof in the direction of the more caudally and ventrally located atrioventricular canal (fig. 11-11*A*). The latter now shows local thickenings of mesenchyme covered by endocardium (the *endocardial cushions*) on its anterior and posterior walls (fig. 11-12). The opening which temporarily exists between the septum primum and the septum developing in the atrioventricular canal is

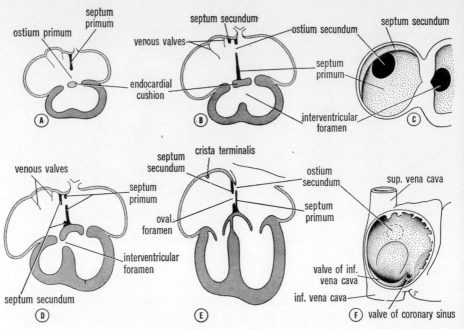

Figure 11-11. *Schematic representation of the atrial septa at various stages of development. A, At 6 mm. (approximately 30 days); B, 9 mm. (approximately 33 days); C, same stage as in B, but seen from the right; D, 14 mm. (approximately 37 days); E, newborn; F, view of the atrial septum seen from the right, same stage as in E.*

called the *ostium primum* (fig. 11-11*A*). Further growth of the septum primum finally causes it to fuse with the partition formed in the atrioventricular canal, thus closing the ostium primum.

Before the two atria are completely separated, however, the upper part of the septum primum ruptures, thereby forming a new opening, the *ostium secundum* (fig. 11-11*B*, *C*).

SEPTUM SECUNDUM. While these events occur another crescentic septum, the *septum secundum*, appears in the roof of the right atrium during the seventh week of development (fig. 11-11*C*, *D*, *E*). This septum never forms a complete partition in the atrial cavity. Only its anterior limb grows downward to the septum in the atrioventricular canal, thereby following the base of the septum primum.[11, 12] Its free concave edge eventually overlaps the ostium secundum, and the passage between the two atrial cavities is now an obliquely elongated cleft, the *oval foramen* (fig. 11-11*D*, *E*, *F*). Since, during fetal life, the pressure is higher in the right atrium than in the left, the oval foramen allows the highly oxygenated blood to flow directly from the right to the left side of the heart. After birth, however, when the lung circulation begins and the blood pressure in the left atrium rises above that in the right, the upper edge of the septum primum is pressed against the septum secundum, thus obliterating the oval foramen and separating the right and left atria.

Atrioventricular Valves

After fusion of the endocardial cushions has divided the atrioven-tricular canal into right and left orifices (fig. 11-12), each orifice is sur-rounded by localized proliferations of mesenchymal tissue (fig. 11-13*A*), When subsequently the tissue located on the ventricular surface of these proliferations becomes hollowed out, the newly formed valves remain attached to the ventricular wall by muscular cords only (fig. 11-13*B*). Finally the muscular tissue in the cords on the ventricular side of the valves degenerates and is replaced by dense connective tissue. The valves then consist of connective tissue covered by endocardium and are connected to thickened trabeculae in the wall of the ventricle, the *papillary muscles*, by means of the *chordae tendineae* (fig. 11-13*C*). In this manner two valve leaflets are formed in the left atrioventricular canal, the *bicuspid* or *mitral valve*, and three on the right side, the *tri-cuspid valve*.

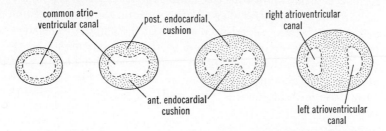

Figure 11-12. *Formation of the septum in the atrioventricular canal. From left to right 4-, 6-, 9-, and 12-mm. stages, respectively. The initial circular opening becomes gradually widened in transverse direction.*

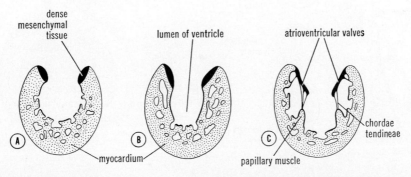

Figure 11-13. *Formation of the atrioventricular valves and chordae tendineae. Note how the valves are hollowed out from the ventricular side, but remain attached to the ventric-ular wall by the chordae tendineae (modified after Gegenbauer).*

Septum Formation in the Bulboventricular Region

At the end of the fourth week of development (5-mm. stage) a muscular ridge, known as the *muscular part of the interventricular septum*, appears in the floor of the bulboventricular region (fig. 11-11*B*, *D*). Further growth of this muscular septum is caused partly by dilatation of the bulboventricular cavity on each side of it and partly by active proliferation. Its posterior limb extends in the direction of the posterior atrioventricular cushion and its anterior limb toward the septum developing in the bulbus. The middle portion forms a concave upper border (fig. 11-15), and the opening between the right and left ventricles present at this stage is known as the *interventricular foramen* (fig. 11-11*B*, *C*, *D*).

In the meantime a pair of opposing ridges, the *truncoconal ridges*, composed of mesenchymal tissue and covered by endocardium, appears in the cephalic part of the truncus (fig. 11-15). With further growth these ridges cut deep into the lumen and descend in the direction of the ventricles, thereby following a spiral course. After fusion, the ridges form a septum known as the *aorticopulmonary septum* (fig. 11-14*A*). As a result of the spiral shape of the septum, the aorta and pulmonary artery are twisted round each other. In the distal area of the truncus, the pulmonary artery is located to the left and dorsal to the aorta (fig. 11-14*B*; in the region of the conus, the pulmonary artery is situated to the right and ventral to the aorta. In this manner the aorta enters the left side of the heart and the pulmonary artery the right side.

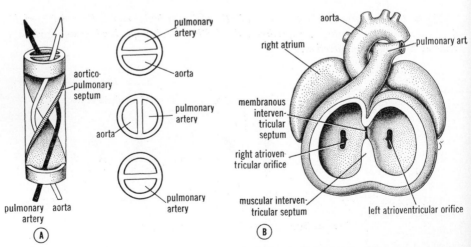

Figure 11-14. *A, Diagram to show the spiral shape of the aorticopulmonary septum. B, Position of aorta and pulmonary artery at 25-mm. stage (eighth week). Note how the aorta and pulmonary artery twist around each other.*

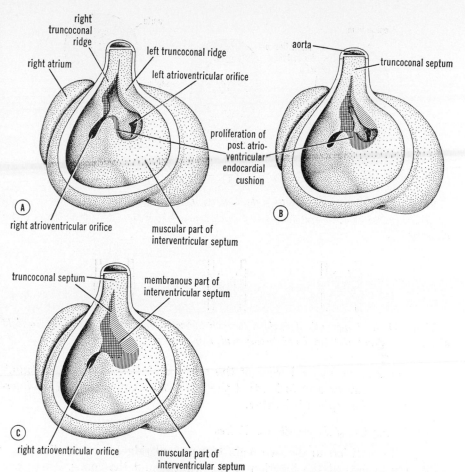

Figure 11-15. *Schematic drawings showing the development of the truncoconal ridges and the closure of the interventricular foramen. The proliferations of the right and left truncoconal ridges, combined with the proliferation of the posterior atrioventricular cushion, eventually close the interventricular foramen and form the membranous portion of the interventricular septum. A, At 6 weeks (12 mm.); B, beginning of seventh week (14.5 mm.); C, end of seventh week (20 mm.) (modified after Hamilton, Boyd, and Mossman).*

The left truncoconal ridge grows along the right side of the anterior limb of the muscular interventricular septum (fig. 11-15A), while the right truncoconal ridge terminates above the right atrioventricular orifice. Later it crosses this opening and fuses with the posterior limb of the muscular interventricular septum (fig. 11-15B).

By the end of the seventh week the interventricular foramen is closed by proliferations from three sources (fig. 11-15A, B, C): (1) the *left truncoconal ridge*, (2) the *right truncoconal ridge*, and (3) material from the *posterior atrioventricular endocardial cushion*, which grows out along

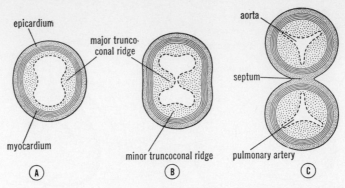

Figure 11-16. *Transverse sections through the truncus arteriosus at the level of the semilunar valves at 5, 6, and 7 weeks of development (A, B, and C, respectively) (after Kramer).*

Figure 11-17. *Longitudinal sections through the semilunar valves. From left to right sixth, seventh, and ninth weeks of development, respectively.*

the concave upper border of the muscular interventricular septum.[13] It is in this area of fusion that the future *membranous part of the interventricular septum* is located.

Formation of the Semilunar Valves

In addition to the two main truncoconal ridges, two smaller ridges are formed at the junction of the truncus and the conus. These new ridges alternate in position with the main ones (fig. 11-16A, B). After fusion of the main ridges, the aorta and pulmonary artery each show three thickenings of loose connective tissue covered by endocardium (fig. 11-16C). Gradually these become hollowed out on their upper surface, thus forming the *semilunar valves* (fig. 11-17).

References —Normal Development of the Heart

1. EVANS, H. M. The development of the vascular system. In *Manual of Human Embryology*, edited by F. Keibel and F. P. Mall. J. B. Lippincott Co., Philadelphia, 1912.
2. REAGAN, F. P. Experimental studies on the origin of vascular endothelium and of erythrocytes. Amer. J. Anat., **21:** 39, 1917.
3. HUGHES, A. F. W. The histogenesis of the arteries of the chick embryo. J. Anat., **77:** 266, 1943.
4. HIS, W. Lecithoblast und Angioblast der Wirbeltiere. Abhandl. Math.-Phys. Kl. Sächs. Akad. Wiss. Leipzig, **26:** 173, 1900.
5. McCLURE, C. F. W. The endothelial problem. Anat. Rec., **22:** 219, 1921.

Special Embryology

6. Goss, C. M. The development of the median coordinated ventricle from the lateral hearts in rat embryos with three to six somites. Anat. Rec., **112**: 761, 1952.

7. Davis, C. L. Development of the human heart from its first appearance to the stage found in embryos of 20 paired somites. Contrib. Embryol., **19**: 245, 1927.

8. Barry, A. The functional significance of the cardiac jelly in the tubular heart of the chick embryo. Anat. Rec., **102**: 289, 1948.

9. Kramer, T. C. The partitioning of the truncus and conus and the formation of the membranous portion of the interventricular septum in the human heart. Amer. J. Anat., **71**: 343, 1942.

10. Los, J. A. The development of the pulmonary veins and the coronary sinus in the human embryo. Doctoral thesis, University of Leyden, 1958.

11. Odgers, P. N. B. The formation of the venous valves, the foramen secundum and the septum secundum in the human heart. J. Anat., **69**: 412, 1935.

12. Van Mierop, L. H. S., Alley, R. D., Kausel, M. W., and Stranahan, A. The anatomy and embryology of endocardial cushion defects. J. Thor. Cardiov. Surg., **43**: 71, 1962.

13. Odgers, P. N. B. The development of the pars membranacea septi in the human heart. J. Anat., **72**: 247, 1939.

ABNORMAL DEVELOPMENT OF THE HEART

- **ANOMALIES OF THE ATRIAL SEPTUM:** *probe patency; ostium secundum defect; common atrium; premature closure of the oval foramen*
- **ANOMALIES OF THE ATRIOVENTRICULAR CANAL:** *persistent atrioventricular canal; ostium primum defect; tricuspid atresia*
- **ANOMALIES OF THE INTERVENTRICULAR SEPTUM:** *defect of the membranous septum; common ventricle*
- **ANOMALIES OF THE TRUNCUS AND CONUS:** *tetralogy of Fallot; persistent truncus arteriosus; transposition of the great vessels*
- **ANOMALIES OF THE SEMILUNAR VALVES:** *pulmonary valvular stenosis and atresia; aortic valvular stenosis and atresia*
- **ANOMALIES IN POSITION OF THE HEART:** *dextrocardia; ectopia cordis*
- **CAUSES OF CARDIOVASCULAR ANOMALIES:** *fetal environment; genetic factors; experimentally produced malformations*

Until recently the study of congenital heart malformations was largely of academic interest only. Rapid advances in cardiac diagnosis and surgery and the possibility of correcting many of the previously fatal abnormalities justify a brief account in this chapter of some of the more common malformations.

Anomalies of the Atrial Septum

Under normal conditions the septum primum and septum secundum fuse in such a manner that no opening remains between the right and left atria. In 20 to 25 per cent of all adult hearts, however, a probe can be passed through the oval foramen obliquely upward from the right atrium toward the left. This condition, known as *probe patency of the oval foramen*, does not normally allow intracardiac shunting of blood. Since it occurs frequently in otherwise normal hearts, the condition is not considered a true anomaly.[1]

A more serious anomaly is the *ostium secundum* defect. This condition, which is characterized by a large opening between the left and right atrium, is caused either by excessive resorption of the septum primum (fig. 11-18*A*) or by inadequate development of the septum secundum (fig. 11-18*B*). Depending on the size of the opening, considerable intracardiac shunting may occur.[2]

The most serious anomaly in this group is the complete failure of the septum to form (fig. 11-18*C*). This condition, known as *common atrium* or *cor triloculare biventriculare*, is usually associated with defects elsewhere in the heart.[3]

Occasionally the oval foramen closes during prenatal life. This anomaly, known as *premature closure of the oval foramen*, leads to massive

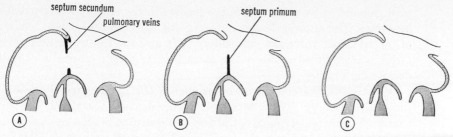

Figure 11-18. *A, Ostium secundum defect caused by excessive resorption of the septum primum. B, Similar defect caused by failure of development of the septum secundum. C, Common atrium or cor triloculare biventriculare—complete failure of the septum primum and septum secundum to form.*

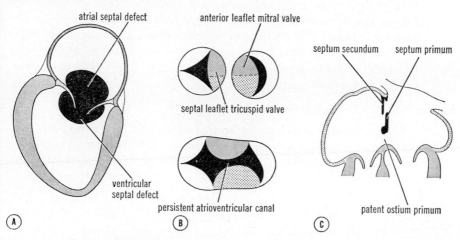

Figure 11-19. *A, Persistent common atrioventricular canal. This anomaly is always accompanied by a septum defect in the atrial as well as in the ventricular portion of the cardiac partition. B, Valves in the atrioventricular orifices under normal conditions (top) and in the case of a persistent atrioventricular canal (below). C, Ostium primum defect caused by incomplete fusion of the atrioventricular endocardial cushions.*

hypertrophy of the right atrium and ventricle, and underdevelopment of the left side.[4] Death usually occurs shortly after birth.

Anomalies of the Atrioventricular Canal

Under normal conditions the endocardial cushions of the atrioventricular canal not only divide this canal into a right and left orifice, but also participate in the formation of the membranous portion of the interventricular septum and in the closure of the ostium primum. Thus, whenever these cushions fail to fuse, the result is a *persistent atrioventricular canal*, combined with a defect in the cardiac septum (fig. 11-19*A*). This septal defect has an atrial and ventricular component, separated by abnormal valve leaflets in the single atrioventricular orifice. The anterior leaflet of the mitral valve and the septal leaflet of the tricuspid valve are completely cleft and their anterior and posterior portions fuse to form the large leaflets which cross the septal defect (fig. 11-19B).

Occasionally the endocardial cushions in the atrioventricular canal fuse only partially. The interatrial communication is then similar to that in the previous anomaly, but the interventricular septum is closed (fig. 11-19C). This defect, known as *ostium primum defect*, is usually combined with a cleft in the anterior leaflet of the mitral valve and in the septal leaflet of the tricuspid valve.[5]

Another important anomaly of the atrioventricular canal, presumably caused by an early obliteration of the right atrioventricular orifice, is the *tricuspid atresia* (fig. 11-20A). It is characterized by the absence or fusion of the tricuspid valves, and is always associated with: (1) patency of the oval foramen, (2) patency of the interventricular foramen, (3) underdevelopment of the right ventricle, and (4) hypertrophy of the left ventricle.[6]

Anomalies of the Interventricular Septum

Under normal conditions the membranous part of the interventricular septum is formed by proliferation of the right and left truncoconal ridges and by migration of material from the posterior atrioventricular

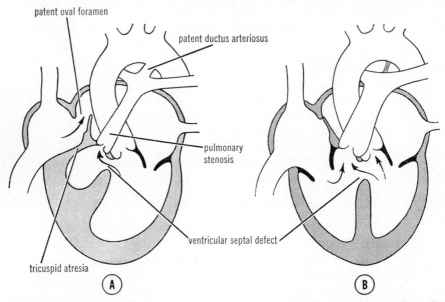

Figure 11-20. *A, Tricuspid atresia. Note the small right ventricle and the large left ventricle. B, Isolated defect in the membranous portion of the ventricular septum.*

cushion. Considering the complicated formation of this portion of the interventricular septum, it is not surprising that defects may easily arise. Indeed, a *defect of the membranous septum* is frequently seen (fig. 11-20B). Although it is commonly found as an isolated lesion, it may be associated with anomalies in the partition of the truncoconal region. Depending on the size of the opening, the blood carried by the pulmonary artery may be 1.2 to 1.7 times more abundant than that carried by the aorta.[4] Occasionally the defect is not restricted to the membranous part, but involves the muscular part of the septum as well.[7]

Finally, the interventricular septum may be completely absent. This condition is usually seen in combination with transposition of the great vessels.[8]

Anomalies of the Truncus and Conus

The most frequently seen abnormality of this region is the *tetralogy of Fallot* (fig. 11-21A). Classically, this cardiac anomaly is described as consisting of: (1) pulmonary stenosis, (2) ventricular septal defect, (3) overriding aorta, and (4) hypertrophy of the right ventricle. Hence the term "tetralogy." The basic defect in this cardiac malformation is an unequal division of the conus, due to an anterior displacement of the aorticopulmonary septum. This results in a narrow right ventricular outflow region, that is, an *infundibular stenosis*, and a large defect of the interventricular septum. The aorta arises directly above the septal defect from both ventricular cavities, and the resulting high pressure on

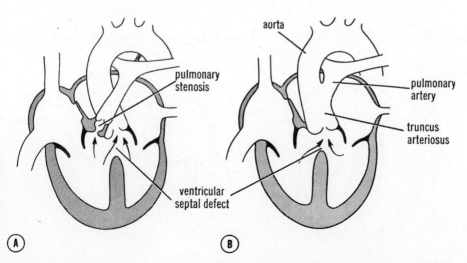

A **B**

Figure 11-21. *A, Tetralogy of Fallot characterized by: (1) stenosis of the pulmonary tract, (2) overriding aorta, (3) ventricular septal defect, and (4) hypertrophy of the right ventricle. B, Persistent truncus arteriosus. The pulmonary artery originates from the common truncus.*

the right side causes hypertrophy of the right ventricular wall. This abnormality is regarded as the most important type of malformations causative of cyanosis, but is compatible with life.[9, 10]

Under normal conditions the truncus and conus are divided into aorta and pulmonary artery by the fusion of the two spiral ridges. If these ridges fail to fuse and to descend toward the ventricles, a *persistent truncus arteriosus* results (fig. 11-21B). In such a case the pulmonary artery arises some distance above the origin of the undivided truncus. Since the ridges also participate in the formation of the conal septum and part of the interventricular septum, the persistent truncus is always accompanied by a defective interventricular septum. The undivided truncus thus overrides both ventricles and receives blood from both sides.[11]

Sometimes the descending aorticopulmonary septum fails to follow its normal spiral course, but descends straight downward (fig. 11-22A). As a consequence the aorta originates from the right ventricle, and the pulmonary artery from the left. This condition, known as *transposition of the great vessels*, is one of the most common cardiac anomalies. Sometimes it is associated with a defect in the membranous part of the interventricular septum.[12, 13]

Anomalies of the Semilunar Valves

In this important group of abnormalities the semilunar valves of the pulmonary artery or aorta are fused for a variable distance and

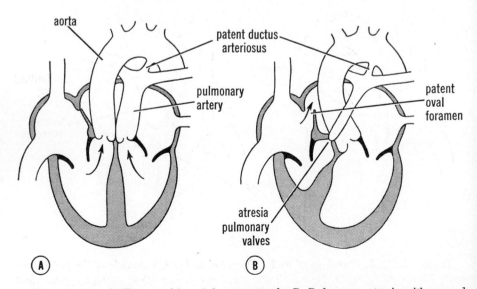

Figure 11-22. *A, Transposition of the great vessels. B, Pulmonary atresia with normal aortic root. The only access route to the lungs is by way of the patent ductus arteriosus.*

Special Embryology

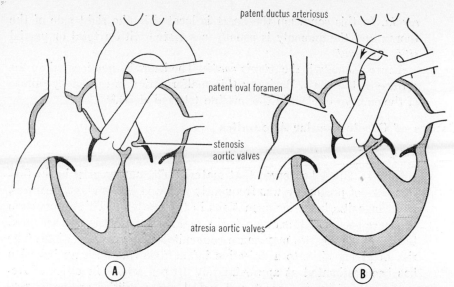

Figure 11-23. *A, Aortic valvular stenosis. B, Aortic atresia. Arrow in arch of the aorta indicates direction of blood flow. The coronary arteries are supplied by this retroflux. Note the small left ventricle and the large right ventricle.*

may even form an imperforated diaphragm. In case of a *valvular stenosis of the pulmonary artery* the fused cusps may form a dome, which projects into a poststenotic dilatation of the pulmonary artery.[14] When the valves are completely fused the trunk of the pulmonary artery is narrow or even atretic (fig. 11-22B). The patent oval foramen then forms the only outlet for blood from the right side of the heart. The ductus arteriosus is always patent and represents the only access route to the pulmonary circulation.[15]

In case of *aortic valvular stenosis* (fig. 11-23A), the fusion of the thickened valves may be so complete that only a pinhole opening remains. The size of the aorta itself, however, is usually normal.[16] Occasionally a *subaortic stenosis* may be seen. In these cases a ring of fibrous tissue is found circling the outflow tract of the left ventricle just below the aortic valves.[17]

When the fusion of the semilunar aortic valves is complete—a condition known as *aortic valvular atresia* (fig. 11-23B) —the aorta, left ventricle, and left atrium are markedly underdeveloped. The anomaly is usually accompanied by a wide open ductus arteriosus, which delivers blood into the aorta.[18]

Anomalies in the Position of the Heart

In addition to the malformations described above, the position of the heart itself may be abnormal. Most frequently seen is the *dextro-*

cardia. In this condition the heart is located in the right side of the thorax and the anomaly is usually associated with a total or partial *situs inversus.*[19]

A rare anomaly is the *ectopia cordis.* The heart is then located on the surface of the chest. Basically this malformation is caused by failure of the embryo to close in the midline (sternal cleft).[20]

Causes of Cardiovascular Anomalies

Fetal Environment

In 1941, Gregg[21] observed that maternal German measles in the first 10 weeks of pregnancy was frequently followed by cataract, deafness, and congenital heart malformations in the newborn. This observation has since been confirmed repeatedly, and at present it is well accepted that German measles may cause congenital heart malformations. The risk of giving birth to a defective infant following such an infection has been estimated at approximately 10 per cent.[22] In order of frequency the following heart and vessel abnormalities are seen: persistent ductus arteriosus, ventricular septal defect, Fallot's tetralogy, atrial septal defect, and pulmonary valvular stenosis.[22-24]

Genetic Factors

There are many reports of family pedigrees showing more than one member affected with congenital heart anomalies; this suggests that these malformations may be transmitted genetically. In contrast to these reports, however, recent authors are less inclined to incriminate genetic factors. Even though the familial incidence of cardiac anomalies has been noted in some cases, no definite mode of inheritance has so far been determined.[25-28]

Experimentally Produced Heart Malformations

A great variety of congenital cardiovascular anomalies have recently been produced by treating pregnant rats and mice with a number of teratogenic agents, *e.g.,* injection of trypan blue,[29, 30] vitamin A deficiency,[31] oxygen deficiency,[32] x-irradiation,[33] and pteroylglutamic acid deficiency.[34, 35] Although in many instances the anomalies produced were strikingly similar to those observed in man, it must be kept in mind that these results were obtained with animals and are not necessarily applicable to man.

References—Abnormal Development of the Heart

1. WRIGHT, R. R., ANSON, B. J., AND CLEVELAND, H. C. The vestigial valves and the interatrial foramen of the adult human heart. Anat. Rec., 100: 331, 1948.

2. DEXTER, L. Atrial septal defects. Brit. Heart J., **18**: 209, 1956.

3. ROGERS, H. M., AND EDWARDS, J. E. Cor triloculare biventriculare. Amer. Heart J., **45**: 623, 1953.

4. EDWARD, J. E. Congenital malformations of the heart and great vessels. In *Pathology of the Heart,* edited by S. E. Gould, p. 266. Charles C Thomas, Springfield, Ill., 1953.

5. ROGERS, H. M., AND EDWARDS, J. E. Incomplete division of the atrioventricular canal with patent interatrial foramen primum. Amer. Heart J., **36**: 28, 1948.

6. EDWARDS, J. E., AND BURCHELL, H. B. Congenital tricuspid atresia; a classification. Med. Clin. N. Amer., **33**: 1177, 1949.

7. MASON, D. G., AND HUNTER, W. C. Localized congenital defects of the cardiac interventricular septum. Amer. J. Path., **13**: 835, 1937.

8. ROGERS, H. M., AND EDWARDS, J. E. Cor triloculare biatriatum. Amer. Heart J., **41**: 299, 1951.

9. BRINTON, W. D., AND CAMPBELL, M. Necropsies in some congenital diseases of the heart, mainly Fallot's tetralogy. Brit. Heart J., **15**: 335, 1953.

10. BAFFES, T. G., JOHNSON, F. R., POTT, W. J., AND GIBSON, S. Anatomic variations in tetralogy of Fallot. Amer. Heart J., **46**: 657, 1953.

11. COLLETT, R. W., AND EDWARDS, J. Persistent truncus arteriosus. Surg. Clin. N. Amer., **29**: 1245, 1949.

12. HARRIS, J. S., AND FARBER, S. Transposition of the great cardiac vessels. Arch. Path., **28**: 427, 1939.

13. TAUSSIG, H. B. Complete transposition of the great vessels. Amer. Heart J., **16**: 728, 1938.

14. ABRAHAMS, D. G., AND WOOD, P. Pulmonary stenosis with normal aortic root. Brit. Heart J., **13**: 519, 1951.

15. GREENWOLD, P. Congenital pulmonary atresia with intact ventricular septum. In *Proceedings of the 29th Scientific Session of the American Heart Association,* p. 51, 1956.

16. CAMPBELL, M., AND KAUNTZE, R. Congenital valvular stenosis. Brit. Heart J., **15**: 179, 1953.

17. GRUENWALD, P. Subaortic stenosis of the left ventricle. J. Tech. Meth., **27**: 173, 1947.

18. MONIE, J. W., AND DE PAPE, A. D. J. Congenital aortic atresia. Amer. Heart J., **40**: 595, 1950.

19. LICHTMAN, S. S. Isolated congenital dextrocardia. Arch. Int. Med., **48**: 683, 1931.

20. BYRON, F. Ectopia cordis. J. Thor. Cardiov. Surg., **7**: 717, 1948.

21. GREGG, N. M. Congenital cataract following German measles in the mother. Trans. Ophthal. Soc. Aust., **3**: 35, 1941.

22. WARKANY, J. Etiologic factors of congenital heart disease. In *Congenital Heart Disease,* edited by H. S. Kaplan and S. J. Robinson, p. 83. American Association for the Advancement of Science, Washington, D. C., 1960.

23. CAMPBELL, M. Place of maternal rubella in the aetiology of congenital heart disease. Brit. Med. J., **1**: 5227, 1961.

24. BELL, J. On rubella in pregnancy. Brit. Med. J., **1**: 1302, 1959.

25. McKEOWN, T., MACMAHON, B., AND PARSONS, C. G. The familial incidence of congenital malformations of the heart. Brit. Heart J., **15**: 273, 1953.

26. POLANI, P. E., AND CAMPBELL, M. An etiological study of congenital heart disease. Ann. Hum. Genet., **19**: 209, 1955.

27. UCHIDA, J. A., AND ROWE, R. D. Discordant heart anomalies in twins. Amer. J. Hum. Genet., **9**: 133, 1957.

28. Böök, J. A. Heredity and heart disease. Amer. J. Public Health, **50:** 1, 1960.
29. Fox, M. H., AND Goss, C. M. Experimentally produced malformations of the heart and great vessels in rat fetuses; transposition complexes and aortic arch abnormalities. Amer. J. Anat., **102:** 65, 1958.
30. Richman, S., Thomas, W., AND Konikov, N. Survival of rats with induced congenital cardiovascular anomalies. A. M. A. Arch. Path., **63:** 43, 1957.
31. Wilson, J. G., AND Warkany, J. Aortic arch and cardiac anomalies in the offspring of vitamin A deficient rats. Amer. J. Anat., **85:** 113, 1949.
32. Ingalls, T. H., Curley, F. J., AND Prindle, R. Experimental production of congenital anomalies. New Engl. J. Med., **247:** 758, 1952.
33. Wilson, J. G., Jordan, H. C., AND Brent, R. L. Effects of irradiation on embryonic development. II. X-rays on the ninth day of gestation in the rat. Amer. J. Anat., **92:** 153, 1953.
34. Baird, C. D. C., Nelson, M. M., Monie, T. W., AND Evans, H. M. Congenital cardiovascular anomalies by pteroylglutamic acid deficiency during gestation in the rat. Circulat. Res., **2:** 544, 1954.
35. Monie, T. W., Nelson, M. M., Baird, C. D. C., AND Evans, H. M. Pathogenesis of cardiovascular abnormalities in fetal rats following transitory maternal pteroylglutamic acid deficiency. Circulation, **12:** 750, 1955.

ARTERIAL SYSTEM

Normal Development

The development of the intra-embryonic vascular system (early somite stage) is characterized by the appearance of numerous blood islands which gradually form plexiform networks throughout the mesenchyme. Shortly afterward, these plexuses fuse and form minute vessels, which in turn give rise to bigger channels.

The first well defined intra-embryonic vessels so formed are the *right and left primitive aortas*. They appear at approximately the 12-somite stage as continuations of the endocardial heart tube, and are located ventrally to the foregut (fig. 11-24). From here, they curve around the pharyngeal gut, embedded in the mesoderm of the first pharyngeal arch, and then continue caudally as the dorsal aortas.

Each dorsal aorta gives off the following branches along its course: the *intersegmental arteries* to the body wall; the *vitelline arteries* to the yolk sac; and the *umbilical arteries* to the placenta (fig. 11-24).

Progressive fusion of the endocardial heart tubes beyond the pericardial cavity subsequently causes the ventral portions of both primitive aortas to unite, thus forming the *aortic sac*.[1] With the further formation of the pharyngeal arches, the aortic sac contributes a branch to each new arch, giving rise to a total of six pairs of arteries which curve around the pharyngeal gut and enter into the dorsal aorta. These arteries, the *aortic arches*, are never present all at the same time, since the first pairs have already been obliterated by the time the last pair arises (fig. 11-3).

Aortic Arches

Although in human development the six aortic arches never exist all at the same time, this basic vascular pattern is useful in understand-

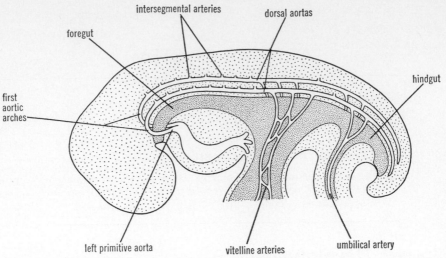

Figure 11-24. *Scheme of the arterial system in a 3-week-old embryo (approximately 2 mm.) (modified after Congdon).*

ing the transformation into the adult arterial system (fig. 11-25). In addition, it may help to understand the vascular abnormalities which frequently occur in this region.

The first aortic arch, or *mandibular arch artery*, disappears at the time that the third aortic arch becomes fully developed. A small part of it persists as the *maxillary artery*.

The second aortic arch, or *hyoid arch artery*, disappears except for small parts which form the *hyoid* and *stapedial arteries*.[2]

The third aortic arch forms the common carotid and the first part of the internal carotid artery. The remainder of the internal carotid is formed by the cranial part of the dorsal aorta. The origin of the external carotid artery is controversial, but in later stages it is found as a new sprout of the third aortic arch, linking up with the remaining parts of the first and second aortic arches (fig. 11-25B).[1]

The fourth aortic arch persists bilaterally, but its ultimate fate is different on right and left sides. On the left it forms the *arch of the aorta*. On the right it forms the *stem of the subclavian artery*, which reaches the arm by way of the right dorsal aorta and the seventh intersegmental artery (fig. 11-25B). Comparing the development of the right subclavian artery with that on the left, it may be noticed that the seventh intersegmental artery is the only portion which is identical in origin in both arteries.

The existence of *the fifth aortic arch* is controversial. If it exists at all, it disappears early.[1]

The sixth aortic arch, often referred to as the *pulmonary arch*, gives

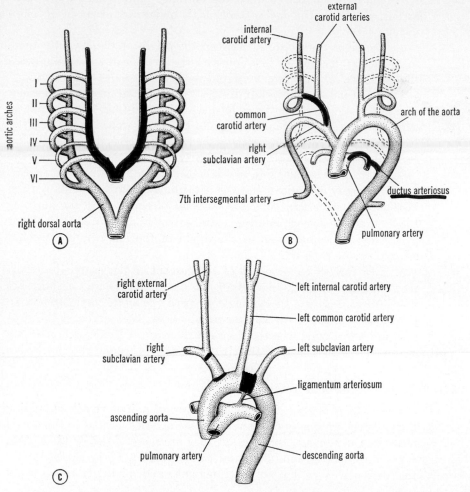

Figure 11-25. *A, Diagram of the aortic arches and dorsal aortas before transformation into the definitive vascular pattern. B, Diagram of the aortic arches and dorsal aortas after the transformation. The obliterated components are indicated by broken lines. Note the patent ductus arteriosus and the position of the seventh intersegmental artery on the left. C, The great arteries in the adult. Compare the distance between the place of origin of the left common carotid artery and the left subclavian in B and C.*

off an important branch which grows toward the lung bud. Whereas on the right the distal part of this arch loses its connection with the dorsal aorta, on the left it persists during intra-uterine life as the *ductus arteriosus of Botallo*. After birth, however, this vessel is obliterated, persisting into adult life as the *ligamentum arteriosum* (fig. 11-25C).

Simultaneously with these alterations in the aortic arch system, a number of other changes occur:

1. The dorsal aorta between the entrance of the third and fourth arches, known as the *ductus caroticus,* is obliterated early in development.

2. The right dorsal aorta between the origin of the seventh intersegmental artery and its junction with the left dorsal aorta disappears (fig. 11-25*B*). If it persists, a double aortic arch results (fig. 11-28).

3. The truncoconal septum divides the aortic sac in such a manner that the aortic trunk continues into the third and fourth aortic arches, while the pulmonary trunk opens into the sixth arches (fig. 11-25*B*).

4. Formation of the neck causes the heart to descend from its initial cervical position into the thoracic cavity. Hence, the carotid and the innominate arteries elongate considerably. As a further result of this descent, it may be noticed that the left subclavian artery, distally fixed in the arm bud, gradually shifts its point of origin from the aorta at the level of the seventh intersegmental artery to an increasingly higher point, until it comes close to the origin of the left common carotid artery (fig. 11-25*B, C*).[3]

5. As a further consequence of the descent of the heart, the recurrent laryngeal nerves (nerves of the sixth pharyngeal arches) are pulled down into the thorax together with the sixth aortic arches. In the adult, therefore, the left recurrent nerve passes around the ligamentum arteriosum, whereas the right, because of lack of a homologue of the ductus arteriosus on the right side, passes around the subclavian artery.

Vitelline and Umbilical Arteries

The *vitelline arteries,* initially a number of paired vessels supplying the yolk sac, gradually fuse and form the arteries located in the dorsal mesentery of the gut. In the adult they are represented by the *coeliac, superior mesenteric,* and *inferior mesenteric arteries.* These vessels supply the derivatives of the foregut, midgut, and hindgut, respectively (see fig. 13-6).

The *umbilical arteries,* initially paired ventral branches of the dorsal aorta, course to the placenta in close association with the allantois (fig. 11-24). During the fourth week, however, each artery acquires a secondary connection with a dorsal branch of the aorta, the *common iliac artery,* and loses its original origin. After birth the proximal portions of the umbilical arteries persist as the *internal iliac* and the *superior vesicle arteries,* while the distal parts are obliterated to form the *lateral vesico-umbilical ligaments.*

Abnormalities of the Great Arteries

Since the aortic arch system undergoes a number of complicated changes in reaching its final pattern, it is not surprising that variations from the normal plan frequently occur.

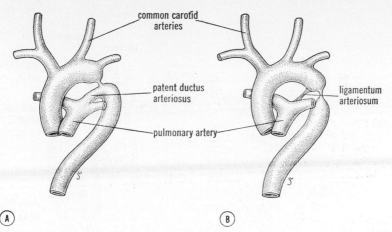

common carotid
arteries

patent ductus
arteriosus

ligamentum
arteriosum

pulmonary artery

(A)　　　　　　(B)

Figure 11-26. *Coarctation of the aorta. A, Preductal type; B, postductal type. The caudal part of the body is supplied by large, hypertrophied intercostal and internal mammary arteries.*

Patent Ductus Arteriosus

Under normal conditions the ductus arteriosus is functionally closed through contraction of its muscular wall shortly after birth.[4] Anatomical closure, however, by means of intima proliferation takes from 1 to 3 months.[5] A patent ductus arteriosus is one of the most frequently seen anomalies of the great vessels and may occur either as an isolated abnormality or in combination with other heart anomalies (figs. 11-20A and 11-22).

Coarctation of the Aorta

Coarctation of the aorta (fig. 11-26A, B), is a condition in which the aortic lumen below the origin of the left subclavian artery is significantly narrowed. Since the constriction may be located above or below the entrance of the ductus arteriosus, two types of coarctation may be distinguished: the *preductal* and *postductal* types. The cause of the aortic narrowing is primarily an abnormality in the media of the aorta followed by intima proliferations.[6] In the preductal type the ductus arteriosus persists, whereas in the postductal type this channel usually is obliterated. A collateral circulation between the proximal and distal parts of the aorta is established by way of large intercostal and internal mammary arteries.[7]

Abnormal Origin of the Right Subclavian Artery

In this condition (fig. 11-27A, B) the right subclavian artery is formed by the distal portion of the right dorsal aorta and the seventh intersegmental artery. The right fourth aortic arch and the proximal part of the right dorsal aorta have been obliterated. With shortening

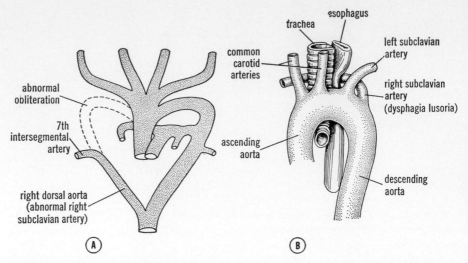

Figure 11-27. *Abnormal origin of the right subclavian artery (dysphagia lusoria). A, Scheme to show the obliteration of the right fourth aortic arch and the proximal portion of the right dorsal aorta, and persistence of the distal portion of the right dorsal aorta. B, The abnormal right subclavian artery crosses the midline behind the esophagus and may compress the latter.*

of the aorta between the left common carotid and the left subclavian arteries,[3] the origin of the anomalous right subclavian artery is finally found just below that of the left subclavian artery. Since its stem is derived from the right dorsal aorta, it must cross the midline behind the esophagus to reach the right arm. This abnormality, which is frequently seen, may occasionally cause difficulties in swallowing.[8, 9] In such instances the recurrent laryngeal nerve does not hook around the right subclavian artery, but passes directly from the vagus to the larynx musculature.

Double Aortic Arch

Under normal conditions the right dorsal aorta disappears between the origin of the seventh intersegmental artery and its junction with the left dorsal aorta. If, however, this fails to occur, a double aortic arch (fig. 11-28*A*, *B*) results. A *vascular ring* is thus formed which surrounds the trachea and esophagus and frequently compresses these structures, causing difficulties in breathing and swallowing.[10, 11]

Interrupted Aortic Arch

This interesting anomaly (fig. 11-29*A*, *B*), which is more serious than the abnormalities previously described, is caused by obliteration of the fourth aortic arch on the left side. It is frequently combined with

Special Embryology

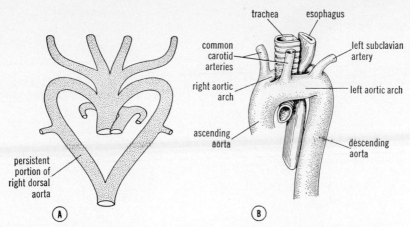

Figure 11-28. *Double aortic arch. A, Scheme showing the persistence of the distal portion of the right dorsal aorta. B, The double aortic arch forms a vascular ring around the trachea and the esophagus.*

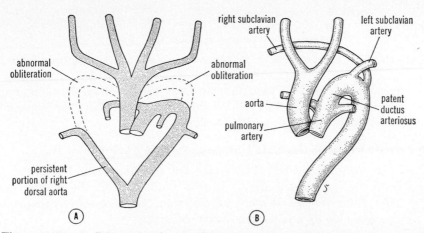

Figure 11-29. *A, Scheme showing the obliteration of the fourth aortic arch on the right as well as on the left and persistence of the distal portion of the right dorsal aorta. B, Case of interrupted aortic arch. The aorta supplies the head; the pulmonary artery by way of the ductus arteriosus supplies the remaining parts of the body.*

an abnormal origin of the right subclavian artery. The ductus arteriosus remains wide open and the descending aorta and subclavian arteries are supplied with blood of low oxygen content. The aortic trunk supplies the two common carotid arteries.[12]

Right Aortic Arch

In such a case (fig. 11-30*A*) the left fourth aortic arch and left dorsal aorta have been completely obliterated and are replaced by the cor-

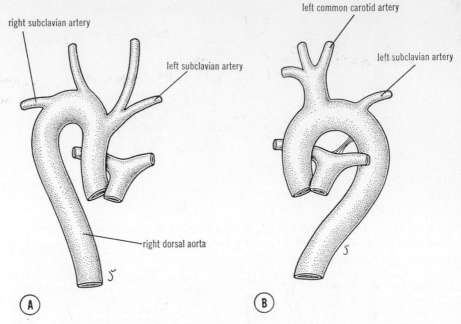

right subclavian artery

left subclavian artery

right dorsal aorta

left common carotid artery

left subclavian artery

A

B

Figure 11-30. *A, Right aortic arch. B, Abnormal origin of left common carotid artery.*

responding vessels on the right side. Occasionally, when the ligamentum arteriosum is situated on the left side and passes behind the esophagus, it may cause complaints with swallowing.[13]

Abnormal Origin of the Left Common Carotid Artery

In such a case (fig. 11-30*B*) the left common carotid artery arises from the innominate artery. It then winds around the anterior surface of the trachea in a cranial direction. This anomaly is frequently accompanied by an abnormal vertebral artery.[14]

References—Arterial System

1. CONGDON, E. D. Transformation of the aortic arch system during development of the human embryo. Contrib. Embryol., 14: 47, 1922.
2. PADGET, D. H. The development of the cranial arteries in the human embryo. Contrib. Embryol., 32: 205, 1948.
3. BARRY, A. The aortic arch derivatives in the human adult. Anat. Rec., 111: 221, 1951.
4. ADAMS, F. H., AND LIND, J. Physiologic studies on the cardiovascular status of the normal newborn infant (with special reference to the ductus arteriosus). A. M. A. J. Dis. Child., 93: 13, 1957.
5. JAGER, B. V., AND WOLLENMAN, O. J. An anatomical study of the closure of the ductus arteriosus. Amer. J. Path., 18: 595, 1942.
6. WIELENGA, G. The relationship between coarctation of the aorta and the ligamentum arteriosum. Thesis, University of Leyden, 1959.

Special Embryology

7. EDWARDS, J. E., CHRISTENSEN, N. A., CLAGETT, O. T., AND McDONALD, J. R. Pathologic considerations in coarctation of the aorta. Proc. Mayo Clin., **23**: 324, 1948.

8. PATTINSON, J. N. Anomalous right subclavian artery. Brit. Heart J., **15**: 150, 1953.

9. LANGMAN, J. Esophagus atresia accompanied by a remarkable vessel anomaly. Arch. Chir. Neerl., **4**: 39, 1952.

10. GRISWOLD, H. E., AND YOUNG, M. D. Double aortic arch. Pediatrics, **4**: 751, 1949.

11. EKSTROM, G., AND SANDBLOM, P. Double aortic arch; embryonic development. Acta Chir. Scand., **102**: 183, 1951.

12. KLEINERMAN, J., YANG, W., HACKEL, D. B., AND KAUFMAN, N. Absence of the transverse aortic arch. A. M. A. Arch. Path., **65**: 490, 1958.

13. BEDFORD, D. E., AND PARKINSON, J. Right sided aortic arch. Brit. J. Radiol., **9**: 776, 1936.

14. MAISEL, H. Some anomalies of the origin of the left vertebral artery. S. Afr. Med. J., **32**: 1141, 1958.

VENOUS AND LYMPHATIC SYSTEMS

NORMAL DEVELOPMENT
- VITELLINE VEINS
- UMBILICAL VEINS
- CARDINAL VEINS: *inferior vena cava; azygos vein; superior vena cava*
- PULMONARY VEINS
- LYMPHATIC SYSTEM

ABNORMAL VENOUS DRAINAGE
- *Double inferior vena cava; absent hepatic portion of the inferior vena cava; left superior vena cava; double superior vena cava; anomalous pulmonary venous drainage*

Normal Development

The 3-week-old embryo (3 mm.) is characterized by the presence of three pairs of veins: (1) the *vitelline* or *omphalomesenteric veins* carrying blood from the yolk sac toward the heart; (2) the *umbilical veins* originating in the chorionic villi and carrying oxygenated blood to the embryo; and (3) the *cardinal veins* draining the body of the embryo proper (fig. 11-3).

Vitelline Veins

The vitelline veins enter the body of the embryo by way of the yolk sac stalk, form an anastomotic network around the duodenum, and then enter the septum transversum on their way to the heart. Here the veins are interrupted by proliferating liver cords, and an extensive vascular network is formed throughout the liver, the *hepatic sinusoids* (fig. 11-31*A*, *B*). Subsequently the vitelline veins enter into the right and left horns of the sinus venosus.

Shortly thereafter the anastomotic network around the duodenum develops into a single vessel, the *portal vein*, partly by obliteration and partly by growth of different portions (fig. 11-31*A*, *B*, *C*). The *superior mesenteric vein* which drains the primitive intestinal loop is considered to be the successor of the right vitelline vein. The distal part of the left vitelline vein disappears completely.

The proximal parts of the vitelline veins drain into the sinus venosus (fig. 11-31*A*, *B*). With the disappearance of the left sinus horn, blood from the left side of the liver is rechanneled toward the right vitelline vein, which gradually enlarges to form the suprahepatic portion of the inferior vena cava (fig. 11-31*C*). The proximal part of the left vitelline vein disappears.

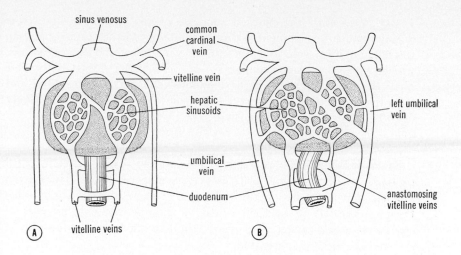

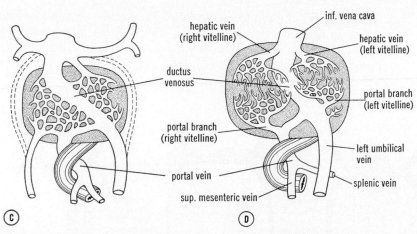

Figure 11-31. *Schemes showing the development of the umbilical and vitelline veins. A, At the end of the fourth week; B, in the fifth week; C, in the sixth week; D, in the third month. Note the formation of the ductus venosus between the left umbilical vein and the inferior vena cava.*

Umbilical Veins

The umbilical veins enter the embryo by way of the connecting stalk and then course through the mesoderm of the septum transversum toward the heart (fig. 11-3). At first they pass on each side along the liver (fig. 11-31A), but soon become connected to the hepatic sinusoids (fig. 11-31B). The proximal part of both umbilical veins as well as the remainder of the right umbilical vein then disappear so that the left vein is the only one to carry blood from the placenta to the liver (fig.

11-31*C*, *D*). With the marked increase of the placental circulation during further development, a direct communication is formed between the left umbilical vein and the inferior vena cava, the *ductus venosus*, which bypasses the sinusoidal plexus of the liver (fig. 11-31*C*, *D*). After birth the left umbilical vein and ductus venosus are obliterated and form the *ligamentum teres hepatis* and *ligamentum venosum*, respectively (see "Circulatory Changes at Birth," p. 190).

Cardinal Veins

The intra-embryonic venous system initially forms a symmetrical pattern. As development progresses this pattern changes in such a manner that the veins on the right side of the embryo enlarge while those on the left shunt their blood to the opposite side by way of transverse anastomoses. As a result, the left-sided vessels diminish in size and are largely obliterated.

Inferior Vena Cava

In the 4-week embryo the *posterior cardinal veins* form two longitudinal vessels draining the dorsal body wall and the mesonephroi (fig. 11-32*A*). During the next 4 weeks a number of other venous systems appear, which gradually take over the drainage of the posterior cardinals.

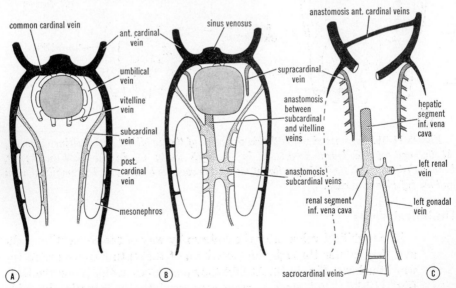

Figure 11-32. *Diagrams showing the development of the inferior vena cava, the azygos veins, and the superior vena cava. A, In the fourth week; B, in the sixth week; C, in the seventh week. Anastomoses are formed between the subcardinals, the sacrocardinals, and the anterior cardinals.*

Special Embryology

The *subcardinal veins* arise along the medial aspect of the mesonephroi and gradually take over the drainage of these organs from the posterior cardinals. In addition, a new vessel develops which connects the right subcardinal vein with the proximal part of the right vitelline vein (fig. 11-32B). This communicating vessel finally forms the *hepatic segment of the inferior vena cava* (fig. 11-32B, C).

While these events occur, anastomotic channels appear between the two subcardinals (fig. 11-32B). The left subcardinal vein proximal to this anastomosis disappears, while the distal portion becomes the *left gonadal vein*. The anastomosis itself becomes the *left renal vein*. The right subcardinal vein develops into the *renal segment of the inferior vena cava* and the *right gonadal vein* (fig. 11-32C).

With continuous growth of the embryo and formation of the lower extremities a third venous system, the *sacrocardinal veins*, appears. These vessels anastomose with the subcardinal veins as well as with each other (fig. 11-32C). The right sacrocardinal vein finally becomes the *sacrocardinal segment of the inferior vena cava*, and the communicating channel between the sacrocardinal veins forms the *left common iliac vein* (fig. 11-33A, B).

Hence, the inferior vena cava is formed by: (1) the proximal portion of the right vitelline vein (*suprahepatic segment*); (2) the anastomosis between the right subcardinal and the right vitelline vein (*hepatic segment*); (3) a portion of the right subcardinal vein (*renal segment*); and (4) a portion of the right sacrocardinal vein (*sacrocardinal segment*).

It has to be kept in mind that the preceding description on the development of the inferior vena cava is much simplified. The veins develop from capillary plexuses and there is much controversy over the fate of the different veins.[1-3]

Azygos Vein

With gradual obliteration of the posterior cardinals, another pair of veins, the *supracardinals*, takes over the drainage of the dorsal body wall (fig. 11-32B, C). These veins drain into the proximal portion of the posterior cardinals. After the development of a communicating vessel between the two supracardinals (fig. 11-33A), the left one loses its contact with the posterior cardinal and forms the hemiazygos vein (fig. 11-33B). The right supracardinal and the proximal portion of the right posterior cardinal form the *azygos vein*.

Superior Vena Cava

During the eighth week of development a large communicating vessel, the left *brachiocephalic vein* (fig. 11-33B), appears between the right and left *anterior cardinal veins*. Most of the blood from the left side is then channeled to the right, and the left anterior cardinal vein

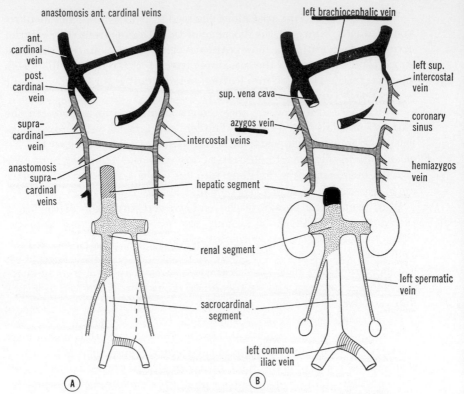

Figure 11-33. *Diagrams showing the further development of the inferior vena cava. A, At 9 weeks; B, full term. Note the anastomosis between the two supracardinal veins (adapted from Gruenwald, McClure, and Butler).*

below the anastomosis loses its connection with the left common cardinal vein (fig. 11-33*A*, *B*). The only portion which persists becomes the *left superior intercostal vein*.

On the right side the *superior vena cava* is formed by the common cardinal vein and the proximal part of the right anterior cardinal vein.

Pulmonary Veins

At approximately the 4-mm. stage the common pulmonary vein can be recognized as an evagination of the dorsal wall of the atrium.[4-6] This bud subsequently grows out into the dorsal mesocardium in the direction of the primitive foregut, which gives rise to the lung buds. With further development of the atrial cavity the stem of the pulmonary vein is progressively incorporated into the wall of the left atrium. Hence, whereas on the right side the smooth-walled part of the atrium originates from the right sinus horn, on the left it develops from the wall of the pulmonary veins. The incorporation of the pulmonary veins continues until two right and two left branches of the pulmonary stem enter the atrial cavity.

Lymphatic System

Initially the lymphatic system was considered to be formed by diverticula of the veins.[7, 8] Later, however, it has been suggested that it develops from clefts in the mesenchyme which connect with the venous system only secondarily.[9, 10] The cells lining the mesenchymal clefts assume an endothelial shape; subsequent sprouting of these cells causes the clefts to fuse, and gradually lymph channels arise.[11]

In the sixth week, local dilatations of some of these lymphatic channels form the lymph sacs. In this manner the *jugular* and *iliac lymph sacs* are formed in close relation to the jugular and common iliac veins, respectively. In addition, a *retroperitoneal lymph sac*, the *cisterna chyli*, arises at the level of the adrenals.

Through continuous budding of lymphatic vessels the abdominal lymph sacs are connected with those in the neck by means of a longitudinal vessel, the *thoracic duct*. This duct drains into the left internal jugular by way of the left jugular lymph sac. The various lymph sacs themselves are later replaced by chains of *lymph glands*, which appear during the third month of development.

Abnormal Venous Drainage

The complicated development of the venae cavae accounts for the fact that deviations from the normal pattern are frequently seen.

Double Inferior Vena Cava at the Lumbar Level

In this abnormality (fig. 11-34A) the left sacrocardinal vein has failed to lose its connection with the left subcardinal, and the left common iliac vein may or may not be present. The left gonadal vein, however, is present as in normal conditions.

Absence of the Inferior Vena Cava

In this case (fig. 11-34B) the right subcardinal vein has failed to make its connection with the liver and shunts its blood directly into the right supracardinal vein (fig. 11-32B). Hence, the blood stream from the caudal part of the body reaches the heart by way of the azygos and superior vena cava. The hepatic vein enters into the right atrium at the site of the inferior vena cava.[12] Usually this anomaly is associated with other heart malformations.

Left Superior Vena Cava

This anomaly (fig. 11-35A) is caused by the persistence of the left anterior cardinal vein and obliteration of the common cardinal and

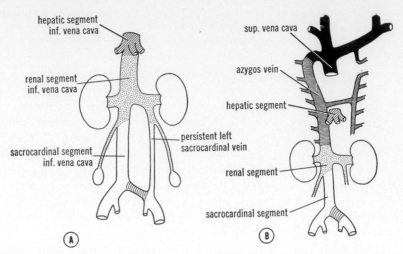

Figure 11-34. *A, Double inferior vena cava at the lumbar level due to the persistence of the left sacrocardinal vein. B, Absent inferior vena cava. The lower half of the body is drained by the azygos vein, which enters the superior vena cava. The hepatic vein enters the heart at the site of the inferior vena cava.*

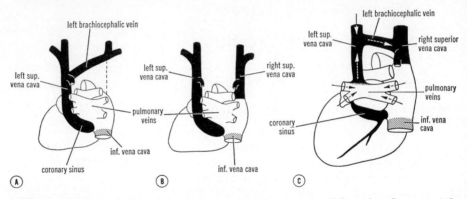

Figure 11-35. *A, Left superior vena cava draining into the right atrium by way of the coronary sinus (dorsal view). B, Double superior vena cava. The communicating vein between the two anterior cardinals has failed to develop (dorsal view). C, Total anomalous pulmonary venous drainage. The pulmonary veins enter the left superior vena cava, which enters the right superior vena cava by way of the brachiocephalic vein (dorsal view).*

proximal part of the anterior cardinal vein on the right. In such a case, the blood from the right is channeled toward the left by way of the brachiocephalic vein.[13]

Double Superior Vena Cava

This condition (fig. 11-35B) is characterized by the persistence of the left anterior cardinal vein and the failure of the left brachiocephalic vein to form. The persistent left anterior cardinal, which is called *left superior vena cava*, drains by way of the coronary sinus into the right atrium.[13]

Anomalous Pulmonary Venous Drainage

Occasionally some or all the pulmonary veins fail to drain into the left atrium (fig. 11-35C). In the partial form, the anomalous veins usually drain into the right atrium or into the superior vena cava. In total anomalous pulmonary venous drainage, they usually drain into a persistent left superior vena cava.[6, 14]

References—Venous and Lymphatic Systems

1. GRÜNWALD, P. Die Entwicklung der Vena Cava Caudalis. Z. Mikroskopischanat. Forsch., **43**: 275, 1938.
2. McCLURE, F. W., AND BUTLER, E. G. The development of the vena cava inferior in man. Amer. J. Anat., **35**: 331, 1925.
3. REAGAN, F. P., AND ROBINSON, A. The later development of the inferior vena cava in man and in carnivora. J. Anat., **61**: 482, 1927.
4. AUER, J. The development of the human pulmonary veins and its major variations. Anat. Rec., **101**: 581, 1948.
5. LOS, J. A. The development of the pulmonary veins and the coronary sinus in the human embryo. Doctoral thesis, University of Leyden, 1958.
6. NEILL, C. A. Development of the pulmonary veins. Pediatrics, **18**: 880, 1956.
7. SABIN, F. R. On the origin of the lymphatic system from the veins and the development of the lymph hearts and thoracic duct in the pig. Amer. J. Anat., **1**: 367, 1902.
8. SABIN, F. R. The origin and development of the lymphatic system. Johns Hopkins Hosp. Rep., **17**: 347, 1916.
9. HUNTINGTON, G. S. The development of the mammalian jugular lymph sac, of the tributary primitive ulnar lymphatic and of the thoracic ducts from the viewpoint of recent investigations of vertebrate lymphatic ontogeny, together with a consideration of the genetic relations of lymphatic and haemal vascular channels in the embryos of amniotes. Amer. J. Anat., **16**: 259, 1914.
10. ZIMMERMAN, A. A. *Origin and Development of the Lymphatic System in the Opossum* (Illinois Medical and Dental Monographs), Vol. 3, p. 1. University of Illinois Press, Urbana, Ill., 1940.
11. YOFFEY, J. M., AND COURTICE, F. C. *Lymphatics, Lymph and Lymphoid Tissue*. Harvard University Press, Cambridge, Mass., 1956.
12. ANDERSON, R. C., HEILIG, W., NOVICK, R., AND JARVIS, C. Anomalous inferior vena cava with azygos drainage. Amer. Heart J., **49**: 318, 1955.
13. WINTER, F. S. Persistent left superior vena cava. Angiology, **5**: 90, 1954.
14. DARLING, R. C., ROTHNEG, W. B., AND CRAIG, J. M. Total pulmonary venous drainage into the right side of the heart. Lab. Invest., **6**: 44, 1957.

CIRCULATORY CHANGES AT BIRTH

Fetal Circulation

Our present knowledge of the fetal circulation is based largely on angiocardiographic investigations in the fetal lamb and in the human fetus.[1-5]

Before birth, oxygenated blood from the placenta returns to the fetus by way of the umbilical vein. On approaching the liver, the main portion of this blood flows through the ductus venosus directly into the inferior vena cava, thereby short-circuiting the liver. A smaller portion enters the liver sinusoids and mixes here with blood from the portal circulation (fig. 11-36). A sphincter mechanism in the ductus venosus, close to the entrance of the umbilical vein, regulates the flow of umbilical blood through the liver sinusoids. It is thought that this sphincter closes when, because of a uterine contraction, the venous return is too high, thus preventing a sudden overloading of the heart.[6]

After a short course in the inferior vena cava the blood enters the right atrium. Here it is guided toward the oval foramen by the valve of the inferior vena cava, and the major portion of the blood stream passes directly into the left atrium. A small portion, however, is prevented from so doing by the lower edge of the septum secundum, the *crista dividens*, and remains in the right atrium. Here it mixes with the desaturated blood returning from the head and arms by way of the superior vena cava.

From the left atrium the blood stream enters the left ventricle and the ascending aorta. Since the coronary and carotid arteries are the first branches of the ascending aorta, the heart musculature and the brain are supplied with well oxygenated blood. The desaturated blood from the superior vena cava flows by way of the right ventricle into the pulmonary trunk. Since the resistance in the pulmonary vessels during fetal life is high, the main portion of this blood passes directly through the *ductus arteriosus* into the descending aorta, where it mixes with blood from the proximal aorta. From here on the blood stream flows toward the placenta by way of the two umbilical arteries. Only at the end of pregnancy, a small portion of the blood carried by the pulmonary artery may pass through the lungs.

During its course from the placenta to the organs of the fetus, the high oxygen content of the blood in the umbilical vein gradually de-

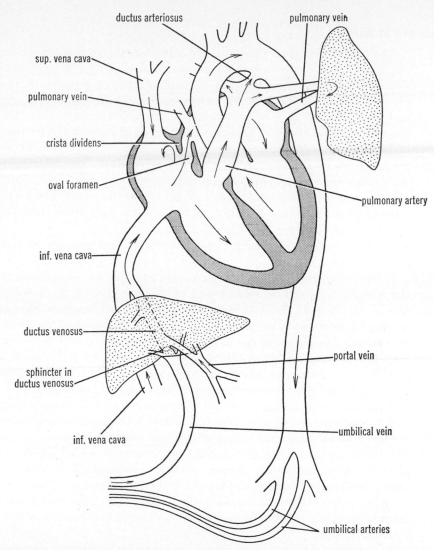

Figure 11-36. *Plan of the human circulation before birth. Arrows indicate the direction of the blood flow.*

creases by mixing with varying amounts of desaturated blood. Theoretically this may occur to a greater or lesser extent in the following places: (1) in the liver by mixture with a small amount of blood returning from the portal system; (2) in the inferior vena cava, which carries deoxygenated blood returning from the lower extremities, pelvis, and kidneys; (3) in the left atrium by mixture with blood returning from the lungs; and (4) at the entrance of the ductus arteriosus into the descending aorta.

Changes at Birth

The sudden changes occurring in the vascular system of the newborn are caused by the cessation of the placental blood flow and the beginning of the lung respiration. As a result of the compression of the chest at birth, the amnion fluid in the bronchial tree is replaced by air, and the lungs suddenly become aerated. Since, at the same time, the ductus arteriosus closes by muscular contraction of its wall, the amount of blood flowing through the lung vessels increases rapidly. This, in turn, results in a rise in pressure in the left atrium. Simultaneously with these changes on the left, the pressure in the right atrium decreases as a result of interruption of the placental blood flow. The septum primum is then apposed to the septum secundum, and the oval foramen closes functionally.

Summarizing, the following changes occur in the vascular system after birth (fig. 11-37):

1. *Closure of the umbilical arteries* is accomplished by contraction of the smooth musculature in the wall of the vessels and is probably caused by thermal and mechanical stimuli and a change in oxygen tension.[7] Functionally, the arteries are closed a few minutes after birth. The actual obliteration of the lumen by fibrous proliferation, however, may take from 2 to 3 months.[8, 9] The distal parts of the umbilical arteries then form the *lateral vesico-umbilical ligaments*, while the proximal portions remain open as the *superior vesical arteries*.

2. *Closure of the umbilical vein and ductus venosus* occurs shortly after that of the umbilical arteries. Hence, blood from the placenta may enter the newborn for some time after birth and an additional quantity equal to 1 to 4.5 per cent of the child's body weight may be added before the placental flow completely ceases. After obliteration, the umbilical vein forms the *ligamentum teres hepatis* in the lower margin of the falciform ligament. The ductus venosus, which courses from the ligamentum teres to the inferior vena cava, is also obliterated and forms the *ligamentum venosum*.

3. *Closure of the ductus arteriosus* by contraction of its muscular wall occurs almost immediately after birth. Angiocardiography and cardiac catheterization, however, have revealed that during the first days after birth a left-to-right shunt is not unusual.[7, 10] Complete anatomical obliteration by proliferation of the intima is thought to take from 1 to 3 months.[8] In the adult, the obliterated ductus arteriosus forms the *ligamentum arteriosum*.

4. *Closure of the oval foramen* is caused by an increased pressure in the left atrium combined with a decrease in pressure on the right side. With the first good breath the septum primum is pressed against the septum secundum. During the first days of life, however, this closure

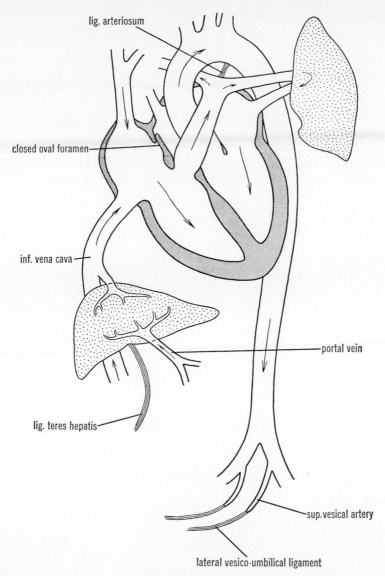

lig. arteriosum

closed oval foramen

inf. vena cava

lig. teres hepatis

portal vein

sup. vesical artery

lateral vesico-umbilical ligament

Figure 11-37. *Plan of the human circulation after birth. Arrows indicate the direction of the blood flow.*

is reversible. Crying of the baby creates a shunt from right to left, thus accounting for the cyanotic periods in the newborn. Constant apposition gradually leads to fusion of the two septa in about 1 year. In 20 to 25 per cent of all individuals, however, perfect anatomical closure may never be obtained.[9]

References—Circulatory Change at Birth

1. BARCLAY, Q. E., FRANKLIN, K. L., AND PRICHARD, M. M. L. *The Foetal Circulation*. Blackwell Scientific Publications, Oxford, 1944.
2. BARCROFT, J. *Researches on Prenatal Life*. Blackwell Scientific Publications, Oxford, 1946.
3. LIND, J., AND WEGELIUS, C. Human fetal circulation in: the mammalian fetus; physiological aspects of development. Symposia Quant. Biol., **19**: 109, 1954.
4. BARCROFT, J. Foetal and neonatal physiology. Brit. Med. Bull., **17**: 247, 1961.
5. DAWES, J. S. Changes in the circulation at birth and the effects of asphyxia. In *Recent Advances in Pediatrics*, edited by D. Gairdner. Little, Brown & Co., Boston, 1958.
6. GRIBBE, G., HIRVONEN, L., LIND, J., AND WEGELIUS, C. Cineangiocardiographic recordings of the cyclic changes in volume of the left ventricle. Cardiologia, **34**: 348, 1959.
7. ADAMS, F. H., AND LIND, J. Physiologic studies on the cardiovascular status of normal newborn infants with special reference to the ductus arteriosus. Pediatrics, **19**: 431, 1957.
8. ODÉ, E. De ductus arteriosus. Doctoral thesis, University of Leyden, 1951.
9. PATTEN, B. M. The development of the heart. In *Pathology of the Heart*, Ed. 1, edited by S. E. Gould, p. 20. Charles C Thomas, Springfield, Ill., 1953.
10. LIND, J., BOESEN, T., AND WEGELIUS, C. Selective angiocardiography in congenital heart disease. Progr. Cardiov. Dis., **2**: 293, 1959–1960.

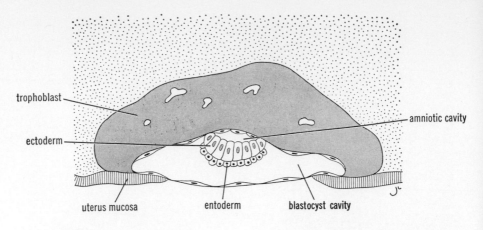

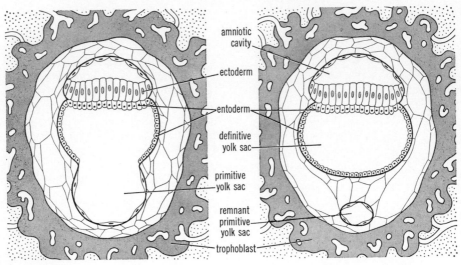

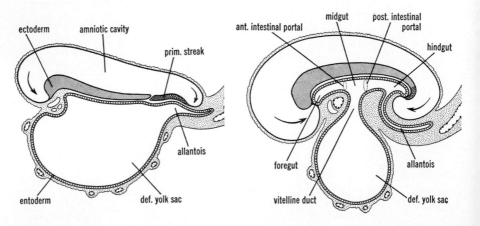

Special Embryology

CHAPTER 12

Digestive Tube and Its Derivatives

When the embryo is approximately 8 days old the entodermal germ layer can be distinguished as a continuous sheet of flat epithelial cells, located immediately under the ectodermal disc (fig. 12-1). From here, the entodermal cells gradually extend along the wall of the primitive yolk sac, and on the 15th day of development form the inner lining of the definitive yolk sac (figs. 12-2 and 12-3) (see Chapter 3).

With subsequent formation of the head fold and tail fold, the entoderm-lined cavity is divided into an intra-embryonic portion, the *primitive gut*, and two extra-embryonic portions, the *yolk sac* and *allantois* (figs. 12-4 and 12-5). In the cephalic as well as the caudal part of the embryo the primitive gut forms a blind-ending tube, the *foregut* and *hindgut*, respectively. Its middle part, the *midgut*, remains connected temporarily to the yolk sac by means of the *omphalomesenteric* or *vitelline duct* (fig. 12-5) (see Chapter 4).

In this chapter, the development of the primitive gut and its derivatives is discussed in four sections: (1) the *cranial part of the foregut*,

Figure 12-1. *Schematic drawing of a 7½-day embryo, showing the entodermal cells located immediately under the ectodermal disc.*

Figure 12-2 (middle left). *Drawing of a 13-day embryo. The entodermal cells extend along the inside wall of the primitive yolk sac.*

Figure 12-3 (middle right). *Drawing of a 15-day embryo. The entodermal cells form the internal lining of the definitive yolk sac.*

Figure 12-4 (bottom left). *Schematic representation of a longitudinal section through a 21-day embryo. The arrows indicate the direction of the anteroposterior folding of the embryo.*

Figure 12-5 (bottom right). *Schematic drawing of a longitudinal section through a 30-day embryo. The intra-embryonic portion of the entoderm-lined cavity is now divided into the foregut, midgut, and hindgut. The midgut is connected to the yolk sac by the vitelline duct. The allantois extends into the connecting stalk.*

which extends from the buccopharyngeal membrane to the tracheo-bronchial diverticulum; (2) the *caudal part of the foregut*, lying caudal to the tracheobronchial diverticulum and extending to the origin of the liver bud; (3) the *midgut*, beginning caudal to the liver bud (the anterior intestinal portal) and extending to a point where, in the adult, the junction of the right two-thirds and left one-third of the transverse colon is found (known, in the embryo, as the posterior intestinal portal); (4) the *hindgut*, extending from the posterior intestinal portal to the cloacal membrane.

CRANIAL PART OF THE FOREGUT

NORMAL DEVELOPMENT
- **PHARYNGEAL POUCHES:** *tympanic cavity; Eustachian tube; palatine tonsil; parathyroid glands; thymus; ultimobranchial body*
- **FLOOR OF THE PHARYNX:** *tongue; thyroid gland*
- **PHARYNGEAL CLEFTS:** *external auditory meatus; cervical sinus*
- **PHARYNGEAL ARCHES:** *Meckel's cartilage; ossicles; hyoid bone; laryngeal cartilages*
- **RESPIRATORY SYSTEM:** *trachea; bronchi; lungs; alveoli*

CONGENITAL MALFORMATIONS
- *Lateral cervical cyst and fistula; pre-auricular fistula; anomalies of the tongue; thyroglossal cyst and fistula; anomalies of the lungs*

Normal Development

At its cephalic end the cranial part of the foregut, also referred to as the *pharyngeal gut*, is in direct contact with the ectoderm at the bottom of the stomodeum, and the entoderm-ectoderm membrane so formed is known as the *buccopharyngeal membrane* (figs. 12-5 and 12-6A). At the end of the third week this membrane ruptures, thereby establishing an open connection between the stomodeum and the foregut (fig. 12-6B). The primitive mouth cavity is then formed by the ectodermal stomodeum and the cephalic end of the foregut (see also Chapter 17).

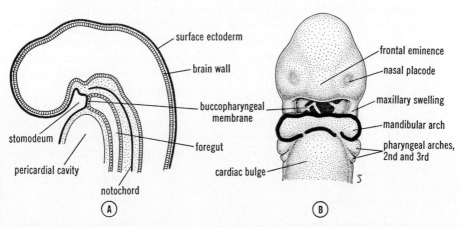

Figure 12-6. *A, Sagittal section through the cephalic end of an embryo of approximately 25 days (crown-rump length, 3.5 mm.). The buccopharyngeal membrane is formed by the epithelial lining of the foregut and the ectodermal lining at the bottom of the stomodeum. B, Front view of a slightly older embryo, showing the rupture of the buccopharyngeal membrane.*

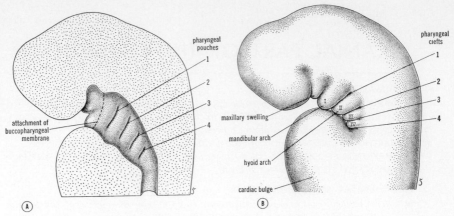

Figure 12-7. *A, Sagittal section through the cephalic end of a 5-week embryo (approximately 6 mm.), showing the pharyngeal pouches along the right lateral wall of the pharyngeal gut. Broken line represents the approximate site of attachment of the buccopharyngeal membrane. B, The pharyngeal arches and clefts in a 5-week embryo.*

Since the peripheral attachment of the buccopharyngeal membrane disappears without trace, it is thought that the boundary line between the two components may be indicated by a line just behind the gums.

During the fourth and fifth weeks of development a series of grooves, the *pharyngeal pouches*, appears along the lateral walls of the pharyngeal gut (fig. 12-7*A*). At the same time, four ectodermal grooves appear on the surface of the embryo (fig. 12-7*B*). The level of these grooves, known as the *pharyngeal clefts*, corresponds to that of the pharyngeal pouches, but although the clefts and pouches come in close contact, they rarely communicate with each other in the form of open gills.

As a result of the formation of the deep clefts and pouches, the loose mesodermal tissue surrounding the pharyngeal gut is gradually pushed aside and a number of bars of dense mesodermal tissue, the *branchial* or *pharyngeal arches*, make their appearance (fig. 12-7). In the lower vertebrates there may be six or more pharyngeal arches; the human embryo has only five, the tailmost one being poorly defined. On the inside of the pharynx, however, this last arch may cause a slight swelling.

Pharyngeal Pouches

The human embryo has five pairs of pharyngeal pouches, located along the lateral walls of the pharyngeal gut and approaching each other ventrally across or toward the midline (figs. 12-7*A* and 12-8*A*). The last one of these pouches is atypical and often considered as part of the fourth. Since the epithelial entodermal lining of the pouches

Special Embryology

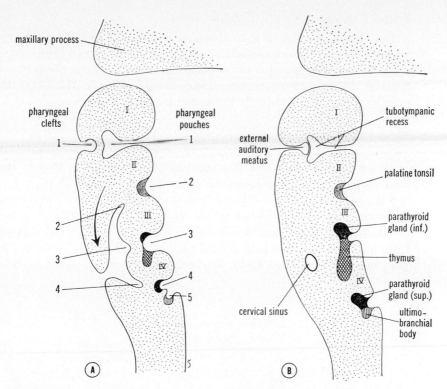

Figure 12-8. *A, Schematic representation of the development of the pharyngeal clefts and pouches. Note how the second arch grows over the third and fourth arches, thereby burying the second, third, and fourth pharyngeal clefts. B, The remnants of the second, third, and fourth pharyngeal clefts form the cervical sinus temporarily. Note also the differentiation of the epithelium in the wall of the entodermal pharyngeal pouches (modified after Starck).*

gives rise to a number of important organs, the fate of each pouch is discussed separately.

First Pharyngeal Pouch (*Tympanic Cavity, Eustachian Tube*)

While the ventral portion of this pouch is gradually obliterated by the developing tongue (fig. 12-10*A*), its dorsal portion forms an outpocketing in a lateral direction; this outpocketing reaches the epithelial lining of the first pharyngeal cleft (fig. 12-8*A, B*). The distal portion of this outpocketing widens into a saclike structure, the *primitive tympanic* or *middle ear cavity*, whereas the proximal part remains narrow, forming the *pharyngotympanic* or *Eustachian tube*. The entodermal lining of the tympanic cavity later aids in the formation of the *tympanic membrane* or *eardrum* (see Ear, Chapter 16).

Digestive Tube and Derivatives

Second Pharyngeal Pouch (Palatine Tonsil)

The ventral portion of this pouch as well is obliterated by the developing tongue. The epithelial lining of the remaining part proliferates and is secondarily invaded by mesodermal tissue to form the primordium of the *palatine tonsil* (fig. 12-8A, B). During the third to fifth months the tonsil is gradually infiltrated by lymphatic tissue.

Third Pharyngeal Pouch (Inferior Parathyroid Gland, Thymus)

In the fifth week of development the epithelium of the dorsal part of this pouch differentiates into *parathyroid tissue*, while that of the ventral part forms the primordium of the *thymus* (fig. 12-8A, B).

Further growth of the thymus and parathyroid tissues causes obliteration of the lumen of the pouch, and at the sixth week the gland primordia lose their connection with the pharyngeal wall.[1] The thymus then begins to migrate in a caudal and medial direction, pulling the parathyroid with it (fig. 12-9). While the main portion of the thymus

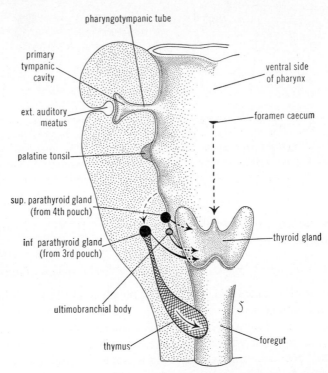

Figure 12-9. *Schematic representation of the migration of the thymus, parathyroid glands, and ultimobranchial body (anterior view). The thyroid gland originating in the ventral wall of the pharynx at the level of the foramen caecum descends to the level of the first tracheal rings (modified after Starck).*

Special Embryology

moves rapidly to its final position in the thorax, where it fuses with its counterpart from the opposite side, its tail portion becomes thin and elongated and eventually breaks up into small fragments. These fragments usually disappear but may sometimes persist embedded in the thyroid gland or as isolated thymic nests.[2, 3]

The parathyroid tissue of the third pouch finally comes to rest on the dorsal surface of the thyroid gland and, in the adult, forms the *inferior parathyroid gland*. Occasionally, this parathyroid tissue descends too far and may then be found at the lower pole of the thyroid or even in the thorax close to the thymus.

Fourth Pharyngeal Pouch (Superior Parathyroid Gland)

The epithelium of the dorsal portion of this pouch forms the *superior parathyroid gland*. Although the fate of the ventral portion of the pouch is uncertain, it is believed that it may give rise to a small amount of thymus tissue which, soon after its formation, disappears without contributing to the definitive gland.

Soon after the parathyroid gland has lost its contact with the wall of the pharynx, it attaches itself to the caudally migrating thyroid and finally is found on the dorsal surface of this gland (fig. 12-9).

Fifth Pharyngeal Pouch (Ultimobranchial Body)

This is the last of the pharyngeal pouches to develop and is usually considered to be a part of the fourth pouch. It gives rise to the *ultimobranchial body*, which is later incorporated in the thyroid gland.[4] In the adult, the cells of the ultimobranchial body can sometimes be distinguished as groups of large pale cells. Although many theories have been proposed with regard to the function and ultimate fate of this body, no general agreement has been reached.[3, 5-7]

Floor of the Pharynx

Tongue

The tongue appears in embryos of approximately 4 weeks in the form of two *lateral lingual swellings* and one medial swelling, the *tuberculum impar* (fig. 12-10A). These three swellings result from proliferation of mesoderm in the ventral parts of the mandibular arch. Shortly thereafter a second median swelling, the *copula* or *hypobranchial eminence*, is formed by mesoderm of the second, third, and part of the fourth arch. Finally, a third median swelling, formed by the posterior part of the fourth arch, marks the development of the *epiglottis*. Immediately behind this is the *tracheobronchial groove* or *laryngeal orifice*, which is flanked by the *arytenoid swellings*.

Further proliferation and ingrowth of underlying mesoderm into the

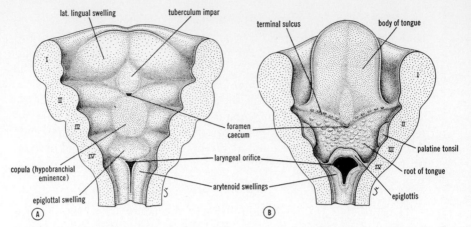

Figure 12-10. *The ventral portions of the pharyngeal arches seen from above, to show development of the tongue. The cut pharyngeal arches are indicated by numbers I to IV, respectively. A, At 5 weeks (approximately 6 mm.). B, At fifth month; note the foramen caecum, the site of origin of the thyroid primordium, and the terminal sulcus which forms the dividing line between the first and second pharyngeal arches.*

lateral lingual swellings, followed by fusion of the two sides, results in the formation of the anterior two-thirds or the *body of the tongue* (fig. 12-10*B*). The mucosa covering the body of the tongue thus originates from the first pharyngeal arch, and is innervated by the mandibular branch of the trigeminal nerve. It is separated from the posterior third of the tongue by a V-shaped groove, the *terminal sulcus*.

The posterior part or *root of the tongue* develops from the second, third, and part of the fourth pharyngeal arches. Since its mucosa is innervated by the glossopharyngeal nerve, it seems likely that tissue of the third arch has overgrown that of the second. The extreme posterior part of the tongue as well as the epiglottis are innervated by the superior laryngeal nerve, indicating their development from the fourth arch.

Thyroid Gland

The thyroid gland appears at the 17th day of development (the early somite stage) as an epithelial proliferation in the floor of the pharyngeal gut between the tuberculum impar and the copula, a point later indicated by the *foramen caecum* (fig. 12-10).[8] Shortly thereafter (19 days) the thyroid primordium penetrates the underlying mesoderm and descends in front of the pharyngeal gut as a bilobed diverticulum (fig. 12-9). During this migration the gland remains connected to the floor of the pharyngeal gut by means of a narrow canal, the *thyroglossal duct*. This duct later solidifies and disappears subsequently.

Special Embryology

In the meantime, the thyroid gland continues to move downward in front of the hyoid bone and the laryngeal cartilages, and reaches its final position in front of the trachea in the seventh week (fig. 12-14). By then it has acquired a small median isthmus and two lateral lobes. Whether or not part of the thyroid gland is formed by epithelial proliferation of the fourth pharyngeal pouch is still a point of discussion.[2, 4, 5, 9]

The thyroid begins to function at approximately the end of the third month, at which time the first follicles containing colloid become visible.

From the above description it is evident that the pharyngeal gut in the embryo gives rise to an important part of the oral cavity, the tongue, the thyroid gland, and the various organs developing from the epithelial lining of the pharyngeal pouches. Only then does it become comparable to the definitive pharynx in the adult, which is divided into the naso- and oropharynx. The laryngeal division of the definitive pharynx is situated immediately dorsal to the cartilaginous components of the larynx and forms the most caudal portion of the cranial part of the foregut.

As the development of the pharyngeal clefts and arches is intimately associated with that of the entodermal pouches, their fate is discussed in the following sections.

Pharyngeal Clefts

The 5-week embryo is characterized by the presence of four pharyngeal clefts of which only the first one contributes to the definitive structure of the embryo. The dorsal part of this cleft grows into the underlying mesoderm in the direction of the first pharyngeal pouch and gives rise to the *external auditory meatus*. The epithelial lining at the bottom of this meatus participates in the formation of the *eardrum* (see Ear, Chapter 16).

Active proliferation of the mesodermal tissue in the second arch causes it to grow caudally, thereby overlapping the third and fourth arches. Finally, the second arch fuses with the lower part of the neck (fig. 12-8*A*, *B*). As a result of this overgrowth the second, third, and fourth clefts are gradually buried and lose contact with the outside (fig. 12-8*B*). Temporarily, the clefts form a cavity lined with ectodermal epithelium, the *cervical sinus*, but with further development this sinus disappears entirely.

Pharyngeal Arches

When the embryo is approximately 4 weeks old (crown-rump length, 5 mm.) the pharyngeal clefts are separated by ridges, the *pharyngeal arches* (fig. 12-7*B*). During further development each of these arches acquires a cartilaginous skeleton and a muscular component, as well

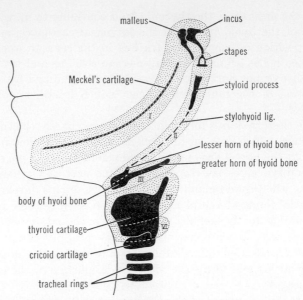

Figure 12-11. *Drawing showing the structures formed by the cartilaginous components of the various pharyngeal arches (modified after Giroud).*

as a characteristic artery and nerve. While some of the cartilaginous parts eventually vanish, others persist throughout life as bony, cartilaginous, or ligamentous structures (fig. 12-11). Although the muscles of the different arches migrate in various directions, their origin can always be traced since, despite their migration, their nerve supply comes from the arch of origin (for discussion on the development of the arteries, see Chapter 11).

First Pharyngeal Arch

The cartilaginous component of the *first* or *mandibular arch* consists of a small dorsal portion, known as the *maxillary process*, extending forward beneath the region of the eye, and a much larger ventral portion, the *mandibular process* or *Meckel's cartilage*. During further development the maxillary process, and Meckel's cartilage as well, retrogress and disappear, except for two small portions at their dorsal ends which persist and form the *incus* and *malleus*, respectively (fig. 12-11).[10] The *mandible* is formed secondarily by intramembranous ossification of mesodermal tissue surrounding Meckel's cartilage (see Chapter 8).

The musculature of the mandibular arch (that is, the *muscles of mastication*, the *anterior belly of the digastric*, and the *tensor tympani*) is innervated by the *mandibular branch of the trigeminal nerve*, the nervous component of the first arch. In addition, this nerve innervates

Special Embryology

the skin over the mandible and the anterior two-thirds of the mucosa of the tongue.

Second Pharyngeal Arch

The cartilaginous component of the *second* or *hyoid arch* is formed by *Reichert's cartilage*. It gives rise to the *stapes*, the *styloid process of the temporal bone*, the *stylohyoid ligament*, and, in its ventral portion, to the *lesser horn* and the *cranial part of the body of the hyoid bone* (fig. 12-11).

The muscles of the hyoid arch (the *stapedius*, the *stylohyoid*, the *posterior belly of the digastric*, and the *muscles of facial expression*) are supplied by the *facial nerve*, the nervous component of the second arch.

Third Pharyngeal Arch

The cartilage of this arch produces the *caudal part of the body* and the *greater horn of the hyoid bone* (fig. 12-11).

The musculature of this arch is limited to the *stylopharyngeal muscle*, which is innervated by the *glossopharyngeal nerve*, the nervous component of the third arch. Since part of the tongue is also derived from this arch, its sensory innervation is likewise partly supplied by the glossopharyngeal nerve.

Fourth, Fifth, and Sixth Pharyngeal Arches

The cartilaginous components of these arches fuse to form the *thyroid*, *cricoid*, and *arytenoid cartilages* of the larynx.

The muscles of the fourth arch (the *cricothyroid* and the *constrictors of the pharynx*) are innervated by the *superior laryngeal branch of the vagus*, the nerve of the fourth arch. The intrinsic muscles of the larynx, however, are supplied by the *recurrent laryngeal branch of the vagus*, the nervous component of the sixth arch.

Respiratory System

When the embryo is approximately 3 weeks old (crown-rump length, 3 mm.) the primordium of the respiratory system appears as a diverticulum from the ventral wall of the foregut immediately caudal to the last pharyngeal pouch (figs. 12-10A and 12-12A). Hence, the respiratory system is of entodermal origin.

Initially, the *respiratory diverticulum* is openly connected to the foregut but is soon separated from it by the *esophagotracheal septum*, except at the entrance to the laryno (figs. 12-10B and 12-12B). Above this level the respiratory primordium maintains its communication with the foregut through the *laryngeal orifice* (fig. 12-10B). Hence, the foregut is divided into a ventral portion, the *respiratory primordium*,

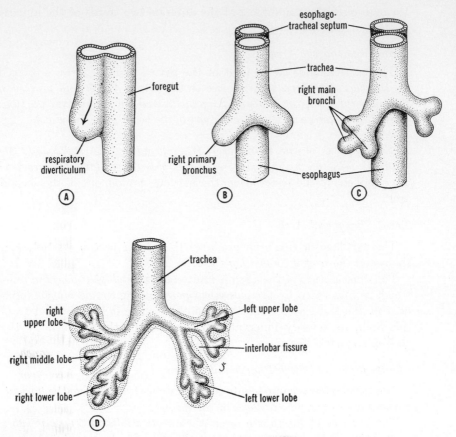

Figure 12-12. *Successive stages in the development of the trachea and lungs. A, At 3 weeks, lateral view; B, 4 weeks, ventral view; C, 5 weeks, ventral view; D, 6 weeks, ventral view (adapted from several sources).*

which forms the epithelial lining of the larynx, trachea, bronchi, and alveoli; and a dorsal portion, the *laryngopharynx* and the *esophagus*. The supporting components of the respiratory system, such as cartilage and muscle, develop from the surrounding mesenchyme.

Trachea, Bronchi, and Lungs

Shortly after its separation from the foregut, the respiratory primordium grows in a caudal direction, thereby forming a midline structure, the *trachea*, and two lateral outpocketings, the *lung buds* (fig. 12-12B). The right lung bud subsequently divides into three branches, the *main bronchi*, and the left into two main bronchi (fig. 12-12C), thus foreshadowing the presence of three lobes on the right side and two on the left (fig. 12-12D).

During further development the main bronchi divide repeatedly in a dichotomous fashion, and by the end of the sixth month approximately 17 generations of subdivisions have been formed, the last ones known as *respiratory bronchioli*. Before the bronchial tree has reached its final shape, however, an additional six divisions are formed. These appear during postnatal life.[11, 12] During the course of their development the lungs migrate caudally and by the time of birth the bifurcation of the trachea is opposite the fourth thoracic vertebra.

Alveoli

With the onset of respiration, the distal end of the terminal bronchioli expands into the *alveoli*, which are lined with flat epithelial cells of entodermal origin.[11] Although it was believed initially that the epithelial cells of the alveoli disappear, thus leaving the endothelial wall of the capillaries in direct contact with the alveolar air,[13, 14] it is now well accepted that the epithelial alveolar cells persist and are in intimate contact with the endothelial wall of the surrounding capillaries.[15, 16]

Although respiratory-like chest movements may occur *in utero*, in stillborn infants the alveoli are collapsed and the bronchial tree is filled with amniotic fluid. Under normal conditions the amniotic fluid is rapidly absorbed shortly after birth, and by the third postnatal day all alveoli have expanded.

Congenital Malformations

Lateral Cervical or Branchial Cyst and Fistula

Normally, the second pharyngeal arch grows caudally over the third and fourth arches and fuses with the lower part of the neck. It thereby buries the second, third, and fourth pharyngeal clefts (fig. 12-8*A*, *B*). When this fails to occur the remnants of the clefts remain in contact with the surface by way of a narrow canal, known as the *branchial fistula* (fig. 12-13*A*). Such a fistula, found on the lateral aspect of the neck directly in front of the sternomastoid muscle, usually provides drainage for a *lateral cervical cyst*. These cysts are remnants of the cervical sinus and are most often located just below the angle of the jaw (fig. 12-13*B*).[17] They may, however, be found anywhere along the anterior border of the sternomastoid muscle.[18] Frequently, a branchial cyst is not recognized at birth, but enlarges later in life and then becomes obvious.

A rare anomaly is the *internal branchial fistula*. The cervical sinus is then connected to the lumen of the pharynx by a small canal, which usually opens in the tonsillar region (fig. 12-13*C*). Such a fistula seems

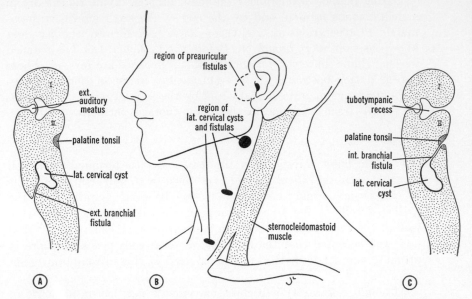

Figure 12-13. *A, Schematic drawing of a lateral cervical cyst opening at the lateral side of the neck by way of a branchial fistula. B, Localization of lateral cervical cysts and fistulas in front of the sternocleidomastoid muscle. Note also the region of localization of the pre-auricular fistulas. C, A lateral cervical cyst opening into the pharynx at the level of the palatine tonsil.*

to indicate a rupture of the membrane between the second pharyngeal cleft and pouch at some time during development.[19]

Pre-auricular Fistula or Earpit

This is a narrow pit in front of the ear (fig. 12-13B). It is thought to develop either from the dorsal end of the first branchial cleft or to be due to the incomplete disappearance of one of the sulci between the auricular tubercles[20] (see Ear, Chapter 16).

Anomalies of the Tongue

It is sometimes noted at birth that the tongue is proportionately larger than other oral structures and slightly protruding from the mouth. With further growth, however, the other oral structures grow at such a rate as to make the tongue appear normal. True *macroglossia*, based on hypertrophy of the tongue musculature, is usually seen in cases of mongolism and cretinism.

A rare abnormality is the *bifid tongue*. It is caused by failure of the two lateral lingual swellings to fuse and may be associated with a cleft of the lower lip.[21]

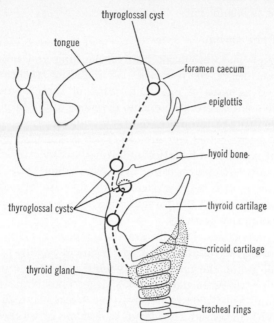

Figure 12-14. *Schematic drawing indicating the localization of the thyroglossal cysts These cysts, most frequently found in the hyoid region, are always located close to the midline. Broken line indicates the migratory path followed by the thyroid gland during its descent from the foramen caecum to its definitive position in front of the trachea.*

Thyroglossal Cyst and Fistula

A thyroglossal cyst may be found at any point along the migratory path followed by the thyroid gland. As indicated by its name, it is a cystic remnant of the thyroglossal duct which, in the embryo, connects the thyroid gland with the floor of the pharynx. Although approximately 50 per cent of these cysts are located close to or even behind the hyoid bone (fig. 12-14), they may also be found at the base of the tongue, sublingually, or on the side of the thyroid cartilage.[22, 23]

Sometimes a thyroglossal cyst is connected to the outside by a fistulous canal, the *thyroglossal fistula*. Such a fistula usually arises secondarily after rupture of a cyst, but may be present at birth.

Aberrant thyroid tissue may also be found anywhere along the path taken by the thyroid gland in its downward descent. It is most commonly found in the base of the tongue,[24, 25] just behind the foramen caecum, and is subject to the same diseases as the gland itself.

Congenital *hypoplasia* or *aplasia of the thyroid* is rarely observed. Recently, it has been suggested that antibodies circulating in the maternal blood stream during pregnancy may be the cause of sporadic athyrotic cretinism.[26,27] Evidence for this auto-immunization theory, however, is insufficient.

Anomalies of the Lungs

Although many abnormalities of the lung and bronchial tree have been described in the past, *e.g.*, blind-ending trachea with absence of lungs and agenesis of one lung, most of these anomalies are rare.[28] More frequently seen are unusual divisions of the bronchial tree, sometimes resulting in the presence of supernumerary lobules. These variations of the bronchial tree are of little functional significance, but may cause unexpected difficulties in bronchoscopy.

More interesting are *ectopic lung lobes* which arise from the trachea or esophagus. It is believed that these lobes are formed from additional respiratory buds of the foregut which develop independently of the main respiratory system.

Most important clinically are the *congenital cysts of the lung*. Such cysts, formed by dilatation of the terminal or larger bronchi, may be multiple, giving the lung a honeycomb appearance on x-ray, or they may be restricted to one or more larger ones. Since cystic structures of the lung usually drain poorly, they frequently cause chronic infections. With increased knowledge and scope of thoracic surgery, however, many of the cystic conditions of the lung have now become operable.

References—Cranial Part of the Foregut

1. Norris, E. H. The parathyroid glands and the lateral thyroid in man; their morphogenesis, histogenesis, topographic anatomy and prenatal growth. Contrib. Embryol., 26: 247, 1937.
2. Norris, E. H. The morphogenesis and histogenesis of the thymus gland in man; in which the origin of the Hassall's corpuscles of the human thymus is discovered. Contrib. Embryol., 27: 193, 1938.
3. Gilmour, J. R. The embryology of the parathyroid glands, the thymus and certain associated rudiments. J. Path. Bact., 45: 507, 1937.
4. Kingsbury, B. F. The question of a lateral thyroid in mammals, with special reference to man. Amer. J. Anat., 65: 333, 1939.
5. Van Dyke, J. H. Behaviour of the ultimobranchial tissue in the postnatal thyroid gland. Amer. J. Path., 76: 201, 1945.
6. Weller, G. L. Development of the thyroid, parathyroid and thymus glands in man. Contrib. Embryol., 24: 93, 1933.
7. Boyd, J. D. Development of the thyroid and parathyroid glands and the thymus. Ann. Roy. Coll. Surg. Engl., 7: 455, 1950.
8. Sgalitzer, K. E. Contribution to the study of the morphogenesis of the thyroid gland. J. Anat., 75: 389, 1941.
9. Watzka, H. Vergleichende Untersuchungen über den Ultimobranchialen Körper. Z. Mikroskopischanat. Forsch., 34: 485, 1933.
10. Hanson, J. R., Anson, B. J., and Best, T. H. The early embryology of the auditory vesicles in man. Quart. Bull. Northw. Univ. Med. Sch., 33: 350, 1959.

11. Broman, T. Zur Kenntnis der Lungenentwicklung. Anat. Anz., **57**: 83, 1923.
12. Wilson, H. G. Postnatal development of the lung. Amer. J. Anat., **41**: 97, 1928.
13. Clements, L. P. Embryonic development of the respiratory portion of the pig's lung. Anat. Rec., **70**: 575, 1938.
14. Loosli, C. G., and Potter, E. L. The prenatal development of the human being. Anat. Rec., **109**: 320, 1951.
15. Low, F. N. The pulmonary alveolar epithelium of laboratory mammals and man. Anat. Rec., **117**: 241, 1953.
16. Bertalanffy, F. D., and Leblond, C. P. Structure of respiratory tissue. Lancet, **2**: 1365, 1955.
17. Gross, R. E., and Ladd, W. E. *Abdominal Surgery of Infancy and Childhood.* W. B. Saunders Co., Philadelphia, 1953.
18. Neel, H. B., and Pemberton, J. deJ. Lateral cervical (branchial) cysts and fistulas. Surgery, **18**: 267, 1945.
19. Douglas, J. Branchiogenetic cyst with sinus leading into pharynx. Ann. Surg., **67**: 240, 1918.
20. Martins, A. G. Lateral cervical and pre-auricular sinuses. Brit. Med. J., **5**: 255, 1961.
21. Grieg, D. M. Schistoglossus and double tongue. Edinburgh Med. J., **32**: 1, 1925.
22. Marshall, S. F., and Beeker, W. F. Thyroglossal cysts and sinuses. Ann. Surg., **129**: 642, 1949.
23. McClintock, J. C., and Mahaffey, D. E. Thyroglossal tract lesions. In *Transactions of the American Goiter Association.* Charles C Thomas, Springfield, Ill., 1950.
24. Goetsch, E. Lingual goiter. Ann. Surg., **127**: 291, 1948.
25. Montgomery, M. L. Lingual thyroid; a comprehensive review. Western J. Surg., **44**: 54, 1936.
26. Blizzard, R. M., Chandler, R. W., Landing, B. H., Petit, M. D., and West, C. D. Maternal auto-immunization to thyroid as probable cause of athyrotic cretinism. New Engl. J. Med., **263**: 327, 1960.
27. Sutherland, J. M., Esselborn, V. M., Burket, R. L., Shillman, T. B., and Benson, J. T. Familial non-goitrous cretinism apparently due to maternal antithyroid antibody. New Engl. J. Med., **263**: 336, 1960.
28. Thomas, L. B., and Boyden, E. A. Agenesis of the right lung. Surgery, **31**: 429, 1952.

CAUDAL PART OF FOREGUT

Normal Development

Esophagus

The esophagus develops from that part of the foregut which extends from the respiratory diverticulum to the fusiform dilatation which forms the stomach (fig. 12-15). With the descent of the heart and lungs, the esophagus lengthens rapidly. Its muscular coat, differentiating from the surrounding mesenchyme, is striated in its upper two-thirds and smooth in the lower one-third.

Stomach

The stomach appears first as a fusiform dilatation of the foregut in the fifth week of development (fig. 12-15*A*, *B*). It is then attached to the dorsal and ventral body walls by peritoneal folds, the *dorsal and ventral mesogastrium*, respectively (see Chapter 13, fig. 13-6). During the following weeks the appearance and position of the stomach changes greatly. This is due to a different rate of growth in various regions of its wall, and to a change in position of the surrounding organs, such as the fast-growing liver.[1] The positional changes of the stomach are most easily explained by assuming that, during its growth, the stomach rotates around longitudinal and anteroposterior axes.

Rotation along Longitudinal Axis

When viewed from above, the stomach carries out a 90° clockwise rotation along its longitudinal axis, causing its left side to face anteriorly and its right side, posteriorly (fig. 12-16*A*, *B*, *C*). Hence, the left vagus nerve comes to innervate the anterior wall of the stomach, and the right vagus the posterior wall. During this rotation the original

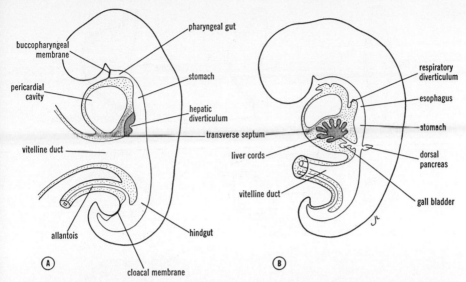

Figure 12-15. *A, Sagittal section through a 3-mm. embryo (approximately 25 days). The stomach is visible as a slight dilatation of the foregut; the hepatic diverticulum appears as a proliferation of the entodermal epithelial lining of the terminal part of the foregut. B, Similar section through a 5-mm. embryo (approximately 32 days). The liver cords now penetrate the mesenchyme of the transverse septum.*

posterior part of the stomach grows faster than the original anterior portion and this results in the formation of the *greater and lesser curvatures* (fig. 12-16*A, B, C*). As the stomach is suspended between the dorsal and ventral mesogastrium, rotation around the longitudinal axis is thought to pull the dorsal mesogastrium to the left, thus helping in the formation of the *omental bursa,* a pouch of the peritoneum located behind the stomach (fig. 12-16*D, E, F*).

Rotation along Anteroposterior Axis

The cephalic and caudal ends of the stomach are originally located in the midline, but rotation along an anteroposterior axis displaces the caudal or *pyloric part* to the right and upward, and the cephalic or *cardiac portion* to the left and slightly downward (fig. 12-16*G, H*). The stomach thus assumes its final position, and its longitudinal axis runs from above left to below right. The greater curvature finally faces downward and the lesser curvature upward and to the right (figs. 12-16 and 13-11).

Duodenum

This section of the intestinal tract is formed by the terminal part of the foregut and the cephalic part of the midgut. The junction of the

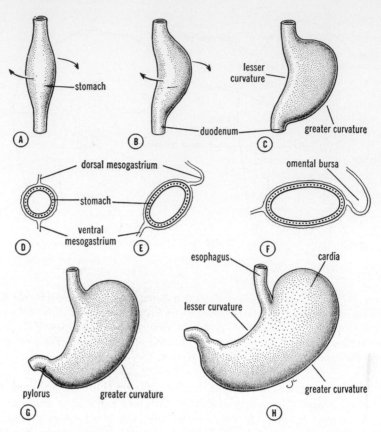

Figure 12-16. *Schematic representation of the positional changes of the stomach. A, B, and C show the rotation of the stomach along its longitudinal axis as seen from anterior; D, E, and F show, in transverse section, the effect of rotation on the peritoneal attachments; G and H show the rotation of the stomach around the anteroposterior axis (seen from anterior).*

two parts is located directly distal to the origin of the hepatic and pancreatic buds. As the stomach rotates, the duodenum takes on the form of a U-shaped loop, rotates to the right, and finally comes to lie retroperitoneally (see Chapter 13). During the second month the lumen of the duodenum may temporarily be obliterated. Under normal conditions, however, the lumen is reestablished shortly afterward.

Liver and Gall Bladder

The liver primordium appears in the middle of the third week as a thickening of the entodermal epithelium at the distal end of the foregut (fig. 12-15A). This thickened area, known as the *hepatic diverticulum*, consists of rapidly proliferating cells which penetrate the *septum*

Special Embryology

transversum, that is, the mesodermal plate between the pericardial cavity and the stalk of the yolk sac (fig. 12-15*A*, *B*). The hepatic diverticulum soon splits into two components: the *pars hepatica*, which will form the liver and biliary duct system; and a smaller caudal portion, the *pars cystica*, destined to become the gall bladder and the cystic duct (fig. 12-15*B*). During further ingrowth into the septum transversum, the entodermal epithelial liver cords intermingle extensively with the blood sinuses of the vitelline and umbilical veins, thereby forming the parenchymatous tissue of the liver. The connective tissue of the liver, however, is formed by the mesoderm of the septum transversum.

Owing to continuous rapid growth, the liver gradually protrudes more and more into the ventral mesogastrium, a duplication of peritoneum which connects the lesser curvature of the stomach to the anterior body wall (figs. 12-17*A*, *B* and 13-6). Finally, the liver is surrounded by peritoneum, except on its cranial surface, where it remains in contact with the septum transversum. This region will later form the bare area of the liver, which is in direct contact with the caudal side of the diaphragm (fig. 12-17*B*).

In the 10th week of development the weight of the liver is approximately 10 per cent of the total body weight. Though this may be attributed partly to the presence of a large number of sinusoids from the vitelline and hepatic veins, another important factor contributing

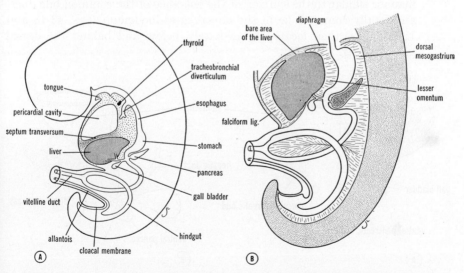

Figure 12-17. *A, Sagittal section through a 9-mm. embryo (approximately 36 days). The liver expands into the ventral mesogastrium. B, Similar section through a slightly older embryo, showing the liver expanded into the ventral mesogastrium, which is divided into the falciform ligament and the lesser omentum (see Chapter 13). Note the bare area of the liver.*

to the weight of the liver at this stage of development is its *hematopoietic function*. Large nests of proliferating cells, which produce red and white blood cells, are found between the hepatic cells and the walls of the vessels. This activity subsides gradually during the last 2 months of intra-uterine life and only small hematopoietic islands remain at birth. The weight of the liver is then only 5 per cent of the total body weight.

Meanwhile, the caudal portion of the hepatic diverticulum has developed into the *gall bladder* and *cystic duct*, located in the lower part of the ventral mesogastrium (fig. 12-17B). The cystic duct joins the hepatic duct to form the *common bile duct*, which enters the duodenum. As a result of the positional changes of the duodenum, the entrance of the bile duct gradually shifts from its initial anterior position to a posterior one, and consequently the common bile duct is found to be passing behind the duodenum (figs. 12-18 and 12-19).

Pancreas

The pancreas is formed by proliferation of the entodermal epithelium of the duodenum as two separate buds, the *dorsal and ventral pancreatic buds* (fig. 12-18A). While the dorsal bud is located opposite and slightly above the hepatic diverticulum, the ventral bud is found in the angle below the hepatic rudiment.

The ventral pancreatic bud subsequently migrates dorsally, in a manner similar to the shifting of the entrance of the common bile duct, and finally comes to lie in the dorsal mesoduodenum (figs. 12-18 and 12-19). It is then located immediately below and behind the dorsal pancreas (fig. 12-19A).

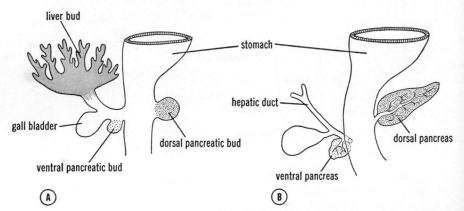

Figure 12-18. *Successive stages in the development of the pancreas. A, At 30 days (approximately 5 mm.); B, 35 days (approximately 7 mm.). The ventral pancreatic bud is initially located close to the hepatic diverticulum, but later migrates posteriorly around the duodenum in the direction of the dorsal pancreatic bud.*

Special Embryology

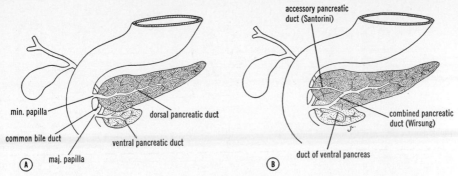

Figure 12-19. *A, The pancreas during the sixth week of development (approximately 10 mm.).The ventral pancreatic bud is in close contact with the dorsal pancreatic bud. The dorsal pancreatic duct enters the duodenum at the minor papilla and the ventral pancreatic duct at the major papilla. B, Drawing showing the fusion of the pancreatic ducts. The combined pancreatic duct of Wirsung now enters the duodenum in combination with the common bile duct at the major papilla. The accessory pancreatic duct of Santorini enters the duodenum at the minor papilla (modified after Starck).*

Later the parenchyme as well as the duct systems of the dorsal and ventral pancreatic buds fuse (fig. 12-19*B*). The *combined pancreatic duct* or *duct of Wirsung* is formed by the distal part of the dorsal pancreatic duct and the entire ventral pancreatic duct (fig. 12-19*B*). As this duct becomes the main drainage channel of the pancreas, the proximal part of the dorsal pancreatic duct either is obliterated or persists as a small channel, the *accessory pancreatic duct of Santorini.* The main pancreatic duct enters the duodenum at the site of the major papilla; the entrance of the duct of Santorini is at the site of the minor papilla. In about 10 per cent of all cases the duct systems fail to fuse and the original double system persists.[2]

The pancreatic islets develop from the parenchymatous pancreatic tissue in the third month of fetal life and are scattered throughout the gland. Insulin secretion begins at approximately the fifth month.

Congenital Malformations

Atresia of the Esophagus and Esophagotracheal Fistula

In the most common form of this anomaly the proximal part of the esophagus ends as a blind sac, whereas the distal part is connected to the trachea at a point just above the bifurcation by a narrow canal (fig. 12-20*A*).[3] This anomaly is thought to result either from a spontaneous deviation of the esophagotracheal septum in a posterior direction, or from some mechanical factor pushing the dorsal wall of the foregut anteriorly.[4, 5] Occasionally, the fistulous canal between the

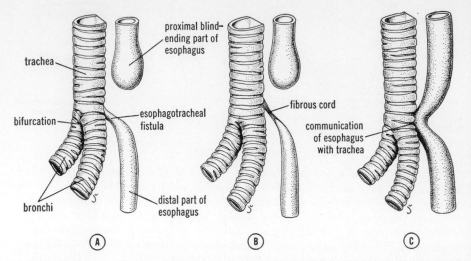

Figure 12-20. *A, Atresia of the esophagus and esophagotracheal fistula. B, Atresia of esophagus. The connection between the distal part of the esophagus and trachea is formed by a fibrous cord. C, The proximal and distal parts of the esophagus are both connected to the trachea by a narrow canal.*

trachea and the distal portion of the esophagus is replaced by a ligamentous cord (fig. 12-20B). Rarely do the proximal and distal portions of the esophagus open into the trachea (fig. 12-20C).[6]

Atresia of the esophagus prevents the normal passage of amniotic fluid into the intestinal tract; this results in the accumulation of excess fluid in the amniotic sac and consequently an enlarged uterus. Although a newborn child with atresia of the esophagus may appear normal, at its first attempt to drink the proximal portion of the esophagus will fill rapidly and milk will flow over into the trachea and lungs. Such a condition will usually lead to aspiration pneumonia. If recognized early, the defect may be repaired successfully.

Pyloric Stenosis

In this lesion there is a hypertrophy of the circular and, to a lesser degree, of the longitudinal musculature of the stomach in the region of the pylorus. It is one of the most common lesions of the stomach in infants and is believed to develop during fetal life. There is extreme narrowing of the pyloric lumen, and the passage of food is obstructed, resulting in severe progressive vomiting. A few cases have been described in which the pylorus was atretic.[7]

Other malformations of the stomach, such as duplications[8] and the presence of a prepyloric septum,[9] are extremely rare.

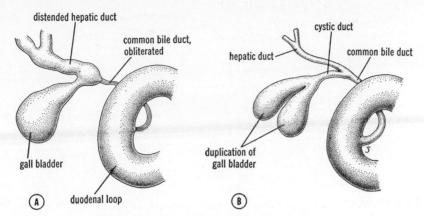

Figure 12-21. *A, Obliteration of the common bile duct, resulting in a distention of the gall bladder and hepatic ducts distal to the obliteration. B, Bifid gall bladder.*

Atresia of the Gall Bladder and Bile Ducts

Normally, the biliary diverticulum is at first hollow, but shortly becomes solid as a result of proliferation of its epithelial lining. The definitive lumen develops by vacuolization of the epithelial cords. When this fails to occur the gall bladder remains atretic and does not develop.[10]

Similarly, the intra- and extrahepatic ducts go through a solid stage in development. If the lumen fails to reopen the ducts will appear as narrow, fibrous cords.[11] Occasionally, such an atresia is limited to a small portion of the common bile duct only (fig. 12-21*A*). The gall bladder and the hepatic duct proximal to the atresia are then considerably distended, and severe, steadily increasing jaundice will become obvious soon after birth.

In addition to atresia there are reports on duplication, partial subdivision, and diverticula of the gall bladder (fig. 12-21*B*).[12]

Annular Pancreas

Under normal conditions, the ventral pancreatic bud shifts in position in such a manner that it reaches the dorsal pancreatic bud in the dorsal mesoduodenum. Occasionally, however, this fails to occur. A portion of the ventral bud then migrates along its normal route, but another part migrates in an opposite direction. In this manner the duodenum is completely surrounded by pancreatic tissue, and an *annular pancreas* is formed (fig. 12-22).[13] Although this malformation usually does not cause any symptoms, sometimes it may constrict the duodenum and may even lead to complete obstruction.

Digestive Tube and Derivatives

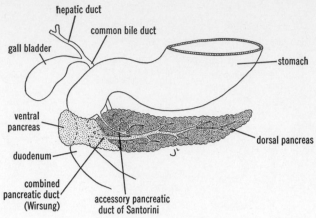

Figure 12-22. *Annular pancreas. The ventral pancreas forms a ring around the duodenum, occasionally resulting in duodenal stenosis.*

Heterotopic Pancreatic Tissue

This condition may be found anywhere from the distal end of the esophagus to the tip of Meckel's diverticulum, a remnant of the vitelline duct. Most frequently this pancreatic tissue is found in the mucosa of the stomach,[14] and in Meckel's diverticulum. Here it may show all the pathological changes characteristic of the pancreas itself.[15] Occasionally, a major part of the ventral pancreatic bud may grow out with the liver bud and form a pancreatic nodule or *pancreatic bladder*, located close to the gall bladder.[16]

References—Caudal Part of the Foregut

1. DANKMEYER, J., AND MIETE, M. Le développement précoce de l'estomac chez l'embryon humain. C. R. Ass. Anat., 103: 341, 1958.
2. DAWSON, W., AND LANGMAN, J. An anatomical-radiological study on the pancreatic duct pattern in man. Anat. Rec., 139: 59, 1961.
3. LADD, W. E. Congenital anomalies of the esophagus. Pediatrics, 6: 9, 1950.
4. GRUENWALD, P. A case of atresia of the esophagus combined with tracheo-esophageal fistula in a 9 mm. human embryo, and its embryological explanation. Anat. Rec., 78: 293, 1940.
5. LANGMAN, J. Esophagus atresia accompanied by vessel anomalies. Arch. Chir. Neerl., 4: 39, 1952.
6. HERWEG, J. C., AND OGURA, J. H. Congenital tracheo-esophageal fistula without esophageal atresia; endoscopic diagnostic technique. J. Pediat., 47: 293, 1955.
7. SALEBURY, A. M., AND COLLINS, R. E. Congenital pyloric atresia. A. M. A. Arch. Surg., 80: 501, 1960.
8. BOTHA MULLER, G. S. Intrathoracic duplications of the foregut. II. S. Afr. Med. J., 34: 259, 1960.
9. RAWLING, J. T. A prepyloric septum. Brit. J. Surg., 47: 162, 1960.
10. HOULE, M. P., AND HILL, P. S. Congenital absence of the gallbladder. J. Maine Med. Assn., 51: 108, 1960.

11. AHRENS, E. H., HARRIS, R. C., MACMAHAN, M. E. Atresia of the intrahepatic bile ducts. Pediatrics, 8: 628, 1951.
12. POPPER, H., AND SHAFFNER, F. *Liver, Structure and Function.* McGraw-Hill Book Co., New York, 1957.
13. WEATHERILL, D., FORGRAVE, E. G., AND CARPENTER, W. S. Annular pancreas producing duodenal obstruction in the newborn. A. M. A. J. Dis. Child., 95: 202, 1958.
14. MARTINEZ, N. S., MORLACH, C. G., DOCKERTY, B., WAUGH, J. M., AND WEBER, H. Heterotopic pancreatic tissue involving the stomach. Ann. Surg., 147: 1, 1958.
15. BARBOSA, J., DOCKERTY, M. B., AND WAUGH, J. Pancreatic heterotopia. Surg. Gynec. Obstet., 82: 527, 1946.
16. BOYDEN, E. A. The problem of the pancreatic bladder. Amer. J. Anat., 36: 151, 1925.

MIDGUT

Normal Development

In the 5-mm. embryo the midgut extends from the *anterior* to the *posterior intestinal portal* and communicates widely with the yolk sac (figs. 12-5 and 12-15A). Although initially the cranial and caudal borders of the midgut are vaguely defined, it is generally accepted that, in the adult, the midgut begins immediately distal to the entrance of the bile duct into the duodenum, and terminates at the junction of the proximal two-thirds of the transverse colon with the distal third.

Further development of the midgut is characterized by rapid elongation, resulting in the formation of the *primary intestinal loop* (figs. 12-23A and 13-6). At its apex, this loop is in open connection with the yolk sac by way of the *vitelline* or *omphalomesenteric duct*. The cephalic limb of the loop develops into the distal part of the duodenum, the jejunum, and part of the ileum. The caudal limb becomes the lower portion of the ileum, the caecum and the appendix, the ascending colon, and the proximal two-thirds of the transverse colon. The junction of the cranial and caudal limbs may be recognized in the adult only if a portion of the vitelline duct persists as *Meckel's diverticulum*.

While the cranial and caudal ends of the primitive intestinal loop become fixed to the posterior abdominal wall, the remaining part continues its rapid elongation to such an extent that the abdominal cavity becomes temporarily too small to contain all the intestinal loops. As a consequence, the loops enter the extra-embryonic coelom in the umbilical cord during the sixth week of development (fig. 12-25).

Coincident with this elongation, the primitive intestinal loop starts to rotate along an axis formed by the superior mesenteric artery. When viewed from ventral, this movement is counterclockwise and extends through 270° (figs. 12-23 and 12-24). The elongation is most marked in the small intestine and consequently the jejunum and ileum form coiled loops. The large intestine, however, fails to participate in this coiling phenomenon.

Because of the regression of the mesonephroi, the reduced growth of the liver, and the actual expansion of the abdominal cavity, the herniated intestinal loops begin to return to the abdominal cavity during the 10th week of development. The proximal part of the jejunum, the

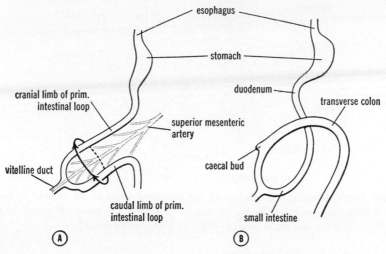

Figure 12-23. *A, Schematic drawing of the primitive intestinal loop before rotation (lateral view). The superior mesenteric artery forms the axis of the loop. Arrow indicates the direction of the anticlockwise rotation. B, Similar view as in A, showing the primitive intestinal loop after 180° anticlockwise rotation. The transverse colon passes in front of the duodenum (modified after Giroud).*

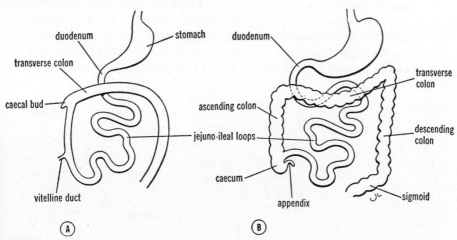

Figure 12-24. *A, Anterior view of the intestinal loops after 270° anticlockwise rotation. Note the coiling of the small intestinal loops and the position of the caecal bud in the right upper quadrant of the abdomen. B, Similar view as in A, with the intestinal loops in the final position. Caecum and appendix are located in the right lower quadrant of the abdomen (modified after Giroud).*

Digestive Tube and Derivatives

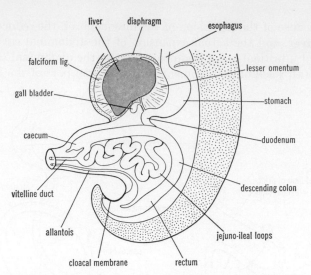

Figure 12-25. *Umbilical herniation of the intestinal loops in an embryo of approximately 8 weeks (crown-rump length, 35 mm.). Coiling of the small intestinal loops and and formation of the caecum is clearly visible (modified after Brödel).*

first part to re-enter, then comes to lie on the left side of the abdomen, while the later returning loops gradually settle more and more to the right. The *caecal swelling*, which appears at about the 12-mm. stage as a small conical dilatation of the caudal limb of the primitive intestinal loop, is the last part of the gut to re-enter the abdominal cavity and is temporarily located in the right upper quadrant directly below the right lobe of the liver (figs. 12-24*A* and 12-26). From here, it descends into the right iliac fossa, thereby forming the ascending colon and the hepatic flexure (fig. 12-24*B*). During this process the distal end of the

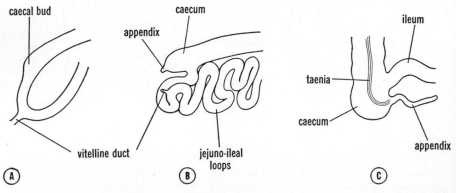

Figure 12-26. *Successive stages in the development of the caecum and appendix. A, At 7 weeks; B, 8 weeks; C, newborn.*

Special Embryology

caecal swelling forms a narrow diverticulum, the *primitive appendix* (fig. 12-26).

Congenital Malformations

Remnants of the Vitelline Duct

Meckel's Diverticulum, Vitelline Fistula, Enterocystoma

Normally, the vitelline or omphalomesenteric duct disappears when the embryo is approximately 6 weeks old. Sometimes, a small portion of the duct persists, forming an outpocketing of the ileum, known as *Meckel's diverticulum*. In the adult, this diverticulum is located about 2 to 3 feet from the ileocaecal valve and does not usually cause any complaints (fig. 12-27A).[1, 2] However, when it contains heterotopic pancreatic tissue or gastric mucosa, a Meckel's diverticulum may show ulceration, cause bleeding, or may even perforate.[3, 4]

If the defect is more extensive, the vitelline duct may remain patent over its entire length, thus forming a direct communication between the umbilicus and the intestinal tract, an anomaly known as *umbilical* or *vitelline fistula* (fig. 12-27C).[5] A fecal discharge may then be found at the umbilicus, and occasionally the ileum may prolapse through the fistula.[6] In another variation, both ends of the vitelline duct are transformed into fibrous cords, while the middle portion forms a large cyst, the *enterocystoma* or *vitelline cyst* (fig. 12-27B). Since the fibrous cords traverse the peritoneal cavity, they may easily cause intestinal strangulation or volvulus.

Omphalocele

The intestinal loops which were herniated into the umbilical cord return to the abdominal cavity in the 10th week of development, as a

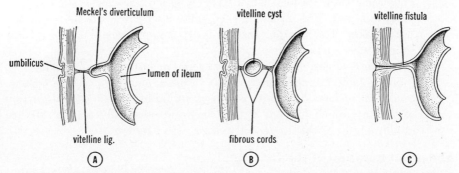

Figure 12-27. *Remnants of the vitelline duct. A, Meckel's diverticulum combined with fibrous cord (vitelline ligament). B, Vitelline cyst attached to the umbilicus and the wall of the ileum by vitelline ligaments. C, Vitelline fistula connecting the lumen of the ileum with the umbilicus.*

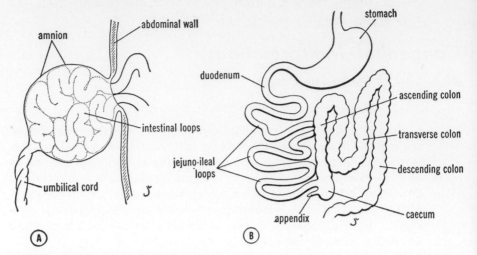

Figure 12-28. *A, Omphalocele—failure of the intestinal loops to return to the abdominal cavity. The herniated loops are surrounded by a membranous sac formed by the amnion. B, Abnormal rotation of the primitive intestinal loop. The colon is located on the left side of the abdomen, and the small intestinal loops on the right. Note that the ileum enters the caecum from the right.*

result of the degeneration of the mesonephroi, reduced growth of the liver, and actual expansion of the abdominal cavity. When this withdrawal from the umbilical cord fails to occur, some intestinal loops remain outside the abdominal cavity, and the resulting defect is known as *omphalocele* (fig. 12-28A).[7, 8]

Congenital Hernia into the Umbilical Cord

In these cases there is a circular defect in the central part of the abdominal wall, through which the intestinal loops protrude into the umbilical cord. The viscera are covered by peritoneum and amnion, but no skin. The sac thus formed is extremely thin and often ruptures shortly after birth.

In more severe cases, all the viscera, including the liver, may be found outside the abdominal cavity. This anomaly, known as *eventration of the abdominal viscera*, is caused by failure of the caudal portion of the anterior abdominal wall to close and is usually associated with abnormalities of the urogenital system (see Chapter 10).

Abnormal Rotation of the Intestinal Loop

The primitive intestinal loop normally rotates 270° anticlockwise. Occasionally, however, rotation amounts to 90° only. When this occurs, the colon and caecum are the first portions of the gut to return from the umbilical cord and they settle on the left side of the abdominal cavity (fig. 12-28B). The later-returning loops then become located more and more to the right.[9, 10]

In some cases, known as *reversed rotation of the intestinal loop*, the primitive loop rotates 90° in a clockwise direction. In such an anomaly the transverse colon passes behind the duodenum.

Duplications of the Gastrointestinal Tract

This condition may occur anywhere along the length of the alimentary canal, from the base of the tongue to the anus.[11, 12] Such a duplication is most frequently located in the region of the ileum, where it may vary in form and size from a small diverticulum to a large cyst. Although duplications of the gut always remain attached to the segment of origin, their mucosa may be greatly different. A duplication of the rectum, for instance, may sometimes be lined with gastric mucosa.[13] With regard to the development of these intestinal duplications, Bremer,[14] suggests that parts of the alimentary canal go through a transient solid state, which is followed by reestablishment of the lumen by means of vacuolization. If, however, some isolated vacuoles do not properly fuse with those forming the main lumen, a duplication may arise.

Atresia and Stenosis of the Gut

These conditions may likewise occur anywhere along the primitive intestinal loop. In case of atresia, a thin diaphragm is usually found across the lumen of the gut. This diaphragm is thought to be due to a localized, incomplete reestablishment of the lumen of the gut. The duodenum is particularly well known for the presence of a *stenosis*.[15] Such a stenosis frequently results in a distention of the proximal part and a marked narrowing of the intestinal loops below the level of the stenosis. The proximal part of the duodenum may exceed even the stomach in size.

References—Midgut

1. BROOKES, V. B. Meckel's diverticulum in children. Brit. J. Surg., 42: 57, 1954.
2. HOWELL, L. M. Meckel's diverticulum. Amer. J. Dis. Child., 71: 365, 1946.
3. ASCHNER, P. W., AND KARELITZ, S. Peptic ulcer of Meckel's diverticulum and ileum. Ann. Surg., 91: 583, 1930.
4. CARD, W. I., AND MIMPRISS, T. W. Peptic ulcer of Meckel's diverticulum. Lancet, 2: 963, 1937.
5. SMITH, J. R. Accessory enteric formations; a classification and nomenclature. Arch. Dis. Child., 35: 87, 1960.
6. HOWARD, S., MOSS, P. D., AND O'DOMHNAILL, S. Patent vitello-intestinal duct with associated fistula and prolapse. Lancet, 2: 968, 1953.
7. McKEOWN, T., MacMAHON, B., AND RECORD, R. G. An investigation of 69 cases of exomphalos. Amer. J. Hum. Genet., 5: 168, 1953.

8. FERGUSON, J. A. Omphalocoele, persistent omphalomesenteric duct, and Meckel's diverticulum. Univ. Hosp. Bull., Ann Arbor, 14: 47, 1948.
9. ESTRADA, R. L. *Anomalies of Intestinal Rotation and Fixation.* Charles C Thomas. Springfield, Ill., 1958.
10. DOTT, N. M. Anomalies of intestinal rotation. Brit. J. Surg., 11: 251, 1923.
11. CHRISTENSEN, C. R. Duplications in the gastro-intestinal tract in children. Danish Med. Bull., 5–6: 281, 1959.
12. GROSS, R. E., HOLCOMB, G. W., AND FARBER, S. Duplications of the alimentary tract. Pediatrics, 9: 449, 1952.
13. CLIFT, M. M. Duplication of the small intestine. J. Amer. Med. Wom. Assn., 9: 396, 1954.
14. BREMER, J. L. *Congenital Anomalies of the Viscera*, p. 67. Harvard University Press, Cambridge, Mass., 1957.
15. SAUNDERS, J. B. DE C. M., AND LINDNER, H. H. Congenital anomalies of the duodenum. Ann. Surg., 112: 321, 1940.

HINDGUT

Normal Development

The hindgut extends from the *posterior intestinal portal* to the *cloacal membrane* (fig. 12-5). It later gives rise to the distal third of the transverse colon, the descending colon, the sigmoid, the rectum, and the upper part of the anal canal. In addition, it participates in the formation of the urogenital sinus.

The *cloaca* forms the terminal portion of the hindgut (fig. 12-29A). At its cephalic end the cloaca continues into the allantois and at its caudal end into the transitory tail gut. Ventrally, the entodermal lining of the cloaca is in direct contact with the surface ectoderm, where it forms the *cloacal membrane* (fig. 12-29A, B).

During further development (crown-rump length, 5 mm.) a transverse septum, the *urorectal septum*, arises in the angle between the allantois and the hindgut (fig. 12-29). This septum gradually descends caudad, thereby dividing the cloaca into an anterior portion, the *primitive urogenital sinus*, and a posterior part, the *anorectal canal* (figs. 12-29 and 12-30).[1] When the embryo is 7 weeks old (crown-rump length, 16 mm.) the urorectal septum reaches the cloacal membrane, at which point the *primitive perineum* is formed. The cloacal membrane is then divided into the posterior *anal membrane*, and the anterior *urogenital membrane* (fig. 12-30) (for discussion of further development of the urogenital sinus, see Chapter 10).

In the meantime, the cloacal membrane is gradually surrounded by mesenchyme derived from the primitive streak, and in the ninth week the anal membrane is found at the bottom of an ectodermal depression, known as *proctodeum*.[2] The surrounding swellings are known as the anal folds. Soon thereafter the anal membrane ruptures and an open pathway is formed between the rectum and the outside. The upper part of the anal canal is thus entodermal in origin and is vascularized by the artery of the hindgut, the *inferior mesenteric artery*. The lower third of the anal canal, however, is of ectodermal origin and is supplied by the systemic rectal arteries, branches of the *internal iliac artery*.

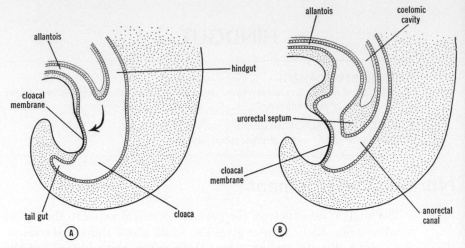

Figure 12-29. *A, Sagittal section through the cloacal region in an embryo of approximately 30 days (crown-rump length, 5 mm.). Arrow indicates the route of descent followed by the urorectal septum. B, Sagittal section through the cloacal region in an embryo of approximately 6 weeks.*

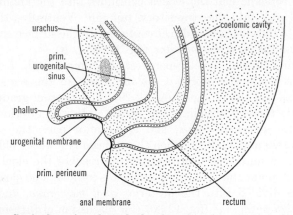

Figure 12-30. *Sagittal section through the cloacal region showing the division of the cloaca into the recto-anal canal and the urogenital sinus. Note the anal membrane, the primitive perineum, and the urogenital membrane.*

Congenital Malformations

Imperforate Anus, Rectal Atresia

Imperforate anus is one of the more common abnormalities of the hindgut.[3] In simple cases, the anal canal ends blind at the anal membrane, which then forms a diaphragm between the entodermal and ectodermal portions of the anal canal (fig. 12-31A). In more serious

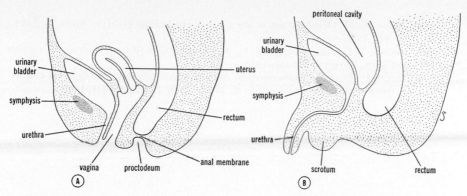

Figure 12-31. *A, Imperforate anus. The anal membrane persists as a diaphragm between the upper and lower portions of the anal canal. B, Rectal atresia. The ampulla of the rectum has failed to develop, while in addition the proctodeum is absent.*

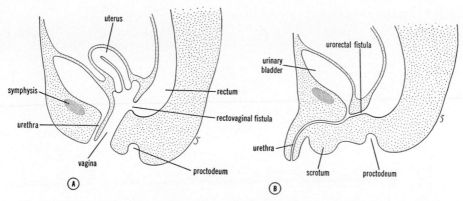

Figure 12-32. *A, Rectovaginal fistula combined with rectal atresia, due to a defect in the formation of the urorectal septum. B, Uro-rectal fistula combined with rectal atresia.*

cases, a thick layer of connective tissue may be found between the terminal end of the rectum and the surface, either due to a failure of the proctodeum to develop, or due to an atresia of the ampullar part of the rectum, *rectal atresia* (fig. 12-31*B*).[4]

Rectal Fistulas

Rectal fistulas are frequently observed in association with an imperforate anus, and may be found between the rectum and the vagina, the urinary bladder, or the urethra (fig. 12-32). Occasionally, such a fistula may open to the surface in the terminal region.

References—Hindgut

1. POLITZER, G. Über die Entwicklung des Dammes beim Menschen. Z. Anat. Entwicklungsgesch., **95**: 734, 1931.

2. TENCH, E. M. Development of the anus in the human embryo. Amer. J. Anat., 59: 333, 1936.
3. MOORE, T. C., AND LAWRENCE, C. A. Congenital malformations of the rectum and anus. Surgery, 32: 352, 1952.
4. BACON, H. E., AND SHERMAN, S. F. Surgical management of congenital malformations of the anus and rectum. A. M. A. Arch. Surg., 64: 331, 1952.

CHAPTER 13

Coelomic Cavity and Mesenteries

NORMAL DEVELOPMENT
- **FORMATION AND PARTITIONING OF THE COELOMIC CAVITY:** *diaphragm; pleuroperitoneal and pleuropericardial membranes*
- **MESENTERIES:** *ventral mesentery, falciform ligament and lesser omentum; dorsal mesentery; lesser peritoneal sac; dorsal mesoduodenum; mesentery of the primitive intestinal loop*

CONGENITAL MALFORMATIONS
- *Diaphragmatic hernia; mobile caecum and colon*

Normal Development

Formation and Partitioning of the Coelomic Cavity

At the end of the third week the intra-embryonic mesoderm on each side of the midline differentiates into a paraxial portion, an intermediate portion, and a lateral plate (fig. 13-1*A*). With the subsequent appearance and coalescence of numerous intercellular clefts, the lateral plates are divided into two layers: the *somatic mesoderm layer*, which is continuous with the extra-embryonic mesoderm covering the wall of the amniotic cavity; and the *splanchnic mesoderm layer*, which is continuous with the mesoderm of the wall of the yolk sac (fig. 13-1*B*). The newly formed spaces bordered by these layers are the *intra-embryonic coelomic cavities*.

At first the right and left intra-embryonic coelomic cavities are widely connected with the extra-embryonic coelom. With further development, however, after the body of the embryo is folded off from the yolk sac, they lose this connection. The two intra-embryonic coelomic cavities are then separated by a double-layered membranous

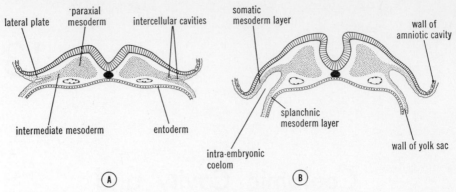

Figure 13-1. *A, Schematic transverse section through an embryo of approximately 19 days showing the differentiation of the mesoderm into the paraxial, intermediate, and lateral plate components. The first intercellular cavities are visible in the lateral plate. B, Similar section as in A, through an embryo of approximately 20 days. The lateral plate is divided into the somatic and splanchnic mesoderm layers which line the intra-embryonic coelomic cavities.*

partition, formed by fusion of the right and left splanchnic mesoderm layers (fig. 13-2A, B). While in some parts of the body, *e.g.*, the upper abdominal region, this septum persists indefinitely, in others, *e.g.*, the thorax, it partially disappears, thus uniting the right and left coelomic cavities (fig. 13-3A, B).

In the fifth week of development the intra-embryonic coelom con-

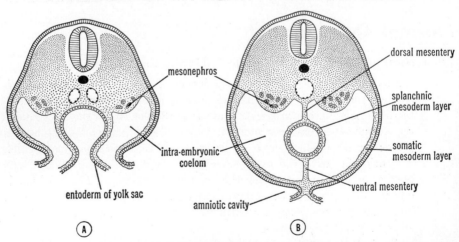

Figure 13-2. *A, Transverse section through a 21-day embryo in the region of the mesonephros. The intra-embryonic coelomic cavities communicate with the extra-embryonic coelom. B, Similar section as in A, at the end of the fourth week. The splanchnic mesoderm layers are fused in the midline and form a double-layered membrane between the right and left intra-embryonic coelom.*

Special Embryology

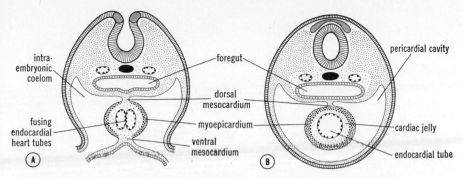

Figure 13-3. *A, Transverse section through an embryo of approximately 21 days in the region of the heart. B, Similar section at approximately 22 days. Note the disappearance of the ventral mesocardium and the communication between the right and left sides of the pericardial cavity.*

sists of a thoracic and an abdominal component, connected by a canal located on each side of the foregut (fig. 13-4A). In the adult, however, the intra-embryonic coelom is divided into three well defined compartments: (1) the pericardial cavity containing the heart; (2) the pleural cavities containing the lungs; and (3) the peritoneal cavity containing the viscera caudal to the diaphragm. The septum between the thoracic and abdominal cavities is formed by the *diaphragm*, and that between the pericardial and pleural cavities by the *pleuropericardial membranes*.

Diaphragm

The most important component of the diaphragm is formed by the *septum transversum*, a thick mesodermal plate initially occupying the space between the base of the thoracic cavity and the stalk of the yolk sac. Contrary to the diaphragm in the adult, this septum does not separate the thoracic and abdominal cavities entirely but leaves a large opening on each side of the gut connecting the two (fig. 13-4A). The canals thus formed are known as the *pleural canals*.

During the sixth week of development the lung buds expand into the pleural canals. Soon, however, because of the continuing rapid growth of the lungs, the space available in the canals is insufficient and room for further expansion can be found only by pushing the body wall in lateral and dorsal directions. The small bilateral outpocketing so formed at the level of the third, fourth, and fifth cervical segments is caudally delimited by a crescent-shaped fold, the *pleuroperitoneal fold*.[1-3] This fold subsequently extends in anterior direction, and by the seventh week fuses with the mesentery of the esophagus and with the septum transversum. The pleural canals connecting the thoracic and abdominal cavities are then closed (fig. 13-4B).

Coelomic Cavity and Mesenteries

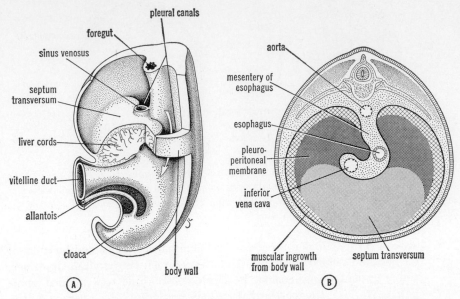

Figure 13-4. *A, Model of a portion of a human embryo of approximately 5 weeks. Parts of the body wall and the septum transversum have been removed to show the pleural canals, connecting the pericardial and peritoneal cavities. The liver cords penetrate the mesenchyme of the septum transversum. B, Schematic representation of the definitive diaphragm, indicating the origin of the various components (after Broman).*

The adult diaphragm is derived from the following structures: (1) the septum transversum, which forms the centrum tendineum; (2) the two pleuroperitoneal membranes; (3) the esophageal mesentery; and (4) the peripheral muscular portions contributed by the cervical and thoracic myotomes (fig. 13-4*B*).

The muscle fibers of the diaphragm derived from the third, fourth, and fifth cervical segments are innervated by the *phrenic nerve*, whereas those added later are innervated by the *intercostal nerves*.

Pleuropericardial Membranes

The thoracic portion of the coelom is divided into the pericardial and pleural cavities by the pleuropericardial membranes. The development of these membranes is closely related to the development of the common cardinal veins,[4] and they first appear as small folds projecting into the primitive undivided thoracic cavity (fig. 13-5*A*). When subsequently, owing to the descent of the heart and positional changes of the sinus venosus, the common cardinal veins shift toward the midline, the pleuropericardial folds are drawn out in mesentery-like fashion. They finally fuse with the dorsal mesocardium and then

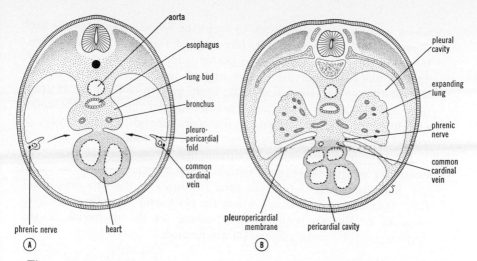

Figure 13-5. *A, Schematic representation showing the pleuropericardial folds and their relation to the common cardinal veins. B, Similar diagram at a later stage of development showing the division of the thoracic cavity into the pericardial and two pleural cavities. Note the expansion of the lungs into the pleural cavities (modified after Clara).*

divide the thoracic cavity into a single pericardial cavity and two pleural cavities (fig. 13-5*B*).

Mesenteries

With closure of the abdominal wall and formation of the peritoneal cavity, the two apposing splanchnic mesoderm layers fuse and form a double-layered membrane, the *primitive mesentery* (fig. 13-2*A*, *B*).

Ventral Mesentery

The stomach and upper part of the duodenum are initially in direct contact with the septum transversum, the bulk of which is formed by the outgrowing liver cords (fig. 13-4*A*). With the formation and closure of the abdominal wall, these structures draw away from the septum and their ventral border is then connected to the underside of the septum transversum and the anterior abdominal wall by the ventral mesentery (fig. 13-6).

During the formation of the ventral mesentery, the liver grows so rapidly that it can no longer be accommodated in the septum transversum and it starts to protrude between the two leaves of the ventral mesentery. The mesentery is then divided into an anterior portion, the *falciform ligament*, extending from the liver to the anterior abdominal wall, and a posterior portion, the *lesser omentum*, extending from the liver to the ventral border of the stomach and duodenum (fig. 13-6). The free edge of the falciform ligament contains the umbilical vein, which is obliterated after birth to form the *round ligament of the liver* (*ligamentum teres hepatis*). The free edge of the lesser omentum contains the common bile duct, the portal vein, and the hepatic artery. At first, the lesser omentum has a sagittal position, but as a result of the rotation of the stomach and the rapid growth of the liver, it gradually acquires a frontal position. Its lower border then forms the upper margin of the *epiploic foramen of Winslow*, through which entrance is gained into the lesser peritoneal sac behind the stomach.

The liver itself is completely surrounded by the ventral mesentery except for an area on its upper surface where it remains in contact with the diaphragm (fig. 13-6). This area is known as the *bare area of the liver*. At the lines of reflection, where the peritoneal covering of the liver becomes continuous with the peritoneum on the underside of the diaphragm, the *coronary ligaments* are formed.

Dorsal Mesentery

The dorsal mesentery extends from the lower end of the esophagus to the rectum. In the region of the stomach it is known as the *dorsal mesogastrium* or *greater omentum*; in the region of the duodenum, as the *dorsal mesoduodenum*; and in the region of the colon, as the *dorsal mesocolon*. The dorsal mesentery of the jejunal and ileal loops is known as the *mesentery proper*. Throughout its length the mesentery serves as a pathway to the gut for the blood vessels, nerves, and lymphatics (fig. 13-6).

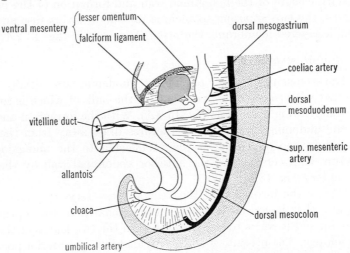

Figure 13-6. *Schematic drawing showing the primitive dorsal and ventral mesenteries viewed from the left side. The liver divides the ventral mesentery into the falciform ligament and the lesser omentum. The superior mesenteric artery continues toward the yolk sac as the vitelline artery.*

Special Embryology

Lesser Peritoneal Sac or Omental Bursa

In the fourth week of development small intercellular clefts appear in the mesoderm lateral to the foregut. These clefts fuse rapidly, and the formation of a cavity, the *pneumato-enteric recess*, results. Though this recess initially is bilateral, it is obliterated on the left side soon after its formation. On the right side it extends cranially between the esophagus and the right lung bud.[5] With development of the pleuro-peritoneal membranes, the cranial portion of the recess becomes isolated and forms a small supradiaphragmatic bursa, the *infracardiac bursa*.[6, 7] In the adult, remnants of this bursa may be found as small cysts lined with peritoneum.[8]

Simultaneously with the appearance of the pneumato-enteric recess, and closely related to it, is the formation of another recess which appears on the right side of the dorsal mesogastrium. Continuous expansion of this recess toward the left side of the body results in the formation of the *omental bursa* (fig. 13-7*A*, *B*). In effect, this bursa is an extension of the right half of the peritoneal cavity.[9]

After rotation of the stomach has been completed (see Chapter 12), the dorsal mesogastrium continues to grow and forms a duplicature, extending like an apron in front of the transverse colon and small intestinal loops (figs. 13-8 and 13-9). This double-leaved apron is the *greater omentum*. Later its leaves fuse to form a single sheet hanging from the greater curvature of the stomach (figs. 13-8*B* and 13-9*B*). The upper part of the posterior leaf of the greater omentum fuses with the mesentery of the transverse colon (fig. 13-8*B*).

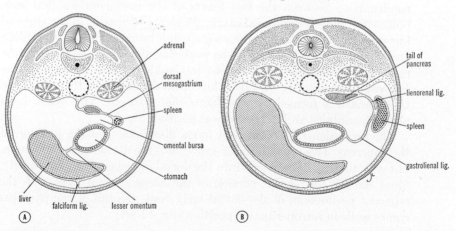

Figure 13-7. *Diagrammatic transverse sections through the region of the stomach, liver, and spleen, showing the formation of the lesser peritoneal sac, the rotation of the stomach, and the position of the spleen and tail of the pancreas between the two leaves of the dorsal mesogastrium. With further development, the pancreas is finally fixed in a retroperitoneal position (adapted from several sources).*

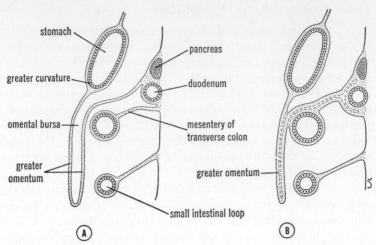

stomach

pancreas

greater curvature

duodenum

omental bursa

mesentery of
transverse colon

greater
omentum

greater omentum

small intestinal loop

(A)

(B)

Figure 13-8. *A, Schematic longitudinal section showing the relationship between the greater omentum, stomach, transverse colon, and small intestinal loops at 4 months. The pancreas and duodenum have already acquired a retroperitoneal position. B, Similar section as in A, in the newborn. The leaves of the greater omentum have fused with each other and with the transverse mesocolon. The transverse mesocolon covers the already retroperitoneally located duodenum.*

The development of the dorsal mesogastrium is made more complex by the formation of the spleen (fig. 13-7A, B). The primordium of this organ appears in the fifth week of development as a mesenchymal condensation between the two leaves of the mesogastrium, but soon bulges into the left peritoneal cavity. With the formation of the omental bursa, a portion of the dorsal mesogastrium located between the spleen and dorsal midline fuses with the posterior abdominal wall, while the remaining part connects the spleen to the kidney and is known as the *lienorenal ligament* (fig. 13-7B). The connection between the spleen and the stomach is formed by the *gastrolienal ligament*. The spleen itself always maintains an intraperitoneal position.

The formation of the omental bursa also influences the position of the pancreas. This organ initially grows into the dorsal mesoduodenum, but with time its tail expands into the dorsal mesogastrium (fig. 13-7A). Since the left leaf of this portion of the mesogastrium fuses with the adjacent peritoneum of the dorsal body wall, the tail of the pancreas comes to lie in retroperitoneal position (fig. 13-8B).

Dorsal Mesoduodenum

Rotation of the stomach and duodenum, together with rapid growth of the head of the pancreas, causes the duodenum to swing from its initial midline position to the right side of the peritoneal cavity (fig.

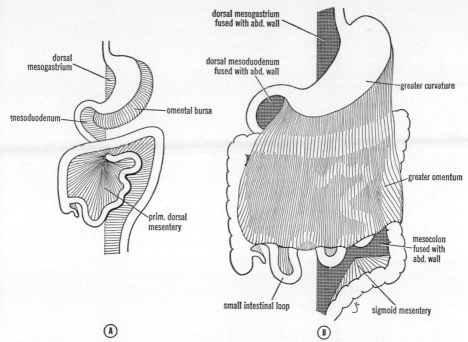

Figure 13-9. *A, Schematic drawing of the dorsal mesentery at the end of the third month.
The dorsal mesogastrium bulges out on the left side of the stomach, where it forms the omental
bursa. B, In the adult, the greater omentum hangs down from the greater curvature of the
stomach in front of the transverse colon and the small intestinal loops. The cross-hatched
areas indicate those parts of the primitive dorsal mesentery which have fused with the abdominal wall (adapted from several sources).*

13-10*A*, *B*). The duodenum and the head of the pancreas are then
pressed against the dorsal body wall, and the right surface of the dorsal
mesoduodenum fuses with the adjacent peritoneum. Both layers subsequently disappear, and the duodenum and head of the pancreas
become fixed in *retroperitoneal position*. The dorsal mesoduodenum
disappears entirely except in the region of the pylorus of the stomach,
where a small portion of the duodenum remains intraperitoneal.

Mesentery of the Primitive Intestinal Loop, or Mesentery Proper

This portion of the original dorsal mesentery undergoes profound
changes with rotation and coiling of the intestinal loops (see Chapter 12,
figs. 12-23 and 12-24). When the lower limb of the primitive intestinal
loop moves to the right side of the abdominal cavity, the dorsal mesentery twists around the origin of the superior mesenteric artery (figs.
13-6 and 13-11). Later, when the ascending and descending portions
of the colon obtain their definitive positions, their mesenteries are

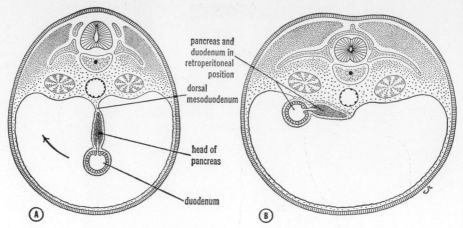

Figure 13-10. *Transverse sections through the region of the duodenum at various stages of development. At first, the duodenum and the head of the pancreas are located in the median plane (A), but later they swing to the right and acquire a retroperitoneal position (B).*

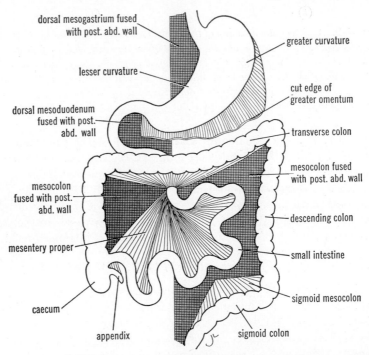

Figure 13-11. *Frontal view of the intestinal loops after removal of the greater omentum. The cross-hatched areas indicate the parts of the dorsal mesentery which fuse with the posterior abdominal wall. Note the line of attachment of the mesentery proper.*

Special Embryology

pressed against the peritoneum of the abdominal wall (fig. 13-11). After fusion of these layers the ascending and descending colons are permanently anchored in a retroperitoneal position. The appendix and the lower end of the caecum, however, retain their free mesentery.

The fate of the transverse mesocolon is different. First, it covers the duodenum with an additional peritoneal layer (fig. 13-8A, B); later, it fuses with the posterior wall of the omental bursa (fig. 13-8B). Its line of attachment finally extends from the hepatic flexure of the ascending colon to the splenic flexure of the descending colon (fig. 13-11).

The mesentery of the jejuno-ileal loops is at first continuous with that of the ascending colon (fig. 13-9A). When the ascending mesocolon fuses with the posterior abdominal wall, the mesentery of the jejuno-ileal loops obtains a new line of attachment which extends from the area where the duodenum becomes intraperitoneal to the ileocaecal junction.

Congenital Malformations

Diaphragmatic Hernia

The diaphragmatic hernia is one of the more common malformations in the newborn and is most frequently caused by failure of the pleuro-peritoneal membranes to close the pleural canals. The peritoneum and parietal pleura are continuous with one another along the posterior body wall, with no line of demarcation between the two. Such a defect, known as the *congenital diaphragmatic hernia of Bochdalek*, allows the abdominal viscera to enter the pleural cavity.[10, 11] In the majority of

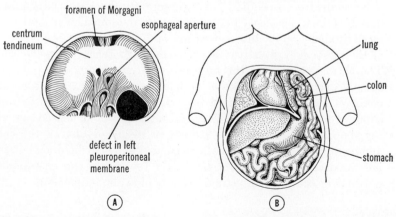

Figure 13-12. *Congenital diaphragmatic hernia. A, Caudal surface of the diaphragm, showing a large defect of the pleuroperitoneal membrane on the left side. B, Hernia of the intestinal loops and part of the stomach into the left pleural cavity. The heart and mediastinum are frequently pushed to the right, while the left lung is compressed.*

cases the hernia is on the left side, and the stomach, spleen, and part of the liver may enter the thoracic cavity (fig. 13-12*A*, *B*). Because of the presence of the abdominal viscera in the chest, the heart is pushed anteriorly, while the lungs are compressed and often hypoplastic. Hence, respiration is difficult and the newborn usually dies shortly after birth. Sometimes, the defective portion of the diaphragm is covered by a membrane composed of pleura and peritoneum. In such cases the intestinal contents penetrating the thoracic cavity are surrounded by the serous membranes.

Occasionally, a small part of the muscular fibers of the diaphragm fails to develop and the defect may then remain undiscovered until the child is several years old. Although such a defect may be located in the posterior portion of the diaphragm, more frequently it is seen in the anterior portion and is then known as the *parasternal hernia of Morgagni*. Such a hernia is located between the sternal and sternocostal portions of the diaphragm, and a small peritoneal sac containing the intestinal loops may then enter the chest.

Another type of diaphragmatic hernia, the *esophageal hernia*, is thought to be due to a congenital shortness of the esophagus. The cardia and upper part of the stomach are retained in the thorax and the stomach is then constricted at the level of the diaphragm.

Although the cause of a diaphragmatic hernia is unknown, it has been shown that the offspring of rats fed a vitamin A-deficient diet have a high percentage of diaphragmatic defects.[12]

Mobile Caecum and Colon

Normally the ascending colon, except for its lower part (approximately 1 inch), is fused to the posterior abdominal wall and covered by peritoneum on its anterior surface and sides. Persistence of a portion of the mesocolon gives rise to what is usually termed a *mobile caecum*. The extreme of this is the failure of the mesentery of the ascending colon to fuse with the posterior body wall, so that the root of the common mesentery is limited to a small area about the origin of the superior mesenteric artery. Such an unusually long mesentery allows for abnormal movements of the gut or even volvulus of the caecum and colon.[13] Similarly, retrocolic pockets may occur behind the ascending mesocolon, and a *retrocolic hernia* represents the entrapment of portions of the small intestinal loops behind the mesocolon.

References

1. BREMER, J. L. The diaphragm and diaphragmatic hernia. Arch. Path., **36:** 539, 1943.
2. WELLS, L. J. Observations on the development of the diaphragm in the human embryo. Anat. Rec., **100:** 778, 1948.

Special Embryology

3. Wells, L. J. Development of the human diaphragm and pleural sacs. Contrib. Embryol., **35:** 107, 1954.
4. Elliott, R. A contribution to the development of the pericardium. Amer. J. Anat., **48:** 355, 1933.
5. Kanagasuntheram, R. Development of the human lesser sac. J. Anat., **91:** 188, 1957.
6. Broman, I. *Die Entwicklungsgeschichte der Bursa Omentalis und ähnlicher Recessbildungen bei den Wirbeltieren.* J. F. Bergmann, Wiesbaden, 1904.
7. Broman, I. Warum wird die Entwicklung der Bursa Omentalis in Lehrbüchern fortwährend unrichtig beschrieben? Anat. Anz., **86:** 195, 1938.
8. Vilkari, S. J. A study on the bursa infra-cardiaca; development, anatomy and surgical pathology. Ann. Chir. Gynaec. Fenn., **39:** 1, 1950.
9. Pernkopf, E. Die Entwicklung der Form des Magendarmkanales beim Menschen. Z. Anat. Entwicklungsgesch., **64:** 136, 1922.
10. Harrington, S. W. Clinical manifestations and surgical treatment of congenital types of diaphragmatic hernia. Rev. Gastroent., **18:** 243, 1951.
11. Harrington, S. W. Esophageal hiatal diaphragmatic hernia. Surg. Gynec. Obstet., **100:** 277, 1955.
12. Andersen, D. M. Effect of diet during pregnancy on incidence of congenital hereditary diaphragmatic hernia in the rat. Amer. J. Path., **25:** 163, 1949.
13. Wolfer, J. A., Beaton, H. E., and Anson, B. J. Volvulus of the cecum: anatomical factors in its etiology; report of a case. Surg. Gynec. Obstet., **74:** 882, 1942.

CHAPTER 14

Nervous System

The nervous system appears at the beginning of the third week of development when the embryo is approximately 1.4 mm. long. An elongated, slipper-shaped plate of thickened ectoderm, the *neural plate*, overlying the notochord and part of the paraxial mesoderm, is then visible in the mid-dorsal region of the embryo just in front of the *node of Hensen*. During the next few days the lateral edges of this plate are elevated to form the *neural folds*, while the depressed midline area between the folds is known as the *neural groove* (fig. 14-1).

With further development the neural folds become more elevated and gradually approach each other in the midline, where they fuse, forming the *neural tube* (fig. 14-2). This fusion begins in the region of the fourth somite and from there proceeds in cephalic and caudal directions (fig. 14-3A). At the cranial and caudal ends of the embryo, however, fusion is somewhat delayed, and the *anterior and posterior neuropores* temporarily form open connections between the lumen of the neural tube and the amniotic cavity (fig. 14-3B). Closure of the anterior neuropore occurs at the 18- to 20-somite stage (23rd day), and that of the posterior neuropore at the 25-somite stage (25th day). The central nervous system then appears as a closed tubular structure with a cylindrical caudal portion, the future *spinal cord*, and a broader cephalic portion which becomes the *brain*.

The cephalic end of the neural tube soon shows three distinct dilatations, the *primary brain vesicles*. From anterior to posterior, these vesicles are known as: (1) the *prosencephalon* or *forebrain*; (2) the *mesencephalon* or *midbrain*; and (3) the *rhombencephalon* or *hindbrain* (fig. 14-4). Coincident with the appearance of these vesicles the neural tube becomes bent in a ventral direction, forming two flexures: the *cervical flexure* at the junction of the hindbrain and the spinal cord; and the *cephalic flexure* located in the midbrain region (fig. 14-4).

When the embryo is 5 weeks old the development of the brain has

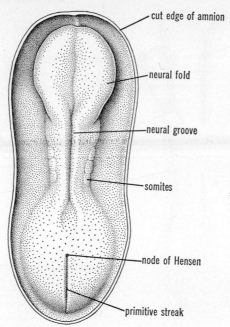

Figure 14-1. *Schematic drawing showing the dorsal aspect of a human embryo in the third week of development (Ingalls). Note the neural folds on either side of the neural groove.*

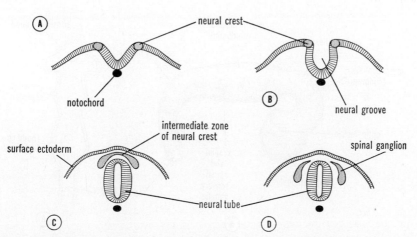

Figure 14-2. *Transverse sections through successively older embryos, showing the formation of the neural folds, neural groove, and neural tube. The cells of the neural crest, initially forming an intermediate zone between the neural tube and surface ectoderm (C), later form the spinal and cranial sensory ganglia.*

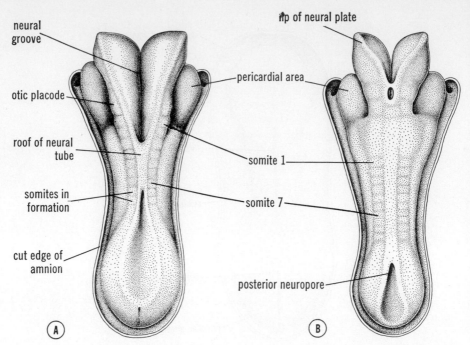

Figure 14-3. *A, Schematic drawing of a human embryo with seven somites; approximately 22 days old (modified after Payne). The neural folds have fused with one another at the level of the fourth to seventh somites. B, Schematic drawing of a human embryo with 10 somites; approximately 23 days old (after Corner). The lumen of the neural tube and the surrounding amniotic cavity are connected with each other through the anterior and posterior neuropores.*

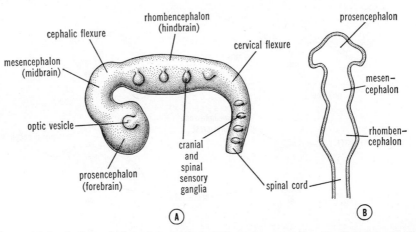

Figure 14-4. *A, Lateral view of the brain vesicles and part of the spinal cord in a 4-week embryo (modified after Hochstetter). Note the ganglia formed by the neural crest on each side of the rhombencephalon and spinal cord. B, Diagram to show the lumina of the three brain vesicles and spinal cord.*

248

made considerable progress, and five components can be distinguished. The prosencephalon has divided into two parts: (1) an anterior portion, the *telencephalon* or *endbrain*, consisting of a mid-portion and two lateral bulges, the *primitive cerebral hemispheres*; and (2) a posterior part, the *diencephalon*, characterized by the outgrowth of the optic vesicles (fig. 14-5). The mesencephalon has undergone little change and is separated from the rhombencephalon by a deep furrow, the *rhombencephalic isthmus*. The rhombencephalon has divided into two parts: (1) an anterior portion, the *metencephalon*, which later forms the *pons* and *cerebellum*; and (2) a posterior portion, the *myelencephalon*, destined to become the *medulla oblongata*. The boundary between these two portions is marked by a concave flexure, known as the *pontine flexure* (fig. 14-5).

The lumen of the spinal cord, the *central canal*, is continuous with that of the brain vesicles, thus allowing the cerebrospinal fluid to circulate freely between the cerebral hemispheres and the most caudal end of the spinal cord. The cavity of the rhombencephalon is known as the *fourth ventricle*, that of the diencephalon as the *third ventricle*, and those of the cerebral hemispheres as the *lateral ventricles* (fig. 14-5C).

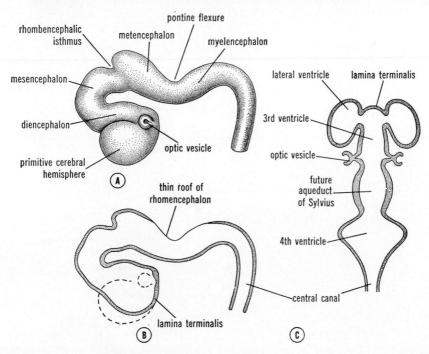

Figure 14-5. *A, Lateral view of the brain vesicles of the human embryo in the beginning of the sixth week (modified after Hochstetter). B, Midline section through the brain vesicles and spinal cord of an embryo of the same age as shown in A. Note the thin roof of the rhombencephalon. C, Diagram to show the lumina of the spinal cord and brain vesicles.*

The third and fourth ventricles are initially connected by the lumen of the mesencephalon. Because of the thickening of the walls of the mesencephalon, however, this canal later becomes very narrow and is then known as the *aqueduct of Sylvius*. The lateral ventricles communicate with the third ventricle through the *interventricular foramina of Monro*.

SPINAL CORD

Normal Development

General Structure

The ectodermal epithelium of the neural plate is initially formed by a single layer of columnar cells. However, by the middle of the fourth week, when the plate has been transformed into the neural tube, the cells of its walls are arranged in three concentric layers (fig. 14-6).

Ependymal Layer

This zone, which borders the lumen of the central canal, consists of a layer of columnar cells, known as the *ependymal cells*. These cells are radially arranged around the lumen and form a pseudo-stratified epithelium. Between the ependymal cells are found a number of large, actively proliferating cells, considered to be the *stem* or *germinal cells* of the nervous system. The stem cells are normally located near the mantle layer and approach the lumen of the tube only during cell division.

Mantle Layer

This zone, adjacent to the ependymal layer, is densely packed with primitive nerve cells or *neuroblasts*, which originate from the stem cells in the ependymal layer. The mantle zone later forms the *gray matter of the spinal cord*.

Marginal Layer

This zone, the outermost layer of the neural tube, contains the nerve fibers emerging from the cells in the mantle layer. It later forms the *white matter of the spinal cord*.

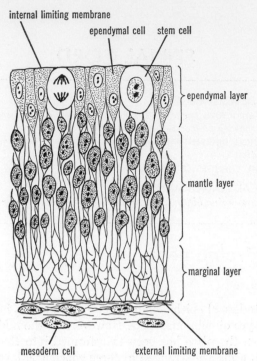

internal limiting membrane

ependymal cell   stem cell

ependymal layer

mantle layer

marginal layer

mesoderm cell   external limiting membrane

Figure 14-6. *Transverse section through a segment of the spinal cord in a 6-week embryo. Note the stem or germinal cells of the nervous system bordering the lumen of the spinal cord. The mesoderm cells at the periphery of the cord will later form the meninges.*

Basal, Alar, Roof, and Floor Plates

As a result of rapid cell proliferation in the ependymal layer, each side of the neural tube shows a ventral and dorsal thickening. The ventral thickenings, the *basal plates*, form the future motor areas of the spinal cord, whereas the dorsal thickenings, the *alar plates*, are destined to become the sensory areas (fig. 14-7A). A longitudinal groove, the *sulcus limitans*, found bilaterally on the inner surface of the tube, marks the boundary between the anterior motor and posterior sensory areas (fig. 14-7A, B). The thin dorsal and ventral midline portions of the neural tube—the *roof* and *floor plates*, respectively—contain no neuroblasts and serve primarily as a pathway for nerve fibers crossing from one side of the spinal cord to the other.

With continuous growth the basal plates bulge forward on each side of the midline, thus causing a deep longitudinal groove to appear on the ventral aspect of the spinal cord (fig. 14-7B). This groove, the *ventral fissure*, later contains the anterior spinal artery. The alar plates expand mainly in a medial direction, thereby compressing the dorsal portion

252   **Special Embryology**

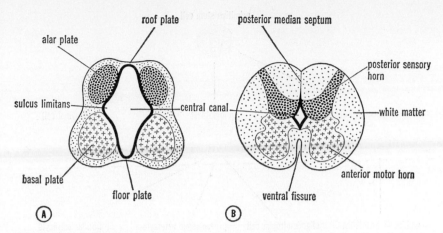

Figure 14-7. *Diagrams to show two successive stages in the development of the spinal cord. Note the formation of the anterior and posterior horns, the ventral fissure, and the posterior median septum.*

of the lumen of the neural tube. When finally the two alar plates fuse in the midline, the *posterior median septum* is formed at the plane of fusion. The spinal cord has then acquired its definitive form with motor horns anteriorly, sensory horns posteriorly, and a small lumen known as the *central canal.*

Histological Differentiation

While the above-described organization of the spinal cord occurs, its cells differentiate into *neuroglia* or *supporting cells,* and *nerve cells.*

Neuroglia Cells

The neuroglia or supporting cells of the nervous system most likely arise from the primitive germinal cells in the ependymal layer. With further differentiation they give rise to many different cell types, among which the ependymal cell is one of the most primitive (fig. 14-8). The majority of the primitive supporting cells, the *spongioblasts,* are found in the mantle and marginal layers, where they differentiate into the *protoplasmic* and *fibrillar astrocytes,* respectively (fig. 14-8).[1,2] Another type of cell to develop from the spongioblasts is the *oligo-dendroglia cell,* which later forms the myelin sheaths around the ascending and descending axons in the marginal layer.

In the third month of development still another type of supporting cell, the *microglia cell,* becomes visible. These cells appear with the invasion of blood vessels into the cord, and are believed to originate in the mesoderm surrounding the neural tube.[3]

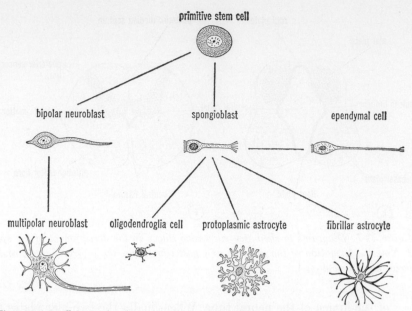

Figure 14-8. *Schematic diagram showing the development of the nerve cell and various types of supporting cells from the primitive stem cell of the nervous system.*

Nerve Cells

The nerve cells likewise arise by division of the germinal cells in the ependymal layer and from there migrate into the mantle layer. Initially they are round, *apolar neuroblasts*, but shortly develop a protoplasmic process on opposite sides of the cell body (*bipolar neuroblasts*) (fig. 14-9). With further differentiation, however, the process at one

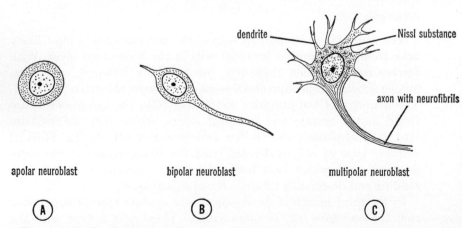

Figure 14-9. *Development of the nerve cell or neuron. A neuron is a structural and functional unit, consisting of the cell body and all its processes.*

Special Embryology

end of the cell is replaced by a number of small cytoplasmic outgrowths, the *primordial dendrites*, while that at the other elongates, forming the *primitive axon* (fig. 14-9C). Such a cell is known as a *multipolar neuroblast*, and with further differentiation becomes the adult nerve cell or *neuron*.

The axons of the neurons in the posterior sensory horn behave differently from those in the anterior motor horn. The former penetrate the marginal layer of the cord, where they either ascend or descend to a higher or lower level (*association neurons*); the latter, on the other hand, break through the marginal zone and become visible on the ventral aspect of the cord, where they are known collectively as the *anterior motor root of the spinal nerve*. These fibers conduct motor impulses from the spinal cord to the periphery (*motor neurons*) (fig. 14-10).

Neural Crest Cells

During the formation of the neural tube, a distinct group of cells appears along each edge of the invaginating neural plate (fig. 14-2B). These cells, ectodermal in origin, and known as the *neural crest cells*, temporarily form an intermediate zone between the tube and the surface ectoderm (fig. 14-2C). This zone extends from the mesencephalon to the level of the caudal somites, and with time divides into two parts, each of which migrates to the dorsolateral aspect of the neural tube.[4-6] There the cells of the neural crest form a series of cell clusters which give rise to the spinal and cranial sensory ganglia (5th, 7th, 9th, 10th, and 11th cranial nerves) (figs. 14-2 and 14-4).

During further development the neuroblasts of the spinal ganglia form two processes (fig. 14-10A). Centrally growing processes penetrate

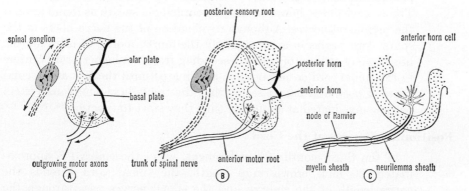

Figure 14-10. *A, Drawing showing the outgrowing motor axons of the cells in the basal plate and the centrally and peripherally growing fibers of the nerve cells in the spinal ganglion. B, The nerve fibers of the ventral moto. and dorsal sensory roots join to form the trunk of the spinal nerve. C, Schematic drawing of an anterior horn cell and its axon surrounded by the neurilemma and myelin sheath.*

the dorsal portion of the neural tube, and either end in the alar plate or ascend through the marginal layer to one of the higher brain centers. These processes are known collectively as the *posterior sensory root of the spinal nerve* (fig. 14-10*B*). The peripherally growing processes join the fibers of the anterior motor root and thus participate in the formation of the trunk of the spinal nerve. Eventually these processes innervate the sensory receptor organs. Hence the neuroblasts of the spinal ganglia give rise to the *posterior root neurons*.

In addition to forming the spinal ganglia and posterior root neurons, there is considerable evidence that the cells of the neural crest may differentiate into sympathetic neuroblasts, Schwann cells, pigment cells, meninges, and cartilage cells of the branchial arches.[7-12]

Myelination

Myelination of the peripheral nerves is accomplished by the *neurilemma cells* or *cells of Schwann*. From their origin in the spinal ganglia these cells migrate peripherally and wrap themselves around the axons, thus forming the *neurilemma sheath* (fig. 14-10*C*). In this manner axons, varying in number from 1 to 20, may be enwrapped by one neurilemma cell.

Beginning at the fourth month of fetal life, the nerve fibers gradually obtain a whitish appearance as a result of the deposition of *myelin* between the axon and the neurilemma. This substance is formed by repeated coiling of the membrane around the axon.[13, 14] Hence, both the neurilemma and the myelin sheath of the peripheral nerve fibers are formed by the neurilemma cells.

The myelin sheath of the nerve fibers in the spinal cord is of completely different origin, since it is formed by the oligodendroglia cells. These nerve fibers, however, lack a neurilemma sheath as found around the peripheral nerves. Although myelination of the nerve fibers in the spinal cord begins in approximately the fourth month of intra-uterine life, some of the motor fibers descending from the higher brain centers to the spinal cord do not become myelinated until the first and second years of postnatal life. It seems that the tracts in the nervous system become myelinated at about the time they start to function.[15]

Positional Changes of the Cord

In the third month of development, when the embryo is approximately 30 mm. crown-rump length, the spinal cord extends the entire length of the embryo and the spinal nerves pass through the intervertebral foramina at their level of origin (fig. 14-11*A*). With increasing age, however, the vertebral column lengthens more rapidly than the neural tube and the terminal end of the spinal cord gradually shifts to a higher level. At birth this end is located at the level of the

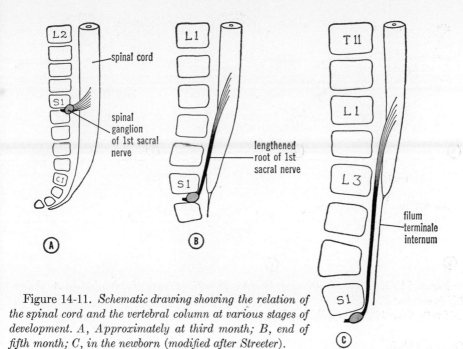

Figure 14-11. *Schematic drawing showing the relation of the spinal cord and the vertebral column at various stages of development. A, Approximately at third month; B, end of fifth month; C, in the newborn (modified after Streeter).*

third lumbar vertebra (fig. 14-11C). As a result of this disproportionate growth, the spinal nerves run obliquely from their segment of origin in the spinal cord to the corresponding level of the vertebral column.

In the adult, the spinal cord terminates at the level of L_2. Below this point the central nervous system is represented only by the *filum terminale internum*, which marks the tract of regression of the spinal cord. The nerve fibers below the terminal end of the cord are known collectively as the *cauda equina* (fig. 14-11C).

Congenital Malformations

By the end of the fourth week the central nervous system forms a closed tubular structure detached from the overlying ectoderm. Occasionally, however, the neural groove fails to close, either because of faulty induction of the surrounding mesodermal structures or because of intrinsic factors of the nervous system itself, and the neural tissue then remains exposed to the surface. Such a defect may extend the length of the neural tube or may be restricted to a small area only (*complete or partial rachischisis*). If localized in the region of the spinal cord, the abnormality is commonly referred to as *spina bifida*, whereas failure of closure in the cephalic region is known as *anencephalus*.

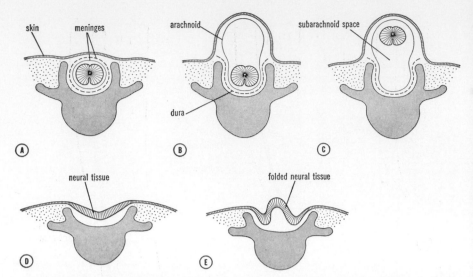

Figure 14-12. *Schematic drawings to show the various types of spina bifida. A, Spina bifida occulta; B, meningocele; C, meningomyelocele; D and E, two types of rachischisis in which the neural tube has failed to close.*

Spina Bifida

The term spina bifida is used to cover a wide range of defects. Literally translated, it indicates a bifid spine and in its most simple form is seen as a failure of the dorsal portions of the vertebrae to fuse with one another. Such an abnormality, usually localized in the sacrolumbar region, is covered by skin and is not noticeable on the surface except for a small tuft of hair sometimes present over the affected area (*spina bifida occulta*) (fig. 14-12A). In such a case the spinal cord and nerves are usually normal.

If more than one or two vertebrae are involved in the defect, the meninges of the spinal cord bulge through the opening and a sac covered with skin is visible on the surface (*meningocele*) (fig. 14-12B). Sometimes this sac is so large that it contains not only the meninges but also the spinal cord and its nerves. The abnormality is then known as *meningomyelocele*, and is usually covered by a thin, easily torn membrane (fig. 14-12C).

Another type of spina bifida results from failure of the neural tube to close, and the nervous tissue is then widely exposed to the surface (*myelocele* or *rachischisis*) (fig. 14-12D, E).[16, 17]

References—Spinal Cord

1. PENFIELD, W. Neuroglia and microglia. The interstitial tissue of the central nervous system. In *Special Cytology*, Ed. 3, edited by E. V. Cowdry. Paul B. Hoeber, Inc., New York, 1932.

Special Embryology

2. GLEES, P. *Neuroglia, Morphology and Function*. Blackwell Scientific Publications, Oxford, 1955.
3. KERSHMAN, J. Genesis of microglia in the human brain. Arch. Neurol. Psychiat., **41**: 24, 1939.
4. BAXTER, J. S., AND BOYD, J. D. Observations on the neural crest of a ten somite embryo. J. Anat., **73**: 318, 1939.
5. THEILER, K. Studien zur Entwicklung der Ganglienleiste und doppelter Spinalganglien. Acta Anat. (Basel), **5**: 206, 1948.
6. THEILER, K. Studien zur Entwicklung der Ganglienleiste. II. Frühentwicklung der Ganglienleiste beim Menschen. Acta Anat. (Basel), **8**: 96, 1949.
7. HARRISON, R. G. Die Neuralleiste. Anat. Anz., **85**: 4, 1937.
8. HARVEY, S., AND BURR, H. Development of the meninges. Arch. Neurol. Psychiat., **15**: 545, 1926.
9. HORSTADIUS, S. *The Neural Crest*. Oxford University Press, London, 1950.
10. BOYD, J. D. Argentophil cells in foetal ectodermal epithelia. J. Anat., **83**: 74, 1949.
11. HUMPHREY, T. Primitive neurons in embryonic human central nervous system. J. Comp. Neurol., **81**: 1, 1944.
12. SEESENIG, E. C. The early development of the meninges of the spinal cord in human embryos. Contrib. Embryol., **34**: 147, 1951.
13. UZMAN, B. G., AND NOGUEIRA, G. G. Electron microscope studies of the formation of node of Ranvier in mouse sciatic nerves. J. Biophys. Biochem. Cytol., **3**: 589, 1957.
14. METUZALS, J. Ultrastructure of myelinated nerve fibers and nodes of Ranvier in the central nervous system of the frog. In *Proceedings of the European Regional Conference on Electron Microscopy, Delft, 1960*, Vol. 2, p. 799.
15. LANGWORTHY, H. A correlated study of the development of reflex activity in fetal and young kittens and the myelinization of tracts in the nervous system. J. Comp. Neurol., **81**: 1, 1944.
16. PATTEN, B. M. Overgrowth of the neural tube in young human embryos. Anat. Rec., **113**: 381, 1952.
17. MACCARTHY, D. Problem of spina bifida. Quart. Rev. Pediat., **12**: 167, 1957.

BRAIN

Normal Development

After closure of the neural tube, the external appearance of its cephalic portion alters rapidly (figs. 14-4, 14-5, and 14-13). Despite these changes the brain vesicles maintain a number of morphological features seen as fundamental components of the spinal cord. For example, the majority of the brain vesicles show a distinct basal and alar plate on each side of the midline, characteristics of the motor and sensory areas, respectively. Even the sulcus limitans, which in the spinal cord forms the boundary between the alar and basal plates, is present in most of the brain vesicles where it likewise forms the dividing line between motor and sensory areas.

In the following account a brief description is given of the fundamental components of each of the five brain compartments. A number of structural specializations, not important to the basic understanding of the development of the brain, are omitted.

Myelencephalon

The myelencephalon, the most caudal of the brain vesicles, extends from the first spinal nerve to the early pontine flexure and eventually gives rise to the *medulla oblongata* (fig. 14-13). It differs from the spinal cord in that the lateral walls rotate around an imaginary longitudinal axis in the floor plate, a movement comparable to the opening of a book (fig. 14-14A).[1] As a result of this movement the roof plate becomes

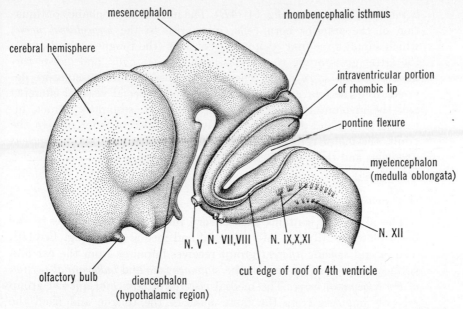

Figure 14-13. *Lateral view of the brain vesicles in an 8-week embryo (crown-rump length approximately 27 mm.) (after Hochstetter). The roof plate of the rhombencephalon has been removed to show the intraventricular portion of the rhombic lip. Note the origin of the cranial nerves.*

stretched and consists of a single layer of ependymal cells. The general structure of the lateral wall, however, remains similar to that of the spinal cord, with alar and basal plates separated by the sulcus limitans (fig. 14-14*A*).

Basal Motor Plate

The basal plate of the myelencephalon contains the motor nuclei, divided into a medial *somatic efferent* group and a lateral *visceral* or

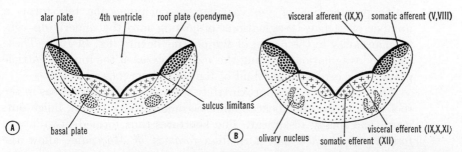

Figure 14-14. *Diagram showing the position and differentiation of the basal and alar plates of the myelencephalon at different stages of development. The arrows indicate the migratory path of the alar plate cells which form the olivary nuclear complex.*

branchial efferent group (fig. 14-14*B*). The former, the cephalic continuation of the anterior horn cells, gives rise to the *hypoglossal nerve*, which supplies the four occipital myotomes (the tongue musculature); the latter gives origin to the *glossopharyngeal, vagus,* and *bulbar portion of the accessory nerve.* These last innervate the musculature derived from the four caudal branchial arches (special visceral efferent) and the involuntary musculature of the heart, respiratory tract, intestinal tract, and glandular tissue (general visceral efferent). In the adult, the motor cells of these nerves are represented by the *nucleus ambiguus* and the *dorsal motor nucleus* of the *vagus* and *salivary nuclei,* respectively.

Alar Sensory Plate

The alar plate contains the sensory relay nuclei which, as in the basal plate, are divided into a lateral and medial group (fig. 14-14*B*). The lateral *somatic afferent* group receives impulses from the ear and surface of the head by way of the *stato-acoustic* and *bulbospinal portion of the trigeminal nerve.* The medial *visceral* or *branchial afferent* group receives impulses from the taste buds of the tongue and from the intestinal tract by way of the *glossopharyngeal* and *vagus nerves.* These cells later form the nucleus of the *tractus solitarius* (special visceral afferent) and the *dorsal sensory nucleus of the vagus* (general visceral afferent).

In addition to the formation of the sensory relay nuclei, other cells of the alar plate migrate downward until they lie ventrolaterally to the basal plate, where they develop into the *olivary nuclear complex* (fig. 14-14*A, B*).

Roof Plate, Choroid Plexus, and Foramina of Luschka and Magendie

The roof plate of the myelencephalon consists of a single layer of ependymal cells, covered by vascular mesenchyme, the *pia mater.* The two combined are known as the *tela choroidea* and, owing to active proliferation of the vascular mesenchyme, the tela forms a number of saclike invaginations projecting into the underlying ventricular cavity in the region of the pontine flexure (fig. 14-16*B*). These tuftlike invaginations forming the *choroid plexus* of the fourth ventricle produce the cerebrospinal fluid of the central nervous system.

When the embryo is approximately 4 months old certain areas in the roof plate of the rhombencephalon become extremely thin, bulge outward, and finally disappear. The apertures thus formed—two lateral *formina of Luschka* and a median *foramen of Magendie*—allow the cerebrospinal fluid to move freely between the ventricular system inside the brain compartments and the surrounding subarachnoidal space (fig. 14-16*B*).[2]

Metencephalon

The metencephalon develops from the anterior portion of the rhombencephalon and extends from the pontine flexure to the rhombencephalic isthmus (figs. 14-4, 14-5, and 14-13). It differs from the myelencephalon in that two new specialized components are formed: a dorsal portion, the *cerebellum*, which functions as the main coordination center for posture and movement; and a ventral portion, the *pons*, which serves as the pathway for nerve fibers between the spinal cord and the cerebral and cerebellar cortices.

Although the lateral walls of the metencephalon reapproach each other, their principal morphological features do not change and a basal motor and alar sensory plate are easily recognizable on each side of the midline (fig. 14-15). As in the myelencephalon, each basal plate contains two groups of motor nuclei; a medial *somatic efferent* group, which gives rise to the *abducens nerve*; and a lateral *visceral* or *branchial efferent* group. The latter gives rise to the branchiomotor components of the *trigeminal* and *facial nerves* which innervate the musculature derived from the first and second branchial arches, respectively (special visceral efferent), and the salivary fibers of the facial nerve (general visceral efferent).

The marginal layer of the basal plates expands considerably as it serves as a bridge for the nerve fibers connecting the cerebral and cerebellar cortices with the spinal cord. Hence, this portion of the metencephalon is known as the *pons*. In addition to these nerve fibers, the pons contains the *pontine nuclei*, which originate in the alar plates of the metencephalon and myelencephalon (fig. 14-15). The axons of these nuclei grow toward the cerebellum and give rise to the *middle cerebellar peduncles*.

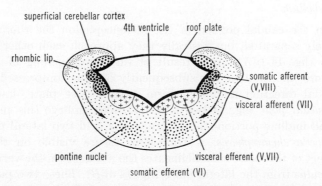

Figure 14-15. *Diagram showing the position and differentiation of the basal and alar plates in the caudal part of the metencephalon. The dorsolateral parts of the alar plates (the rhombic lips) partly project into the lumen of the fourth ventricle and partly above the attachment of the roof plate.*

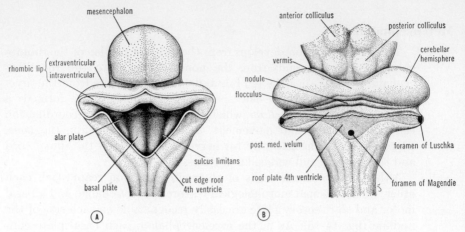

Figure 14-16. *A, Dorsal view of mesencephalon and rhombencephalon in an 8-week embryo. The roof of the fourth ventricle has been removed, allowing a view of the floor of the fourth ventricle (modified after Hochstetter). B, Similar view in a 4-month embryo. Note the choroidal fissure and the lateral and medial apertures in the roof of the fourth ventricle.*

The development of the alar plates of the metencephalon is rather complicated. Their ventromedial portions contain two groups of sensory nuclei: (1) a lateral *somatic afferent* group receiving impulses from the eighth nerve and the pontine portion of the trigeminal nerve; and (2) a medial *visceral afferent* group receiving impulses mainly from the facial nerve (fig. 14-15). The dorsolateral parts of the alar plates, however, bend medially and form the so-called *rhombic lips* (figs. 14-13, 14-15, and 14-16). These lips, projecting partly into the lumen of the underlying fourth ventricle and partly above the attachment of the roof plate (the extraventricular portion), give rise to the *cerebellum.*

Cerebellum

In the caudal portion of the metencephalon the rhombic lips are widely separated, but rostrally they approach each other in the midline (fig. 14-16*A*). As a result of further deepening of the pontine flexure, the rhombic lips subsequently become compressed in cephalocaudal direction and then form a transverse plate, known as the *cerebellar plate* (fig. 14-16*B*). In a 12-week embryo this plate shows a small midline portion, the future *vermis*, and two lateral portions, the *cerebellar hemispheres.* A transverse fissure visible on the posterior aspect of this plate soon delineates the *nodule* from the vermis, and the *flocculus* from the lateral lobes (fig. 14-16*B*). These two parts are considered the most primitive parts of the cerebellum and are connected to the vestibular nuclei.[3, 4] Later, secondary fissures appear which give the cerebellum its characteristic adult appearance (fig. 14-17).[5]

The cell layers of the rhombic lip are initially arranged in ependymal,

Special Embryology

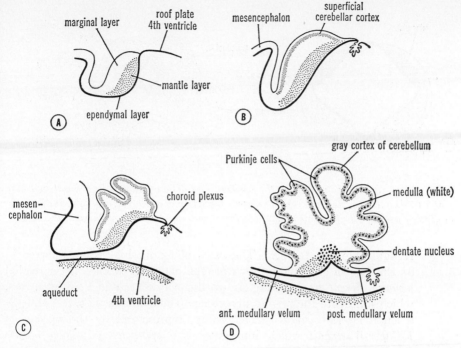

Figure 14-17. *Sagittal sections through the roof of the metencephalon, showing the development of the cerebellum. A, At 8 weeks (approximately 30 mm.); B, 12 weeks (70 mm.); C, 13 weeks; D, 15 weeks (modified after Keibel and Mall).*

mantle, and marginal zones (fig. 14-17*A*). With further development, cells of the mantle zone migrate into the marginal layer where they form the *superficial cortex* of the cerebellum (fig. 14-17*B*). While some of the remaining cells in the mantle layer differentiate into the cerebellar nuclei of which the *dentate nucleus* is the most important, other cells move to the surface of the cerebellum in a second migratory wave. These cells, the *Purkinje cells*, together with the cells of the first wave, the *Golgi* and *granular cells*, form the definitive *cerebellar cortex* (fig. 14-17*D*).

The greater part of the original roof plate of the metencephalon is incorporated into the cerebellum. Those portions located in front of, and behind, the cerebellum remain thin and later are known as the *anterior* and *posterior medullary velum*, respectively (fig. 14-17 *D*).

Mesencephalon

Basal Plate and Crus Cerebri

The mesencephalon is the least modified of the brain vesicles and its basal and alar plates, separated by the sulcus limitans, are easily

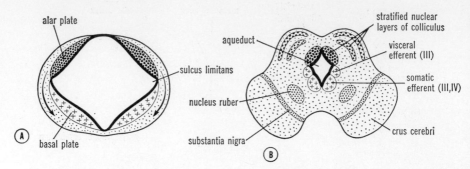

Figure 14-18. *Diagram showing the position and differentiation of the basal and alar plates in the mesencephalon at various stages of development. The arrows in A indicate the migratory path of the alar plate cells which form the nucleus ruber and substantia nigra.*

recognizable (fig. 14-18*A*). The basal plates in this region, referred to as the *tegmentum*, contain two groups of motor nuclei: (1) a medial *somatic efferent* group giving rise to the *oculomotor* and *trochlear nerves*, which innervate the preotic myotomes (the eye musculature); and (2) a small lateral *visceral efferent* group, represented by the *nucleus of Edinger-Westphal*, which innervates the *sphincter pupillary muscle* (fig. 14-18*B*).

The marginal layer of each basal plate greatly enlarges and forms the *basis pedunculi* or *crus cerebri*. These crura serve as pathways for the nerve fibers descending from the cerebral cortex to the lower centers in the pons and spinal cord. In the adult these fibers are known as the *corticospinal, corticobulbar,* and *corticopontine tracts*.

Alar Plate and Colliculi

The alar plates of the mesencephalon, the *tectum*, initially appear as two longitudinal elevations separated by a shallow midline depression (fig. 14-16*A*). With further development, a transverse groove divides each longitudinal elevation into an *anterior* (superior) and *posterior* (inferior) *colliculus* (fig. 14-16*B*). Whereas the nuclei of the posterior colliculi serve as synaptic relay stations for the auditory reflexes, those of the anterior colliculi function as correlation and reflex centers for the visual impulses.

The colliculi are formed by marked proliferation of the cells in the mantle layer and by their subsequent migration into the overlying marginal zone, where they become arranged in stratified layers (fig. 14-18*B*). In addition to the formation of the colliculi, some believe that cells of the alar plate also give rise to the *nucleus ruber* and the *substantia nigra*. Others, however, are of the opinion that these nuclei differentiate *in situ*.[6]

Special Embryology

Diencephalon

This brain vesicle forms the unpaired median portion of the original prosencephalon and is thought to consist of a roof plate and two alar plates, but to lack floor and basal plates.[7] Posteriorly, it is bounded by a plane passing behind the pineal and mammillary bodies, while its anterior boundary is formed by a plane passing just rostral to the optic chiasma and encircling the *foramen of Monro* (fig. 14-19*A*). The lamina terminalis is part of the telencephalon.

The roof plate of the diencephalon consists of a single layer of ependymal cells covered by vascular mesenchyme, and the two combined later give rise to the *choroid plexus* of the third ventricle (figs. 14-19, 14-20, and 14-22). The most caudal part of the roof plate, however, does not participate in the formation of the choroid plexus, but develops into the *pineal body* or *epiphysis*. This body initially appears as an epithelial thickening in the midline, but by the seventh week begins to evaginate (figs. 14-20 and 14-22). Eventually it becomes a solid organ located on the roof of the mesencephalon (fig. 14-24). Though many theories have been proposed as to its function, no satisfactory answer has yet been found.[8, 9] In the adult, calcium is frequently deposited in the epiphysis and it then serves as a landmark on an x-ray of the skull.

Occasionally the roof plate of the diencephalon forms another evagination close to the interventricular foramen, known as the *paraphysis*.[10] Sometimes this organ persists into postnatal life and gives rise to the formation of small cysts.[11]

In addition to the formation of the choroid plexus and epiphysis, it

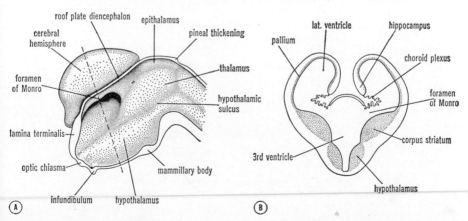

Figure 14-19. *A, Medial surface of the right half of the prosencephalon in a 7-week embryo (modified after Hochstetter). B, Schematic transverse section through the prosencephalon at the level of the broken line in A. The corpus striatum bulges out in the floor of the lateral ventricle and the foramen of Monro.*

has been suggested that the roof plate may also give rise to the *epithalamus*, a group of nuclei located on each side of the midline close to the pineal diverticulum (fig. 14-19*A*). Whether this is correct, or whether these nuclear masses are derived from the alar plate, is unknown. The epithalamic region is at first rather large, but later regresses to a small area which differentiates into the *habenular nuclei*. These nuclei form a link in the olfactory conduction path and are connected to each other across the midline by a group of nerve fibers known collectively as the *habenular commissure*, which is found just rostral to the pineal stalk (figs. 14-22 and 14-24). Caudal to this stalk, the *posterior commissure* appears, likewise connecting two nuclear areas on each side of the midline.

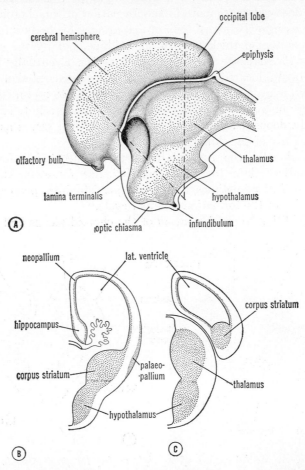

Figure 14-20. *A, Medial surface of the right half of the prosencephalon in an 8-week embryo (modified after Hochstetter). B and C, Schematic transverse sections through the right half of the prosencephalon at the level of the broken lines as indicated in A.*

Special Embryology

The alar plates form the lateral walls as well as the floor of the diencephalon. The side facing the lumen shows a longitudinal groove which divides the plate into a dorsal and ventral region, the *thalamus* and *hypothalamus*, respectively (figs. 14-19, 14-20, and 14-22). Although this groove, the *hypothalamic sulcus*, has been compared to the sulcus limitans of the other brain vesicles, it is of a different nature as it does not form the dividing line between alar and basal plates.

Owing to active proliferation of its nuclei, the thalamus projects into the lumen of the diencephalon. Frequently, this expansion is so great that the right and left thalamic regions fuse in the midline, thereby forming the *massa intermedia* or *interthalamic connexus*. During this rapid growth the nuclear areas of the thalamus are divided into two distinct groups: a *dorsal thalamic group* important for the reception and transmission of visual and auditory impulses, and a *ventral thalamic group* serving mainly as a passage and relay station.

The hypothalamus, forming the lower portion of the alar plate, likewise differentiates into a number of separate nuclei. These nuclear areas, however, serve as regulation centers of the visceral functions such as sleep, digestion, body temperature, emotional behavior, etc. One of these groups, the *mammillary body*, becomes conspicuous and forms a round protuberance on the ventral surface of the hypothalamus on each side of the midline (figs 14-19*A* and 14-22*A*).

Hypophysis

The hypophysis cerebri develops from two completely different parts: (1) an ectodermal outpocketing of the stomodeum immediately in front of the buccopharyngeal membrane, known as *Rathke's pouch*; and (2) a downward extension of the floor of the diencephalon, the *infundibulum* (fig. 14-21).

When the embryo is approximately 3 weeks old, Rathke's pouch

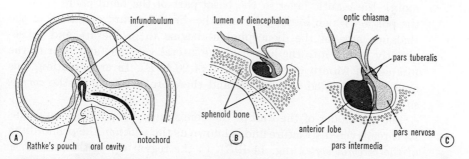

Figure 14-21. *A, Sagittal section through the cephalic part of a 6-week embryo, showing Rathke's pouch as a dorsal outpocketing of the oral cavity, and the infundibulum as a thickening of the floor of the diencephalon. B and C, Sagittal sections through the developing hypophysis in the 11th and 16th week, respectively.*

appears as a distinct evagination of the stomodeum, growing dorsally toward the infundibulum. By the end of the second month it loses its connection with the oral cavity and comes into close contact with the infundibulum. Occasionally a small portion of the pouch persists in the wall of the pharynx (*pharyngeal hypophysis*).[12]

During further growth the cells in the anterior wall of Rathke's pouch actively proliferate and form the *anterior lobe of the hypophysis* (fig. 14-21*B*). Later, a small extension of this lobe, the *pars tuberalis*, grows along the infundibular stalk and eventually surrounds it (fig. 14-21*C*). The posterior wall of the pouch develops into the *pars intermedia*, which in man seems to have little significance. In the adult the lumen of the pouch is obliterated, although occasionally a narrow cleft may remain.

The infundibulum gives rise to the *stalk* and the *pars nervosa* or *posterior lobe of the hypophysis*. It is composed of neuroglia cells which later differentiate into the so-called *pituicytes*.[13] In addition, it contains a number of nerve fibers which link the hypothalamic area of the diencephalon to the gland.

Telencephalon

The telencephalon, the most rostral of the brain vesicles, is comprised of two lateral outpocketings, the *cerebral hemispheres*, and a median portion, the *lamina terminalis* (figs. 14-4, 14-5, 14-19 and 14-20). The cavities of the hemispheres, the *lateral ventricles*, communicate widely with the lumen of the diencephalon through the *interventricular foramina of Monro*.

Cerebral Hemispheres

As in other parts of the brain, the cells in the walls of the continuously expanding cerebral hemispheres are arranged in ependymal, mantle, and marginal layers (fig. 14-19*B*). By the middle of the second month the mantle layer in the basal part of the hemisphere (that is, the portion which initially formed the direct forward extension of the thalamic area of the diencephalon) begins to proliferate and subsequently bulges into the lumen of the lateral ventricle and floor of the foramen of Monro (figs. 14-19 and 14-20*A*, *B*). In cross-section, this area has a striated appearance and therefore is known as the *corpus striatum*.

The remainder of the wall of the hemisphere temporarily maintains its three-layered structure and is known as the *pallium*, the primordium of the *cerebral cortex* (fig. 14-19*B*). In the region where the pallium is attached to the roof of the diencephalon, it becomes very thin and consists of a single layer of ependymal cells covered by vascular mesenchyme. These two later form the *choroid plexus*, which projects into the lateral ventricle along a line of invagination known as the *choroidal* *fissure* (figs. 14-19B, 14-20B, and 14-22B). Just above this line of attachment the wall of the pallium is slightly thickened, forming the *hippocampus* (fig. 14-20B). This structure bulges out into the lateral ventricle, where it later produces a longitudinal elevation.

With further posterior expansion the hemispheres gradually cover the lateral aspect of the diencephalon, mesencephalon, and the cephalic portion of the metencephalon (figs. 14-19 to 14-24). The corpus striatum, being a part of the wall of the hemisphere, likewise expands posteriorly and forms a longitudinal ridge in the floor of the lateral ventricle (fig. 14-20C). During this growth the corpus striatum is

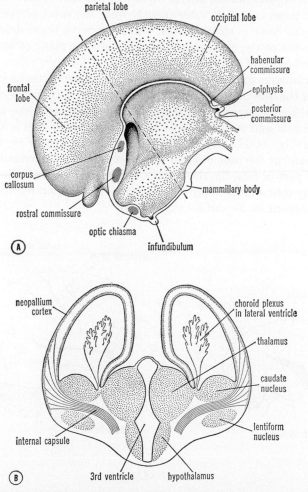

Figure 14-22. *A, Medial surface of the right half of the prosencephalon in a 10-week embryo (modified after Hochstetter). B, Schematic transverse section through the prosencephalon at the level of the broken line as indicated in A.*

Nervous System   271 divided into two parts: (1) a dorsomedial portion which forms the *caudate nucleus*; and (2) a ventrolateral portion which develops into the *lentiform nucleus* (fig. 14-22*B*). This division is accomplished by an ever increasing number of afferent and efferent axons passing to and from the differentiating cortex of the hemisphere and breaking through the nuclear mass of the corpus striatum. The fiber bundle so formed is known as the *internal capsule* (fig. 14-22*B*).[14] The lentiform nucleus is later divided into a lateral portion, the *putamen*, and a medial lightly staining portion, the *globus pallidus*.

As a result of the posterior expansion of the hemisphere its medial surface approaches the lateral surface of the diencephalon (fig. 14-20*C*). When these two walls subsequently fuse, the caudate nucleus and the thalamus come in close contact, while the nerve fibers descending from the cortex of the hemisphere pass through the plane of fusion to enter the peduncles of the mesencephalon (fig. 14-22*B*).[15]

Continuous growth of the cerebral hemispheres results in the formation of the frontal, temporal, and occipital lobes. However, as the region lateral to the corpus striatum lags in development, the area between the frontal and temporal lobes becomes depressed and is known as the *insula* (fig. 14-23*A*). This region is later overgrown by the adjacent lobes and at the time of birth is almost completely covered. During the latter part of fetal life the surface of the cerebral hemispheres grows so rapidly that a great many convolutions (gyri) separated by fissures and sulci appear on its surface (fig. 14-23*B*).

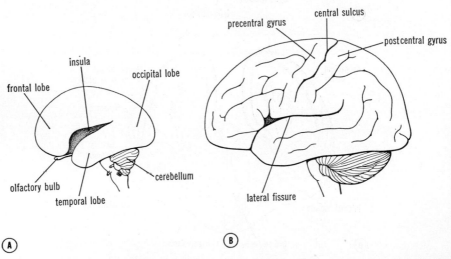

Figure 14-23. *Schematic drawing to show the development of gyri and sulci on the lateral surface of the cerebral hemisphere. A, At seventh month; B, ninth month (modified after Hochstetter).*

Special Embryology

Cortex Development

The cerebral cortex develops from the pallium and may be divided into two regions: (1) the *palaeopallium*, an area located immediately lateral to the corpus striatum; and (2) the *neopallium*, the suprastriatal part of the wall of the hemisphere (figs. 14-20*B* and 14-22*B*).

The palaeopallium appears in the seventh week of development and is formed by a conglomeration of cells migrating from the striated mantle layer to the marginal zone. Here, the cells establish a thin nuclear layer close to the surface that later acts as a relay station for olfactory impulses (fig. 14-20*B*).

Shortly after the appearance of the palaeopallium, the cells of the mantle layer of the neopallium likewise begin to migrate into the marginal zone, where they establish a superficial cortical layer (fig. 14-22*B*). At birth, this layer has a stratified appearance due to successive waves of cells from the mantle layer and to differentiation of the cells in the cortex itself.[16] Different areas of the cortex acquire specific cell types; for example, the motor cortex contains a large number of pyramidal cells, whereas the sensory areas are characterized by granular cells.

Commissures

The lamina terminalis, the mid-portion of the telencephalon, extends from the roof plate of the diencephalon to the optic chiasma (figs. 14-19 to 14-24). Its main function is to form a bridge for nerve bundles crossing from one hemisphere to the other. The first of these to appear is the *anterior commissure*, which becomes visible in the lower part of the lamina terminalis by the third month of development and consists of fibers connecting the olfactory bulb and related brain areas of one hemisphere to those of the opposite side (figs. 14-22 and 14-24).

The second commissure to appear is the *hippocampal* or *fornix commissure*. It is located in the lamina terminalis close to the roof plate of the diencephalon and its fibers connect the hippocampal areas to the mammillary body and hypothalamus by way of the fornix. Under the influence of the corpus callosum, which appears a short time later, the hippocampal commissure regresses greatly.

The most important commissure is the *corpus callosum*. It appears by the 10th week of development and connects the non-olfactory areas of the right and left cerebral cortex. Initially it forms a small bundle in the lamina terminalis immediately rostral to the hippocampal commissure. However, owing to continuous expansion of the neopallium it rapidly extends first anteriorly and then posteriorly, thereby arching over the thin roof of the diencephalon (fig. 14-24). As a result of this growth the area between the corpus callosum and the hippocampal

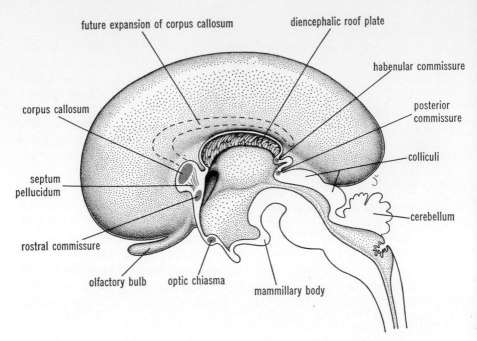

Figure 14-24. *Medial surface of the right half of the brain in a 4-month embryo, showing the various commissures. The broken line indicates the future expansion of the corpus callosum (modified after Hochstetter).*

commissure becomes very thin and is known as the *septum pellucidum* (fig. 14-24). Frequently this septum contains a small cavity, the *cavum septi pellucidi*, which, however, has no relation to the brain ventricles.

In addition to the three above-mentioned commissures developing in the lamina terminalis, three more appear. Two of these, the *posterior* and *habenular commissures*, are found just below and rostral to the stalk of the pineal gland. The third, the *optic chiasma*, appears in the rostral wall of the diencephalon and contains fibers from the medial halves of the retinae which cross the midline on their way to the lateral geniculate body and the anterior colliculus.

Congenital Malformations

Cranium Bifidum

Cranium bifidum indicates a defect in the skull due to faulty ossification. It is most frequently found in the squamous portion of the occipital bone and is often confluent with the foramen magnum. If the opening is small, only the meninges bulge through it, but if the defect is large, part of the brain and even part of the ventricle may penetrate

Special Embryology

into the sac (fig. 14-25). These abnormalities are known as *meningocele*, *meningo-encephalocele*, and *meningohydro-encephalocele*, respectively.[17]

Anencephalus

Anencephalus is characterized by failure of the cephalic part of the neural tube to close and the brain is represented by a mass of degenerated tissue exposed to the surface. The defect is always continuous with an open cord in the cervical region. The vault of the skull is absent, giving the head a characteristic appearance: the eyes bulge forward, the neck is absent, and the surfaces of the face and chest form a continuous plane.

Hydrocephalus

Hydrocephalus is characterized by an abnormal accumulation of cerebrospinal fluid within the ventricular system or, as in the case of external hydrocephalus, between the brain and dura mater. In the majority of cases, hydrocephalus in the newborn is thought to be due to an obstruction in the aqueduct of Sylvius. This prevents the cerebrospinal fluid from the lateral and third ventricles from passing into the subarachnoidal space.[18] This anomaly is often accompanied by a moderate widening of the sutures of the skull, while the bones themselves gradually become thin.

It is obvious that the above-mentioned abnormalities are only the most serious and usually incompatible with life. A great many other defects of the central nervous system, however, may occur without much external manifestation. For example, the corpus callosum may be partially or completely absent without much functional disturbance.

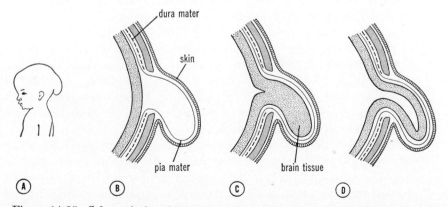

Figure 14-25. *Schematic drawings to show the various types of brain herniation due to faulty ossification of the skull. A, Meningo-encephalocele; B, meningocele; C, meningo-encephalocele; D, meningohydro-encephalocele.*

Likewise, partial or complete absence of the cerebellum may show only a little disturbance of coordination. On the other hand, cases of severe imbecility or idiocy may show hardly any morphological brain abnormalities.

Environmental and Chromosomal Factors

To establish the teratogenicity of an environmental factor, one must show that the malformed children have a history of prenatal exposure to a teratogenic agent more often than non-malformed children. For this reason, only a few environmental teratogens have so far been identified in human beings.

That abnormalities of the central nervous system can occur as the result of fetal infection with the toxoplasma organism is now well established. The affected child may suffer from cerebral calcification, mental retardation, hydrocephalus, or microcephalus.[19] Likewise, radiation during the early stages of development may account for microcephalus.[20-22] Whether virus diseases affecting the fetus during the first trimester of development cause brain abnormalities awaits more information. Some authors have suggested that maternal infection with Asian influenza in the early stages of pregnancy may occasionally result in anencephalus, but that the risk is low;[23, 24] others, however, have reported no significant increase in the malformation rate following maternal influenza.[25, 26] Although the rubella virus can cause abnormalities of the heart, eye, and ear, abnormalities of the central nervous system have been reported only sporadically.[27]

The recent discovery that some congenital malformations are caused by chromosomal abnormalities has had important implications with respect to the problem of mental retardation. That a human defect could be caused by a chromosomal imbalance was first demonstrated by the discovery that children with mongolism had 47 chromosomes, chromosome number 21 being represented three times instead of twice (trisomy).[28, 29] Likewise, 47 chromosomes were found in patients with Klinefelter's syndrome, the extra chromosome being considered as an "X." This syndrome accounts for about 1 per cent of mentally defective children.[30] In addition to Klinefelter's syndrome, it has recently been discovered that many sex chromosome anomalies are associated with mental retardation.[31]

Although little is known about the etiology of malformations of the nervous system in man, over the past years a great many environmental teratogens have been detected as causes of malformations of the central nervous system in the offspring of experimental animals treated during pregnancy. Anencephalus, hydrocephalus, spina bifida, cranium bifidum, exencephalus, meningocele, microcephalus, and cerebellar defects have been produced by a variety of teratogenic factors (vitamin

A, riboflavin, folic acid, pantothenic acid, vitamin E, and nicotinamide deficiencies; maternal fasting; hypervitaminosis A; trypan blue; hypoxia; x-irradiation; and antibody treatment[32-46]). In the chick embryo it has been possible to produce a variety of abnormalities of the neural tube by virus inoculation and antibody treatment.[47-50]

References—Brain

1. AREY, L. B. *Developmental Anatomy*, Ed. 6. W. B. Saunders Co., Philadelphia, 1954.
2. WILSON, J. T. On the nature and mode of origin of the foramen of Magendie. J. Anat., **71:** 423, 1937.
3. LARSELL, O. Development of cerebellum in man in relation to its comparative anatomy. J. Comp. Neurol., **87:** 85, 1947.
4. DOW, R. S. The evolution and anatomy of the cerebellum. Biol. Rev., **17:** 170, 1942.
5. JANSEN, J., AND BRODAL, A. Das Kleinhirn. In *Handbuch des Mikroskopischen Anatomie des Menschen*. Springer-Verlag, Berlin, 1958.
6. SHANER, R. F. Development of nuclei and tracts of mid-brain. J. Comp. Neurol., **55:** 493, 1932.
7. KINGSBURY, B. F. The fundamental plan of the vertebrate brain. J. Comp. Neurol., **34:** 461, 1922.
8. GLADSTONE, R. J., AND WAKELAY, C. P. G. *The Pineal Organ*. Baillière, Tindall & Cox, Ltd., London, 1940.
9. KITAY, J. L., AND ALTSCHULE, M. D. *The Pineal Gland*. Harvard University Press, Cambridge, Mass., 1954.
10. ARIENS KAPPERS, J. Development of the human paraphysis. J. Comp. Neurol., **102:** 425, 1955.
11. BULL, J. W. D., AND SUTTON, D. The diagnosis of paraphysial cysts. Brain, **72:** 487, 1949.
12. BOYD, J. D. Observations on the human pharyngeal hypophysis. J. Endocr., **14:** 66, 1956.
13. SHANKLIN, W. M. Differentiation of pituicytes in the human fetus. J. Anat., **74:** 459, 1940.
14. HEWITT, W. The development of the human internal capsule and lentiform nucleus. J. Anat., **95:** 191, 1961.
15. SHARP, J. A. The junctional region of the cerebral hemisphere and the third ventricle in mammalian embryos. J. Anat., **93:** 159, 1959.
16. CONEL, J. L. *Postnatal Development of the Human Cerebral Cortex*. Harvard University Press, Cambridge, Mass., 1959.
17. INGRAHAM, F. D., AND SCOTT, H W. Spina bifida and cranium bifidum. New Engl. J. Med., **229:** 108, 1943.
18. RUSSELL, D. S. *Observations on the Pathology of Hydrocephalus* (Medical Research Council Special Report No. 265). His Majesty's Stationary Office, London, 1949.
19. FELDMAN, H. A. Toxoplasmosis. Pediatrics, **22:** 559, 1958.
20. MURPHY, D. F. Ovarian irradiation and the health of the subsequent child; a review of more than 200 previously unreported pregnancies in women subjected to pelvic irradiation. Surg. Gynec. Obstet., **48:** 766, 1929.
21. PLUMMER, G. Anomalies occurring in children exposed *in utero* to the atomic bomb in Hiroshima. Pediatrics, **10:** 687, 1952.
22. YAMAZAKI, J. N., WRIGHT, S. W., AND WRIGHT, P. M. Outcome of pregnancy

in women exposed to the atomic bomb in Nagasaki. A. M. A. J. Dis. Child., 87: 448, 1954.

23. COFFEY, V. P., AND JESSOP, N. J. Rubella and incidence of congenital abnormalities. Irish J. Med. Sci., 397: 1, 1959.

24. DOLL, R., AND HILL, A. B. Asian influenza in pregnancy and congenital defects. Brit. J. Prev. Soc. Med., 14: 167, 1960.

25. WALKER, W. M., AND McKEE, A. P. Asian influenza in pregnancy. Obstet. Gynec. (N. Y.), 13: 394, 1959.

26. WILSON, M. G., HEINS, H. L., IMAGAWA, D. T., AND ADAMS, J. M. Teratogenic effects of Asian influenza. J. A. M. A., 171: 638, 1959.

27. ARIENS KAPPERS, J. Les malformations cérébrales consécutives a l'embryopathie rubéoleuse. In *Colloque sur les malformations congénitales de l'encéphalie*, edited by Heyer, Feld, and Gruner. Masson & Cie, Paris, 1959.

28. LEJEUNE, J., GAUTIER, M., AND TURPIN, R. Etudes des chromosomes somatiques de neuf enfants mongoliens. C. R. Acad. Sci. (Par.), 248: 1921, 1959.

29. JACOBS, P. A., BAILIE, A. G., BROWN, W. M. C., AND STRONG, J. A. The somatic chromosomes in mongolism. Lancet, 1: 710, 1959.

30. MACLEAN, N., ET AL. A survey of sex chromosome abnormalities among 4514 mental defectives. Lancet, 1: 293, 1962.

31. HARNDEN, D. G., AND JACOBS, P. A. Cytogenetics of abnormal sexual development in man. Brit. Med. Bull., 17: 206, 1961.

32. KALTER, H., AND WARKANY, J. Experimental production of congenital malformations in mammals by metabolic procedure. Physiol. Rev., 39: 69, 1959.

33. GIROUD, A. Anencéphalie, encéphalocèles, méningocèles par hypervitaminose A. Arch. Franc. Pediat., 15: 835, 1958.

34. GIROUD, A., GOURELLE, H., AND MARTINET, M. Données quantitatives sur le taux de la vitamine A chez le rat lors d'expériences de tératogénèse par hypervitaminose A. Bull. Soc. Chim. Biol. (Par.), 39: 331, 1957.

35. GIROUD, A., Méningocèles rachidiennes et fermeture imparfaite du tube médullaire. Arch. Anat. (Strasb.), 44: 107, 1961.

36. GIROUD, A. Encéphalocèle, méningocèle par hypervitaminose A et considerations cliniques. Rev. Neurol. (Par.), 98: 181, 1958.

37. WARKANY, J., WILSON, J. G., AND GEIGER, J. Myeloschisis and myelomeningocele produced experimentally in the rat. J. Comp. Neurol., 109: 35, 1958.

38. RUNNER, M. N., AND MILLER, J. R. Congenital deformity in the mouse as a consequence of fasting. Anat. Rec., 124: 437, 1956.

39. MILLER, J. R. Clinical and experimental studies on the etiology of skull, vertebra, rib and palate malformations. Ph.D. Thesis, McGill University, 1959.

40. RUSSELL, L. B. X-ray induced developmental abnormalities in the mouse and their use in the analysis of embryological patterns. II. Abnormalities of the vertebral column and thorax. J. Exp. Zool., 131: 329, 1956.

41. HICKS, S. P., ET AL. Migrating cells in the developing nervous system studied by their radiosensitivity and tritiated thymidine uptake. Brookhaven Symposia Biol., 14: 246, 1961.

42. INGALLS, T. H., AVIS, F. R., CURLEY, F. J., AND TEMIN, H. M. Genetic determinants of hypoxia induced congenital anomalies. J. Hered., 44: 185, 1953.

43. PINSKY, H., AND FRASER, F. C. Congenital malformations following a two-hour inactivation of nicotinamide by its analogue, 6-aminonicotinamide in pregnant mice. Brit. Med. J., 2: 195, 1960.

44. RUNNER, M. N., AND DAGG, C. P. Metabolic mechanisms of teratogenic agents during morphogenesis (symposium on normal and abnormal differentiation and development). Nat. Cancer Inst. Monogr., 2: 41, 1960.

45. GLUECKSOHN-WAELSCH, S. The effect of maternal immunization against organ tissues on embryonic differentiation in the mouse. J. Embryol. Exp. Morph., 5: 83, 1957.

46. BRENT, R. L., AVERICH, E., AND DRAPIEWSKI, V. A. Production of congenital malformations using tissue antibodies. Proc. Soc. Exp. Biol. Med., 106: 523, 1961.

47. ROBERTSON, G. G., WILLIAMSON, A. P., AND BLATTNER, R. J. Origin of myeloschisis in chick embryos infected with influenza-A virus. Yale J. Biol. Med., 32: 449, 1960.

48. ROBERTSON, G. G., WILLIAMSON, A. P., AND BLATTNER, R. J. Abnormal formation of neural tube in chick embryos inoculated with influenza-A virus. Anat. Rec., 127: 479, 1957.

49. ROBERTSON, G. G., WILLIAMSON, A. P., AND BLATTNER, R. J. A study of abnormalities in early chick embryos inoculated with Newcastle disease virus. J. Exp. Zool., 129: 5, 1955.

50. LANGMAN, J., MAISEL, H., AND SQUIRES, J. The influence of lens antibodies on the development of lens antigen containing tissues in the chick embryo. J. Embryol. Exp. Morph., 10: 178, 1962.

AUTONOMIC NERVOUS SYSTEM

Functionally, the autonomic nervous system can be divided into two parts: a *sympathetic* portion which is localized in the thoracolumbar region, and a *parasympathetic* portion, found in the cephalic and sacral regions.

Sympathetic Nervous System

In the fifth week of development cells originating in the neural crest of the thoracic region of the embryo, and known as the *sympathetic neuroblasts*, migrate on each side of the spinal cord toward the region immediately behind the dorsal aorta (fig. 14–26). Here they form bilaterally a chain of segmentally arranged sympathetic ganglia interconnected by longitudinal nerve fibers, known as the *sympathetic chains.* From their initial position in the thorax, the neuroblasts migrate toward the cervical and lumbosacral regions, thus extending the sympathetic chains to their full length.

Some of the sympathetic neuroblasts migrate even farther ventrally to form the *pre-aortic ganglia,* such as the *coeliac* and *mesenteric ganglia* found at the roots of the main aortic branches. Still other sympathetic cells migrate to the heart, lungs and gastrointestinal tract, where they give rise to the *sympathetic organ plexuses* (fig. 14–26).

Once the sympathetic chains have been established, nerve fibers originating in the viscero-efferent column of the thoracolumbar segments of the spinal cord penetrate the ganglia of the chain and form synapses around the developing neuroblasts (fig. 14–27). Some of these extend to higher or lower levels in the sympathetic chains or to the *pre-aortic* or *collateral ganglia* before synapsing. They are known as *pre-ganglionic fibers,* have a myelin sheath, and stimulate the sympathetic ganglion cells into action. Passing from the spinal nerves to the sympathetic ganglia, they form the so-called *white communicating rami.*

The axons of the sympathetic ganglion cells are called *post-ganglionic fibers* and have no myelin sheath. They pass either to other levels of the sympathetic chain or extend to the heart, lungs, and intestinal tract (fig. 14–27). Other fibers known as the *gray communicating rami*

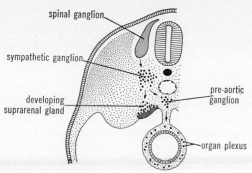

Figure 14-26. *Schematic diagram to show the formation of the sympathetic ganglia. A portion of the sympathetic neuroblasts migrates toward the proliferating mesothelium to form the medulla of the suprarenal gland (modified after Giroud).*

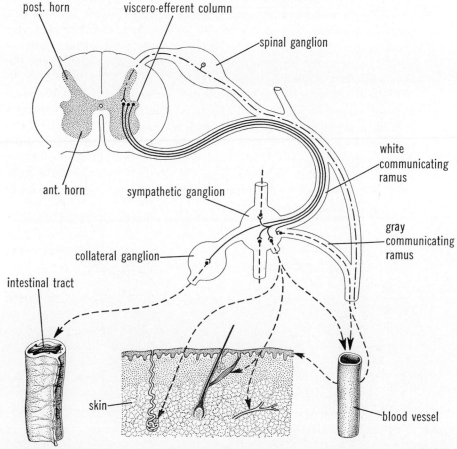

Figure 14-27. *Schematic drawing to show the relationship of the pre-ganglionic and post-ganglionic nerve fibers of the sympathetic nervous system to the spinal nerves. Note the origin of the pre-ganglionic fibers in the viscero-efferent motor column of the spinal cord.*

pass from the sympathetic chain to the spinal nerves and from there to the peripheral blood vessels, hair, and sweat glands.

Suprarenal Gland

The suprarenal gland is formed by two components: (1) a mesodermal portion which develops into the *cortex* of the gland; and (2) an ectodermal portion which forms the *medulla*.

During the fifth week of development, mesothelial cells located between the root of the mesentery and the developing gonad begin to proliferate and penetrate the underlying mesenchyme (fig. 14–26). Here, they differentiate into large acidophilic organs which form the *fetal* or *primitive cortex* of the suprarenal gland (fig. 14–28*A*). Shortly afterward a second wave of cells from the mesothelium penetrates the mesenchyme and surrounds the original acidophilic cell mass. These cells, smaller than those of the first wave, later form the *definitive cortex* of the gland (fig. 14–28*A*, *B*). After birth the fetal cortex regresses rapidly, except for its outermost layer, which differentiates into the basophilic part of the postnatal cortex.

While the fetal cortex is being formed, cells originating in the sympathetic system invade its medial aspect, where they become arranged in cords and clusters. These cells, which give rise to the medulla of the suprarenal gland, do not form nerve processes, but stain brown with chrome salts and hence are called *chromaffin cells* (figs. 14-26 and 14-28). During embryonic life the chromaffin cells are widely scattered throughout the embryo, but in the adult the only persisting group is found in the medulla of the adrenal glands.

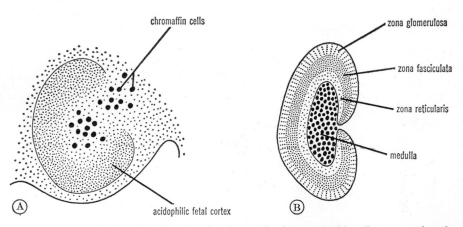

Figure 14-28. *A, Drawing showing the chromaffin (sympathetic) cells penetrating the fetal cortex of the suprarenal gland. B, At a later stage of development, the definitive cortex surrounds the medulla almost completely.*

Parasympathetic Nervous System

The origin of the parasympathetic ganglia found along the oculo-motor, facial, glossopharyngeal, and vagus nerves is rather contro-versial. Some believe that the cells of these ganglia migrate from the central nervous system along the pre-ganglionic fibers of the above-mentioned nerves, whereas others feel that they arise from neuroblasts originating in the sensory ganglia of the fifth, seventh, and ninth nerves.

The post-ganglionic fibers of the parasympathetic ganglia pass to the branchial arches and to the cardiac, pulmonary, and intestinal plexuses. The action of these fibers is thought to be antagonistic to those of the sympathetic nervous system.

Carotid Bodies

These bodies are formed by a mesodermal condensation around the origin of the internal carotid arteries and are supplied by branches of the glossopharyngeal nerve. They are invaded by cells from nearby autonomic ganglia and then develop into chemoreceptor organs, which serve as a reflex system in the regulation of blood pressure.

CHAPTER 15

Eye

NORMAL DEVELOPMENT
- *Optic cup and lens vesicle; retina, iris, and ciliary body; lens; choroid, sclera, and cornea; optic nerve*

CONGENITAL MALFORMATIONS
- *Coloboma iridis; persistent iridopupillary membrane; microphthalmia; anophthalmia; cyclopia; congenital cataract; experimental data*

Normal Development

Optic Cup and Lens Vesicle

The first sign of the developing eye appears in the 18-day embryo as a pair of shallow grooves on each side of the invaginating forebrain (fig. 15-1*A*). With closure of the neural tube, these grooves form outpocketings of the forebrain, the *optic vesicles*, which soon make contact with the surface ectoderm (fig. 15-1*B*). During the following period of intimate contact between the two cell layers, the optic vesicle probably causes chemical changes in the surface ectoderm cells, necessary for lens formation.[1] Shortly thereafter the optic vesicle begins to invaginate and forms the double-walled *optic cup* (fig. 15-1*C*). The inner and outer layers of this cup are initially separated by a lumen, the *intraretinal space*, but with further development this lumen disappears and the two layers are then apposed to each other. The invagination is not restricted to the central portion of the cup but also involves its ventral rim (fig. 15-2*A*). Here it forms the *choroid fissure*, which extends along the undersurface of the optic stalk, where it tapers off. During the seventh week the lips of the choroid fissure fuse,[2, 3] and the mouth of the optic cup then becomes a round opening, the future *pupil*.

While these events are occurring, the cells of the surface ectoderm, initially in contact with the optic vesicle, begin to elongate and form the *lens placode* (fig. 15–1*B, C*). This placode subsequently invaginates and develops into the *lens vesicle*. During the fifth week the

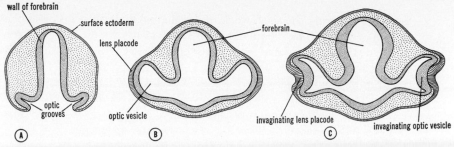

Figure 15-1. *A, Transverse section through the forebrain of an 18-day embryo (approximately seven somites), showing the optic grooves. The neural tube is wide open to the surface (after Heuser). B, Transverse section through the forebrain of a 4-week embryo, showing the optic vesicles in contact with the surface ectoderm. Note the slight thickening of the ectoderm (lens placode). C, Transverse section through the forebrain of a 5-mm. embryo, showing the invagination of the optic vesicle and the lens placode (after Mann).*

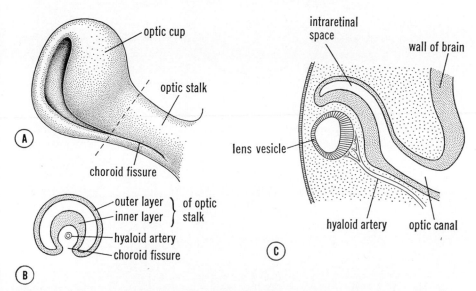

Figure 15-2. *A, Ventrolateral view of the optic cup and optic stalk of a 6-week embryo. The choroid fissure located on the undersurface of the optic stalk gradually tapers off. B, Transverse section through the optic stalk indicated as in A, showing the hyaloid artery in the choroid fissure. C, Section through the lens vesicle, the optic cup, and optic stalk at the plane of the choroid fissure (after Mann).*

lens vesicle loses contact with the surface ectoderm and is then located in the mouth of the optic cup (fig. 15-2C).

Retina, Iris, and Ciliary Body

The development of the outer layer of the optic cup is characterized by the appearance of small pigment granules which arise in its epithelial cells during the sixth week of development. It then becomes the *pigmented layer of the retina* (figs. 15-3 and 15-6).

The development of the inner layer of the optic cup is more complicated. Its posterior four-fifths, known as the *pars optica retinae*, thickens considerably and undergoes a series of changes somewhat similar to those occurring in the wall of the brain vesicles. Bordering the intraretinal space is the ependymal layer which, in the eye, differentiates into the light-receptive elements, the *rods* and *cones* (fig. 15-4). Ad-

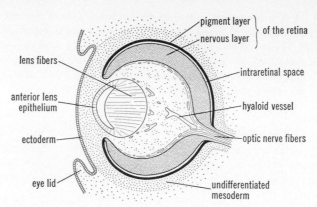

Figure 15-3. *Anteroposterior section through the eye of a 7-week embryo. The eye primordium is completely embedded in mesenchyme. The fibers of the nervous retina converge toward the optic nerve (modified after Mann).*

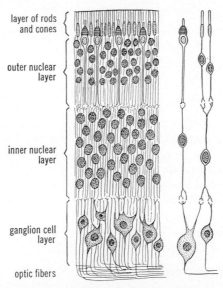

Figure 15-4. *Schematic representation of the various layers of the pars optica retinae in a fetus of approximately 25 weeks (modified after Mann).*

Special Embryology

jacent to the photoreceptive layer is the mantle layer, which, as in the brain, gives rise to the neurons and supporting cells. It differentiates into *the outer nuclear layer, the inner nuclear layer,* and *the ganglion cell layer* as known in the adult (fig. 15-4). On the surface of the mantle layer is found the marginal zone which contains the axons of the nerve cells of the deeper layers. The nerve fibers in this zone converge toward the optic stalk, which develops gradually into the optic nerve (figs. 15-3 and 15-6).

The anterior one-fifth of the inner layer of the optic cup, the *pars caeca retinae,* does not change much and remains one cell layer thick. It is later divided into the *pars iridica retinae,* which forms the inner layer of the iris, and the *pars ciliaris retinae,* which participates in the formation of the ciliary body (fig. 15-5).

Meanwhile, the region between the optic cup and the overlying surface epithelium is filled with loose mesenchyme in which the *sphincter* and *dilatator pupillae* later develop (fig. 15-5*A, B*). Whether in the human embryo these muscle fibers develop from the mesenchymal cells or from the underlying epithelial cells of the optic cup, as has been shown for lower animals, is still not known.[4, 5] In the adult, the iris is formed by the pigment-containing internal and external layers of the

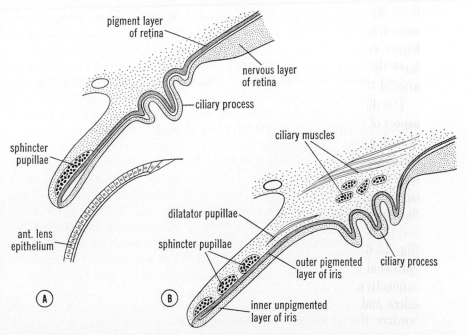

Figure 15-5. *Development of the iris and the ciliary body. The rim of the optic cup is covered by mesenchyme, in which the sphincter and dilatator pupillae develop.*

optic cup as well as by a layer of richly vascularized connective tissue, which contains the pupillary muscles.

The *pars ciliaris retinae* is easily recognized by its marked folding (figs. 15-5*B* and 15-6). Externally it is covered by a layer of mesenchyme which forms the *ciliary muscle*; on the inside, it is connected to the lens by loose mesenchyme which forms the *suspensory ligament*. Contraction of the ciliary muscle changes the tension in the ligament and controls the curvature of the lens.

Lens

Shortly after the formation of the lens vesicle (fig. 15-2*C*), the cells of the posterior wall begin to elongate in an anterior direction and form long fibers which gradually fill the lumen of the vesicle (fig. 15-3). By the end of the seventh week these *primary lens fibers* reach the epithelium of the anterior wall of the lens vesicle and form the so-called *nucleus of the lens* (fig. 15-6). Growth of the lens, however, is not finished at this stage, but new (secondary) lens fibers are continuously added to the central core. These new fibers arise from the cells in the equatorial zone and it is believed that this process continues until the 20th year of life.

Choroid, Sclera, and Cornea

At the end of the fifth week, when the optic cup and the lens vesicle have been formed, the eye primordium is completely surrounded by loose mesenchyme (fig. 15-3). This tissue soon differentiates into an inner layer comparable to the pia mater of the brain and an outer layer comparable to the dura mater. While the inner layer later forms a highly vascularized pigmented layer, known as the *choroid*,[6] the outer layer develops into the sclera and is continuous with the dura mater around the optic nerve (figs. 15-3 and 15-6).

The differentiation of the mesenchymal layers overlying the anterior aspect of the eye is slightly different. Here, the cells arrange themselves in such a manner that a space, known as the *anterior eye chamber*, splits the mesenchyme into a thin inner layer immediately in front of the lens and iris, the *iridopupillary membrane*, and a thick outer layer continuous with the sclera. The anterior eye chamber itself is lined by flattened mesenchymal cells, which form the posterior lining of the cornea as well as the anterior covering of the iridopupillary membrane (fig. 15-6). Hence, the cornea from outside in is formed by: (1) an epithelial layer derived from the surface ectoderm; (2) a layer of dense connective tissue, the *substantia propria*, which is continuous with the sclera and later becomes transparent; and (3) an epithelial layer which borders the anterior eye chamber. The iridopupillary membrane in front of the lens normally disappears completely.

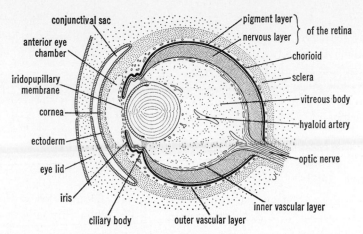

Figure 15-6. *Anteroposterior section through the eye of a 15-week embryo. Note the anterior eye chamber, the iridopupillary membrane, the inner and outer vascular layers, and the outer fibrous layer (sclera and cornea).*

Mesenchyme not only surrounds the eye primordium from the outside, but also invades the inside of the optic cup by way of the choroid fissure. Here, it participates in the formation of the hyaloid vessels, which during intra-uterine life supply the lens and form the vascular layer located on the inner surface of the retina (figs. 15-3 and 15-6). In addition, it forms a delicate network of fibers between the lens and the retina. The interstitial spaces of this network are later filled with a transparent gelatinous substance, the *vitreous body*.

Optic Nerve

Initially the optic cup is connected to the brain by the optic stalk, which on its ventral surface has a groove, the *choroid fissure* (fig. 15-2). In this groove are found the hyaloid vessels and the nerve fibers of the retina returning to the brain (fig. 15-7A). During the seventh week the

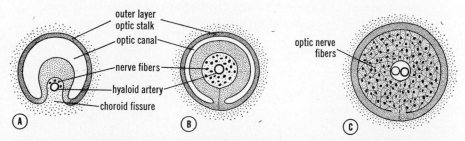

Figure 15-7. *Diagrams showing the transformation of the optic stalk into the optic nerve. A, At sixth week (9 mm.); B, seventh week (15 mm.); C, ninth week. Note the hyaloid vessels in the center of the optic nerve (adapted from several sources).*

choroid fissure closes and a tunnel is formed inside the optic stalk (fig. 15-7B). With further development the inside and outside walls of the stalk fuse (fig. 15-7C) and provide a network of neuroglia cells which support the optic nerve fibers.

The optic stalk is thus transformed into the *optic nerve*. In its center it contains the hyaloid artery, which is later called the *central retinal artery*.

Congenital Malformations

Coloboma Iridis

Under normal conditions the choroid fissure closes during the seventh week of development (fig. 15-7). When this fails to occur, a cleft persists.

Although such a cleft is usually located in the iris only and is known as the *coloboma iridis* (fig. 15-8A), it may extend into the ciliary body, the retina, the choroid, and the optic nerve.[7] This anomaly is frequently seen in combination with other eye abnormalities.[8]

Persistent Iridopupillary Membrane

Usually the iridopupillary membrane disappears entirely during intra-uterine life. Sometimes, however, resorption is not complete and a network of connective tissue is then suspended in front of the pupil (fig. 15-8B). This anomaly usually causes little disturbance of vision.

Microphthalmia

In such a condition the over-all size of the eye is too small, and the eyeball may be reduced to two-thirds of its normal volume. Usually it is not associated with any other ocular abnormalities.

Anophthalmia

Sometimes the eye is grossly absent and it is impossible to detect any trace of the eyeball except by histological means.[9] It is usually accompanied by other serious craniocerebral abnormalities.

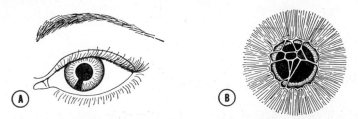

Figure 15-8. *A, Coloboma iridis. B, Partially persistent iridopupillary membrane in an adult.*

Cyclopia

In such an anomaly, both orbits are joined and there is only one median eye. This rare malformation is frequently accompanied by a proboscis and other craniocerebral abnormalities.[10]

Congenital Cataract

This is a condition in which the lens has become opaque during intrauterine life. Although this anomaly is usually genetically determined,[11] it may be caused by environmental factors. In 1941, Gregg[12] observed that children of mothers who suffered from German measles between the fourth and seventh weeks of pregnancy often showed congenital anomalies of which cataract was one of the most common. If, however, the mother was infected after the seventh week of pregnancy, then the lens escaped damage, but the child might be deaf as a result of imperfect differentiation of the cochlea.[13] This seems to indicate that the most actively differentiating parts of the embryo are the most sensitive ones. Indeed, the lens goes through one of its most active stages of development during the sixth week of development, when the primary lens fibers fill the lumen of the lens vesicle.

Experimental Data

In experimental work the primordium of the eye has been proved to be one of the most sensitive organs in the developing embryo, and a great number of eye abnormalities comparable to those in man have been produced.[14] It has been possible to show that a virus may produce eye abnormalities, but just as in the case of the German measles virus in man, it was found that the eye is sensitive only during certain stages of development.[15] Other teratogenic agents successfully used in the production of eye abnormalities are hypoxia,[16, 17] vitamin deficiency,[18-20] hypervitaminosis A,[21, 22] thyroid deficiency,[23] and x-ray.[24, 25] It was surprising to find that certain agents (cysteamine) diminish, whereas others (cortisone) increase, the sensitivity to x-irradiation.[26]

References

1. LANGMAN, J. The first appearance of specific antigens during induction of the lens. J. Embryol. Exp. Morph., 7: 193, 1959.
2. MANN, I. C. The Development of the Human Eye. Grune & Stratton, Inc., New York, 1949.
3. BARBER, A. N. Embryology of the Human Eye. C. V. Mosby Co., St. Louis, 1955.
4. COLLIN, R. Recherches sur le développement du muscle sphincter de l'iris. Bibliographie anat., 11: 183, 1902.
5. NUSSBAUM, M. Die Entwicklung der Binnenmuskeln des Auges der Wirbeltiere. Arch. Mikroskopische Anat. Entwicklungsmech., 58B: 199, 1901.
6. BARTELMEZ, G. W. The formation of neural crest from the primary optic vesicle in man. Contrib. Embryol., 35: 55, 1954.

7. MANN, I. C. *Developmental Abnormalities of the Eye.* J. B. Lippincott Co., Philadelphia, 1957.
8. FRANCOIS, J., KLUYSKENS, J., AND PHILIPS, A. Colobomes iriens compliqués, atypique et unilatéral dans un cas, typique et bilatéral dans un autre. Bull. Soc. Belg. Ophtal., **92**: 188, 1949.
9. REDSLOB, E. Anophtalmie vraie et anophtalmie apparente chez un nouveau-né. Ann. Oculist. (Par.), **169**: 433, 1932.
10. PAPOLCZY, F. Congenital cyclopia and orbital cyst together with other developmental anomalies on the same side of the face. Brit. J. Ophthal., **32**: 439, 1948.
11. FRANCOIS, J. *Heredity in Ophthalmology.* C. V. Mosby Co., St. Louis, 1961.
12. GREGG, N. M. Congenital cataract following german measles in the mother. Trans. Ophthal. Soc. Aust., **3**: 35, 1941.
13. TÖNDURY, G. Zur Kenntnis der Embryopathica rubeolica, nebst Bemerkungen über die Wirkung anderer Viren auf den Keimling. Geburtsh. Frauenheilk., **12**: 865, 1952.
14. TUCHMANN-DUPLESSIS, H., AND MERCIER-PAROT, L. Production of congenital eye malformations particularly in rat fetuses. In *The Structure of the Eye*, edited by G. K. Smelser, p. 507. Academic Press, Inc., New York, 1961.
15. ROBERTSON, G. G., WILLIAMSON, A. P., AND BLATTNER, R. J. A study of abnormalities in early chick embryos inoculated with Newcastle disease virus. J. Exp. Zool., **129**: 5, 1955.
16. WERTHEMANN, A., AND REINIGER, M. Über Augenentwicklungsstörungen bei Rattenembryonen durch Sauerstoffmangel in der Frühschwangerschaft. Acta Anat. (Basel), **11**: 329, 1950.
17. INGALLS, T. H., CURLEY, F. J., AND PRINDLE, R. A. Experimental production of congenital anomalies. New Engl. J. Med., **247**: 758, 1952.
18. GIROUD, A. Phénomènes d'induction et leurs perturbations chez les mammifères. Acta Anat. (Basel), **30**: 297, 1957.
19. NELSON, M. M., BAIRD, C. D. C., WRIGHT, H. V., AND EVANS, H. M. Multiple congenital abnormalities in the rat resulting from riboflavin deficiency induced by the antimetabolite galactoflavin. J. Nutr., **58**: 125, 1956.
20. KALTER, H., AND WARKANY, J. Congenital malformations in inbred strains of mice induced by riboflavin-deficient, galactoflavin-containing diets. J. Exp. Zool., **136**: 531, 1957.
21. COHLAN, S. Q. Excessive intake of vitamin A as a cause of congenital anomalies in the rat. Science, **117**: 535, 1953.
22. GIROUD, A., AND MARTINET, M. Malformations oculaires avec fibrose du vitré chez des embryons de lapin soumis à l'hypervitaminose A. Bull. Soc. Ophtal. Franc., **3**: 191, 1959.
23. LANGMAN, J., AND VAN FAASSEN, F. Congenital defects in the rat embryo. Amer. J. Ophthal., **40**: 65, 1957.
24. WILSON, J. G., JORDAN, H. C., AND BRENT, R. L. Effects of irradiation on embryonic development. II. X-rays on the ninth day of gestation in the rat. Amer. J. Anat., **92**: 153, 1953.
25. HICKS, S. P. Developmental malformations produced by radiation. Amer. J. Roentgenol., **69**: 272, 1953.
26. WOOLLAM, D. H. M., MILLEN, J. W., AND FOZZARD, J. A. F. The influence of cortisone on the teratogenic activity of x-radiation. Brit. J. Radiol., **32**: 47, 1959.

CHAPTER 16

Ear

NORMAL DEVELOPMENT
- **INTERNAL EAR:** *otic vesicle; saccule, cochlea, and organ of Corti; utricle and semi-circular canals*
- **MIDDLE EAR:** *tympanic cavity and Eustachian tube; ossicles*
- **EXTERNAL EAR:** *external auditory meatus; eardrum; auricle*

CONGENITAL MALFORMATIONS
- *Congenital deafness*

Normal Development

Whereas in the adult the ear forms one anatomical unit serving both hearing and equilibrium, in the embryo it develops from three distinctly different parts: (1) the *external ear*, which serves as the sound-collecting organ, develops from the dorsal portion of the first pharyngeal cleft; (2) the *middle ear*, which functions as a sound conductor from the external to the internal ear, arises from the first pharyngeal pouch; and (3) the *internal ear*, which converts the sound waves into nerve impulses and registers changes in equilibrium, is formed by the ectodermal otic vesicle.

Internal Ear

Otic Vesicle

The first sign of the developing ear can be seen in embryos of approximately 18 days (seven somites) as a thickening of the surface ectoderm on each side of the rhombencephalon (fig. 16-1*A*). These thickenings, the *otic placodes*, invaginate rapidly and form the *otic* or *auditory vesicles* (otocysts) (fig. 16-1*B, C, D*). During later development each vesicle divides into (1) a ventral component which gives rise to the saccule and the cochlear duct containing the organ of Corti,

Ear 293

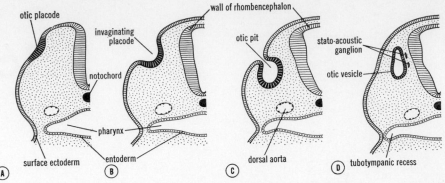

Figure 16-1. *Schematic transverse sections through the region of the rhombencephalon at various stages of development, showing the formation of the otic vesicle. A, At 18 days (approximately eight somites); B, 22 days (approximately 16 somites); C, 25 days (approximately 25 somites); D, 4½ weeks (approximately 5 mm.). Note the appearance of the stato-acoustic ganglion.*

and (2) a dorsal component which forms the utricle, semicircular canals, and endolymphatic duct (figs. 16-2 to 16-5). The epithelial structures so formed are known collectively as the *membranous labyrinth*. Initially, this intricate tubular structure is embedded in mesenchyme. With time, this loose connective tissue is converted into a cartilaginous shell, which in turn ossifies to form the *bony labyrinth*. The membranous labyrinth is then entirely encased in the bony labyrinth, with only narrow perilymphatic spaces separating the two.[1]

During formation of the otic vesicle a small group of cells breaks away from its wall and forms the *stato-acoustic ganglion* (fig. 16-1D).[2, 3] This ganglion subsequently splits into cochlear and vestibular portions which supply the sensory cells of the organ of Corti and those of the saccule, utricle, and semicircular canals, respectively. The proximal processes of the cochlear (spiral) and vestibular ganglia join to form the stato-acoustic nerve which grows toward the brain.

Saccule, Cochlea, and Organ of Corti

In the sixth week of development the saccular portion of the otic vesicle continues its differentiation by forming a tubular-shaped outpocketing at its lower pole (fig. 16-2C). This outgrowth, the *cochlear duct*, penetrates the surrounding mesenchyme in spiral fashion until, at the end of the eighth month, it has completed two and one-half turns (fig. 16-2D, E). Its connection with the remaining portion of the saccule is then confined to a narrow pathway, the *ductus reuniens* (fig. 16-2E).

The mesenchyme surrounding the cochlear duct soon differentiates into a thin, fibrous basement membrane lining the outside of the duct,

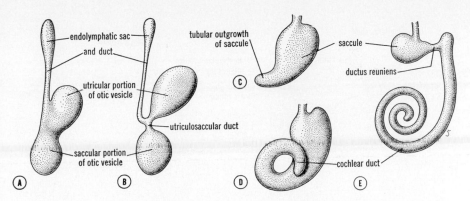

Figure 16-2. *A and B, Further development of the otocyst during the fifth week of development, showing a dorsal utricular portion with the endolymphatic duct, and a ventral saccular portion. C, D, and E, Development of the cochlear duct shown at 6, 7, and 8 weeks, respectively.*

and a large shell of cartilage (fig. 16-3*A*). In the 10th week this cartilaginous shell begins to dissolve in such a manner that two perilymphatic spaces, the *scala vestibuli* and *scala tympani*, are formed (figs. 16-3*B*, *C*).[4] The cochlear duct is then separated from the scala vestibuli by the *vestibular* or *Reissner's membrane*, and from the scala tympani by the *basilar membrane* (fig. 16-3*C*). The lateral wall of the cochlear duct, however, remains attached to the surrounding cartilage by the *spiral ligament*, whereas its median angle is connected to, and partly supported by, a long cartilaginous process, the future axis of the bony cochlea.

The epithelial cells of the cochlear duct are initially alike. With further development, however, some of them proliferate actively and two ridges are formed. The larger of the two, located close to the center of the cochlea, is known as the *inner ridge* (the future spiral limbus), while the other is known as the *outer ridge* (fig. 16-4*A*). The latter forms one row of inner and three or four rows of outer hair cells, the sensory cells of the auditory system (fig. 16-4*B*, *C*). They are covered by the *tectorial membrane*, initially a fibrillar gelatinous substance, which is carried by the spiral limbus and rests with its tip on the hair cells (fig. 16-4).[5, 6] The neuro-epithelial cells and the covering tectorial membrane together are known as the *organ of Corti*, the true organ of hearing. The impulses received by this organ are transmitted to the central nervous system by the auditory fibers of the eighth cranial nerve.

Utricle and Semicircular Canals

During the sixth week of development the semicircular canals appear as flattened outpocketings of the utricular part of the membranous labyrinth (fig. 16-5*A*, *B*). The central portions of the walls of these

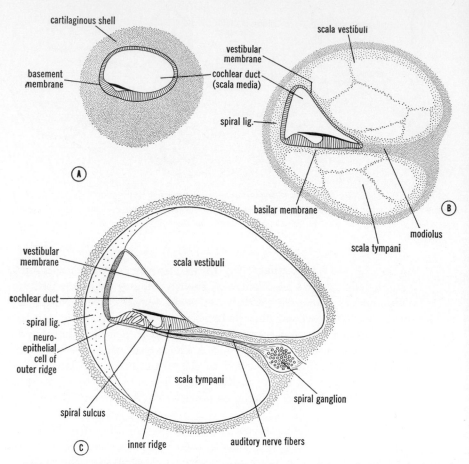

Figure 16-3. *Schematic representation of the development of the scala tympani and scala vestibuli. A, The cochlear duct is surrounded by a fibrous basement membrane and a cartilaginous shell. B, During the 10th week, large perilymphatic spaces appear in the cartilaginous shell. C, The cochlear duct (scala media) is separated from the scala tympani and the scala vestibuli by the basilar and vestibular membranes, respectively. On its lateral aspect it is connected to the bony cochlea by the spiral ligament.*

outpocketings eventually become apposed to each other and disappear, thus giving rise to the three semicircular canals (fig. 16-5E, F). While one end of each canal dilates to form the *crus ampullare*, the other does not widen and is known as the *crus nonampullare* (fig. 16-5E). However, since two of the latter type fuse, only five crura enter the utricle —three with an ampulla and two without.

In the seventh week the cells in the crus ampullare of each semicircular canal form a crest, the *crista ampullaris*, containing the neuroepithelial cells for the maintenance of equilibrium. Similar sensory

Special Embryology

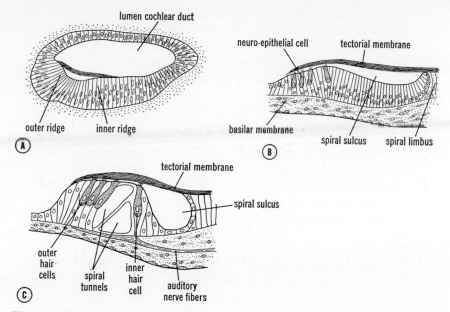

Figure 16-4. *Development of the organ of Corti. A, At 10 weeks; B, approximately 5 months; C, full term. Note the appearance of the spiral tunnels in the organ of Corti.*

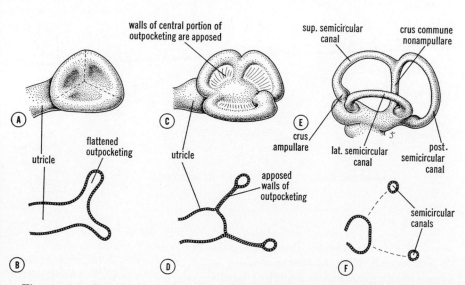

Figure 16-5. *Schematic representation of the development of the semicircular canals at the distal end of the utricle. A, At 5 weeks (7 mm.); C, 6 weeks (13 mm.); E, 8 weeks (30 mm.). B, D, and F show diagrammatically the apposition, fusion, and disappearance of the central portions of the walls of the semicircular outpocketings.*

areas develop in the walls of the utricle and saccule, where they are known as *maculae acousticae*. Impulses generated in the neuro-epithelial cells of the cristae and maculae as a result of a change in position of the body are carried to the brain by the vestibular fibers of the eighth cranial nerve.

Middle Ear

Tympanic Cavity and Eustachian Tube

Contrary to the ectodermal origin of the membranous part of the internal ear, the tympanic cavity is derived from the first pharyngeal pouch, an outpocketing of the foregut (fig. 16-1). This pouch, lined with epithelium of entodermal origin, appears in embryos of approximately 3 weeks, grows rapidly in lateral direction, and temporarily comes in contact with the floor of the first ectodermal cleft. The distal part of the pouch, the *tubotympanic recess*, widens and gives rise to the *primitive tympanic cavity*, while the proximal part remains narrow and forms the *auditory* or *Eustachian tube* (fig. 16-6). The latter is the channel through which the tympanic cavity communicates with the nasopharynx. Its pharyngeal orifice is surrounded by a considerable amount

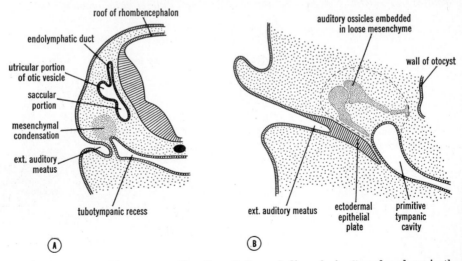

Figure 16-6. *A, Transverse section through the cephalic end of a 7-week embryo in the region of the rhombencephalon, showing the utricular and saccular portions of the otic vesicle, the tubotympanic recess, the external auditory meatus, and the mesenchymal condensation between the otic vesicle and the primitive tympanic cavity, foreshadowing the development of the ossicles. B, Schematic representation of the middle ear, showing the cartilaginous precursors of the auditory ossicles embedded in loose connective tissue. Broken line indicates future expansion of the primitive tympanic cavity. Note the ectodermal epithelial plate extending from the primitive auditory meatus to the future tympanic cavity.*

Special Embryology

of lymphoid tissue, the *tubal tonsil*. Particularly in young children, nasal inflammations associated with swelling of the tubal tonsil frequently result in occlusion of the tube and inflammation of the tympanic cavity (*otitis media*).

Ossicles

By the end of the seventh week the mesenchyme directly above the primitive tympanic cavity shows a number of condensations caused by proliferation of the dorsal tips of the first and second pharyngeal arches. With time, these condensations become the cartilaginous precursors of the *auditory ossicles*, the *malleus, incus,* and *stapes* (fig. 16-7*B*). The malleus and incus are thought to be derived from the cartilage of the first pharyngeal arch, and the stapes from that of the second arch (fig. 16-7*A*)[7-9] (see Chapter 12). Although the ossicles appear during the first half of fetal life they remain embedded in mesenchyme until the eighth month, when the surrounding tissue dissolves. The entodermal epithelial lining of the primitive tympanic cavity then gradually extends along the wall of the newly developing space and wraps itself around the ossicles. When the ossicles are entirely free of mesenchyme the epithelium not only forms the mucosa around them, but also connects them in a mesentery-like fashion to the wall of the cavity. The supporting ligaments of the ossicles later develop in these mesenteries.

Since the malleus is derived from the first pharyngeal arch, its muscle,

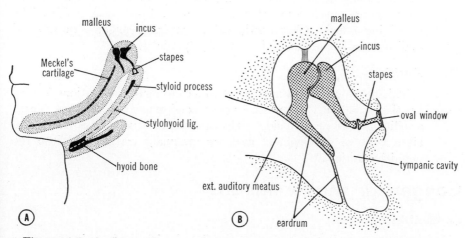

Figure 16-7. *A, Schematic representation of the derivatives of the cartilaginous components of the first three branchial arches. Note the malleus and incus at the dorsal tip of the first arch and the stapes at that of the second arch. B, Schematic representation of the middle ear, showing the malleus in contact with the eardrum and the stapes in contact with the membrane in the oval window.*

the *tensor tympani*, is innervated by the mandibular branch of the trigeminal nerve. Similarly, the *stapedius muscle*, which is attached to the stapes, is innervated by the facial nerve.

External Ear

External Auditory Meatus

The external auditory meatus develops from the dorsal portion of the first pharyngeal cleft, which grows inward as a funnel-shaped tube until it reaches the entodermal lining of the tympanic cavity (fig. 16-6A). Owing to the growth of the head this contact is temporarily lost, but at the beginning of the third month the epithelial cells at the bottom of the meatus begin to proliferate, thereby forming a solid epithelial plate which extends toward the tympanic cavity (fig. 16-6B). In the seventh month this ectodermal plate dissolves and the epithelial lining in the floor of the enlarged meatus then participates in the formation of the definitive eardrum. Occasionally, this solid epithelial plate persists until birth, and congenital deafness results.

Eardrum or Tympanic Membrane

The eardrum is made up of (1) the ectodermal epithelial lining at the bottom of the auditory meatus, (2) the entodermal epithelial lining of the expanded tympanic cavity, and (3) an intermediate layer of loose connective tissue. The major part of the eardrum is firmly attached to the handle of the malleus and arises only after dissolution of the mesenchyme surrounding the ossicles (figs. 16-6B and 16-7B). The remaining, much smaller, portion of the eardrum connects the external auditory meatus to the original tubotympanic recess.

Auricle

This develops from a number of mesenchymal proliferations formed by the dorsal tips of the first and second pharyngeal arches. These swellings, three on each side of the external meatus, appear during the sixth week of development and are gradually transformed into the definitive auricle.[10]

Congenital Malformations

Congenital Deafness

Congenital deafness, usually associated with deaf-mutism, may be caused by abnormal development of the membranous and bony labyrinths, as well as by malformations of the auditory ossicles and eardrum.[11] In the most extreme cases the tympanic cavity and external meatus may be completely absent.

Although congenital deafness was believed to be mainly hereditary,[12, 13] during the last few years it has become evident that environmental factors affecting the mother early in pregnancy may likewise
interfere with normal development of the internal and middle ear of
the embryo. At present, it is generally accepted that the rubella virus,
affecting the embryo in the seventh to eighth week of development,
may cause severe damage particularly to the organ of Corti.[14-16] Although it has been suggested that poliomyelitis, erythroblastosis fetalis,
diabetes, and toxoplasmosis may likewise cause congenital deafness,
these observations await more evidence.[17-20]

Recently it has been possible, by means of x-irradiation, to produce
in the rat anomalies of the ear leading to deafness.[21] On the other hand,
a disturbance of locomotion and posture has been produced by feeding
the animals a manganese-deficient diet during pregnancy.[22]

References

1. Bast, T. H., and Anson, B. J. *The Temporal Bone and the Ear*. Charles C
   Thomas, Springfield, Ill., 1949.
2. Politzer, G. Die Entstehung des Ganglion Acusticum beim Menschen. Acta
   Anat. (Basel), **26**: 1, 1956.
3. Batten, E. H. The origin of the acoustic ganglion in the sheep. J. Embryol.
   Exp. Morph., **6**: 597, 1958.
4. Streeter, J. L. The histogenesis and growth of the otic capsule and its contained periotic tissue spaces in the human embryo. Contrib. Embryol., **7**: 5,
   1918.
5. Van der Stricht, O. The genesis and structure of the membrana tectoria and
   the crista spiralis of the cochlea. Contrib. Embryol., **7**: 55, 1918.
6. Van der Stricht, O. The arrangement and structure of sustentacular cells
   and hair cells in the developing organ of Corti. Contrib. Embryol., **9**: 109,
   1920.
7. Hanson, J. R., Anson, B. J., and Bast, T. H. The early embryology of the
   auditory ossicles in man. Quart. Bull. Northw. Univ. Med. Sch., **33**: 358, 1959.
8. Anson, B. J., and Bast, T. H. Development of the stapes of the human ear.
   Quart. Bull. Northw. Univ. Med. Sch., **33**: 44, 1959.
9. Anson, B. J., and Bast, T. H. Development of the incus of the human ear.
   Quart. Bull. Northw. Univ. Med. Sch., **33**: 110, 1959.
10. Wood-Jones, F., and Wen, J. C. The development of the external ear. J.
    Anat., **68**: 525, 1934.
11. Altmann, F. Malformations, anomalies and vestigial structures of the inner
    ear. A. M. A. Arch. Otolaryng., **57**: 591, 1953.
12. Stevenson, A. C., and Cheeseman, E. A. Hereditary deaf-mutism with
    particular reference to Northern Ireland. Ann. Hum. Genet., **20**: 177, 1956.
13. Stern, C. *Principles of Human Genetics*, Ed. 2, p. 107. W. H. Freeman and
    Co., San Francisco, 1960.
14. Töndury, J. Zur Kenntnis der Embryopathia rubeolica, nebst Bemerkungen
    über die Wirkung anderer Viren auf den Keimling. Geburtsh. Frauenheilk.,
    10: 865, 1952.
15. Gray, J. E. Rubella in pregnancy; fetal pathology in the internal ear. Ann.
    Otol., **68**: 170, 1959.

16. LANCASTER, H. O. The epidemiology of deafness due to maternal rubella. Acta Genet. (Basel), 5: 12, 1954.
17. KELEMAN, J. Acute poliomyelitis of the mother with aural lesions of the premature infant. A. M. A. Arch. Otolaryng., 62: 602, 1955.
18. KELEMAN, J. Erythroblastosis fetalis. Pathologic report on the hearing organs of a newborn infant. A. M. A. Arch. Otolaryng., 63: 392, 1956.
19. KELEMAN, J. Aural changes in the embryo of a diabetic mother. A. M. A. Arch. Otolaryng., 62: 357, 1955.
20. JØRGENSEN, M. B. The influence of maternal diabetes on the inner ear of the fetus. Acta Otolaryng. (Stockh.), 53: 49, 1961.
21. KELEMAN, J. Experimental defects in the ear and the upper airways induced by radiation. A. M. A. Arch. Otolaryng., 61: 405, 1955.
22. HURLEY, L. S., WOOTEN, E., EVERSON, G. L., AND ASLING, C. W. Anomalous development of ossification in the inner ear of offspring of manganese-deficient rats. J. Nutr., 71: 15, 1960.

CHAPTER 17

Face, Nose, and Palate

NORMAL DEVELOPMENT
- *Facial swellings and upper lip; intermaxillary segment; secondary palate; nasal chambers*

CONGENITAL MALFORMATIONS
- *Cleft lip and cleft palate; median cleft lip; oblique facial cleft; macrostomia and microstomia; hereditary factors; environmental factors; experimental data*

Normal Development

Facial Swellings and Upper Lip

Initially, the center of the developing facial structures is a shallow ectodermal depression, known as the *stomodeum*. However, by the time the embryo is 4½ weeks old the stomodeum is bounded by a series of rounded elevations formed by proliferation of the mesenchyme. The *mandibular swellings* can be distinguished caudally to the stomodeum, the *maxillary swellings* laterally, and the *frontal prominence*, a slightly rounded elevation, cranially (fig. 17-1A). On each side of the frontal prominence and just above the stomodeum is a local thickening of the surface ectoderm, the *nasal placode* (fig. 17-1A).

During the fifth week, two fast-growing ridges, the *lateral and medial nasal swellings*, surround the nasal placode which then forms the floor of a depression, the *nasal pit* (fig. 17-1B). The lateral swellings will form the alae of the nose, and the medial swellings will give rise to the middle portions of the nose, the upper lip, and the maxilla as well as to the entire *primary palate*. In the meantime, the maxillary swellings approach the medial as well as the lateral nasal swellings but remain separated from them by well marked grooves (fig. 17-1B).[1]

During the following 2 weeks the development of the face makes considerable progress. The maxillary swellings continue to grow in a medial direction and compress the medial nasal swellings toward the

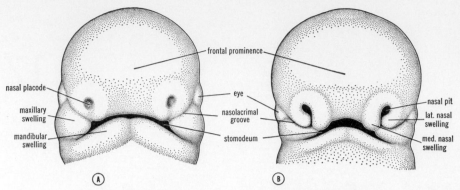

Figure 17-1. *Frontal aspect of the face. A, 5-week embryo; B, 6-week embryo. The nasal swellings are gradually separated from the maxillary swelling by deep grooves.*

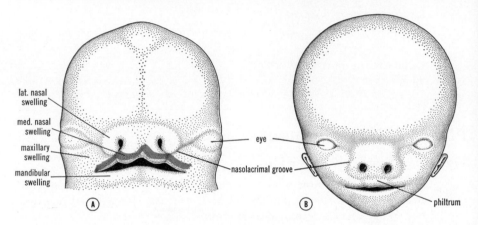

Figure 17-2. *Frontal aspect of the face. A, 7-week embryo; B, 10-week embryo. The maxillary swellings gradually merge with the nasal folds (adapted from several sources).*

midline. Subsequently, these swellings merge with each other—that is, the groove separating them is filled with mesoderm—and at the same time with the maxillary swellings laterally. Hence, the upper lip is formed by the two medial nasal swellings and the two maxillary swellings (fig. 17-2).

In addition to their role in the formation of the upper lip, the maxillary swellings also merge over a short distance with the mandibular swellings. This results in the formation of the cheeks and determines the definitive size of the mouth. The manner in which the maxillary swellings unite with the lateral nasal swellings is slightly more complicated. Initially, these structures are separated by a deep furrow, the *nasolacrimal groove* (fig. 17-2A). Fusion of the swellings is established only when this groove is bridged over to form a portion of the *nasolacrimal duct*.

Special Embryology

Intermaxillary Segment

The merging of the two medial nasal swellings occurs not only at the surface, but also at a deeper level. According to Patten,[2] all the structures of the upper oral arch so formed are called the *intermaxillary segment*, which is thus comprised of : (1) a *labial component*, which forms the philtrum of the upper lip; (2) an *upper jaw component*, which carries the four incisor teeth; and (3) a *palatal component*, which forms the triangular *primary palate* (fig. 17-7). Cranially, the intermaxillary segment is continuous with the rostral portion of the nasal septum, which is formed by the frontal prominence.

Secondary Palate

As pointed out above, the primary palate is derived from the intermaxillary segment. The main part of the definitive palate, however, is formed by two shelflike outgrowths of the deeper parts of the maxillary swellings. These outgrowths, the *palatine shelves*, appear in the sixth week of development and are directed obliquely downward on either side of the tongue (fig. 17-3). In the seventh week, however, the tongue moves downward and the palatine shelves ascend and attain a horizontal position (fig. 17-4*A*, *B*).

During the eighth week the palatine shelves approach each other in the midline, fuse, and form the *secondary palate* (fig. 17-5*A*, *B*). Anteriorly, the shelves fuse with the triangular primary palate, and the incisive foramen may be considered as the midline landmark between the primary and secondary palates. At the same time as the palatine shelves fuse, the nasal septum grows down and joins with the cephalic aspect of the newly formed palate (fig. 17-5*A*).

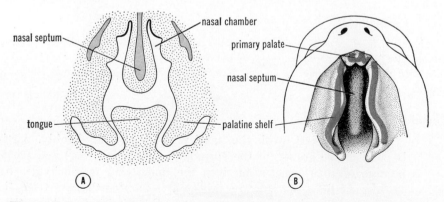

Figure 17-3. *A*, *Frontal section through the head of a 6½-week embryo. The palatine shelves are located in a vertical position on each side of the tongue. B, Ventral view of the palatine shelves after removal of the lower jaw and the tongue. Note the clefts between the primary triangular palate and the palatine shelves.*

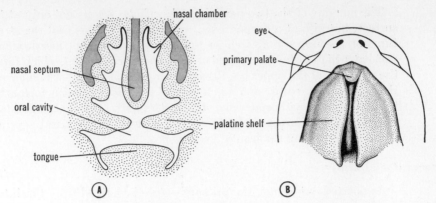

Figure 17-4. *A, Frontal section through the head of a 7½-week embryo. The tongue has moved downward and the palatine shelves have reached a horizontal position. B, Ventral view of the palatine shelves after removal of the lower jaw and the tongue.*

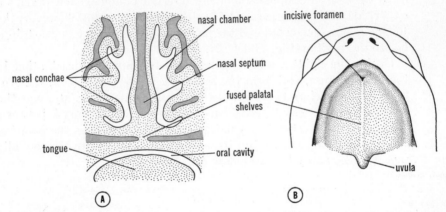

Figure 17-5. *A, Frontal section through the head of a 10-week embryo. The two palatine shelves have fused with each other and with the nasal septum. B, Ventral view of the palate. The incisive foramen forms the midline landmark between the primary and secondary palate.*

Nasal Chambers

During the sixth week the nasal pits deepen considerably, partly because of the growth of the surrounding nasal swellings and partly because of their penetration into the underlying mesenchyme (fig. 17-6A). At first, the *oronasal membrane* separates the pits from the primitive oral cavity, but after its rupture the primitive nasal chambers open into the oral cavity by way of the newly formed foramina, the *primitive choanae* (fig. 17-6B). These choanae are located on each side of the midline and immediately behind the primary palate. Later, with

Special Embryology

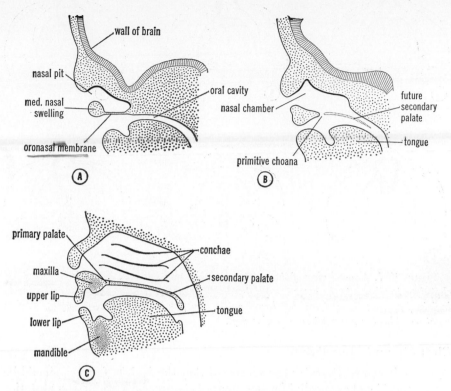

Figure 17-6. *A, Schematic sagittal section through the nasal pit and the lower rim of the medial nasal fold of a 6-week embryo. The primitive nasal cavity is separated from the oral cavity by the oronasal membrane. B, Similar section as in A, showing the primitive nasal cavity in open connection with the oral cavity (7 weeks). C, Median section through the face of a 9-week embryo, showing the intermaxillary segment, comprised of a labial component, a maxillary component, and the primary palate (modified from Clara).*

the formation of the secondary palate and further development of the primitive nasal chambers (fig. 17-6C), the *definitive choanae* are located at the junction of the nasal cavity and the pharynx.

Congenital Malformations

Although the congenital malformations of the face, nose, and palate are compatible with life, they exert a profound influence on the patient's life. A cleft lip not only seriously disfigures the facial contours, but also causes a speech defect, both of which may cause significant psychological and social handicaps to the patient. For these reasons, the cleft lip and cleft palate have been studied in great detail by embryologists, geneticists, plastic surgeons, and speech therapists.

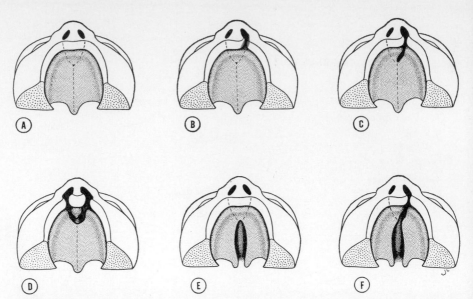

Figure 17-7. *Ventral view of the palate, gum, lip, and nose. A, Normal; B, unilateral cleft lip extending into the nose; C, unilateral cleft involving lip and jaw, and extending to incisive foramen; D, bilateral cleft involving lip and jaw; E, isolated cleft palate; F, cleft palate combined with unilateral anterior cleft.*

Cleft Lip and Cleft Palate

Recently, Stark[1, 3] has suggested that the *incisive foramen* should be considered as the dividing landmark between the anterior and posterior cleft deformities. Those anterior to the incisive foramen are based on the failure of proper mesodermal penetration into the grooves between the medial nasal and maxillary swellings and include the *lateral cleft lip*, the *cleft upper jaw*, and the *cleft* between the *primary and secondary palates* (fig. 17-7B, C, D). Those which lie posterior to the incisive foramen are caused by failure of the palatine shelves to fuse and include the *cleft (secondary) palate* and the *cleft uvula* (fig. 17-7E). The third category is formed by a combination of clefts lying anterior as well as posterior to the incisive foramen (fig. 17-7F). Since the palatine shelves fuse approximately 1 week after completion of the upper lip, and since the closing mechanisms of the lip and secondary palate differ greatly (merging and fusion, respectively), the anterior and posterior clefts must be considered as separate entities.

The anterior clefts may vary in severity from barely visible defects in the vermilion of the lip to clefts extending into the nose (fig. 17-7B). In more severe cases, the cleft extends to a deeper level, thereby forming a cleft of the upper jaw. The maxilla is then split between the lateral incisor and the canine tooth. Frequently, such a cleft extends to the incisive foramen (fig. 17-7C, D).

Special Embryology

The posterior clefts likewise may vary in severity from clefts involving the entire secondary palate to clefts of the uvula only.

Median Cleft Lip

The median cleft lip, a rare abnormality, is thought to be caused by the incomplete merging of the two medial nasal swellings in the midline. This anomaly is usually accompanied by a deep groove between the right and left sides of the nose (fig. 17-8C).

Oblique Facial Cleft

Failure of the maxillary swelling to merge with its corresponding lateral nasal swelling results in an oblique facial cleft. When this occurs the nasolacrimal duct is usually exposed on the surface (fig. 17-8A).

Macrostomia and Microstomia

The maxillary and mandibular swellings may fail to merge, resulting in *macrostomia* (fig. 17-8B), or they may merge to such an extent that the opening of the mouth is too small, a condition known as *microstomia*.

Hereditary Factors

It is now generally accepted that the main etiological factor of the cleft lip and the cleft palate is genetic in nature. There is, however, no genetic correlation between a cleft lip and an isolated cleft palate.[4-6] The cleft lip (approximately 1 : 1000 births) is seen more in males than females; its incidence is slightly higher with increasing maternal age[7] and varies in different population groups.[6]

With reference to the recurrence of the cleft lip, it is known that if the parents are normal and have had one child with a cleft lip, the chance that the next baby will have the same defect is 4 per cent.[9-11] If two siblings are affected the risk for the next child increases to 9 per cent. If, however, one of the parents has a cleft lip, and they have one child with the same defect, the probability that the next baby will be affected rises to 17 per cent.

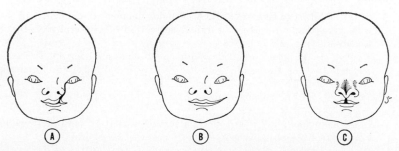

Figure 17-8. *A, Unilateral facial cleft; B, unilateral macrostomia; C, median cleft lip with partially cleft nose.*

With regard to the cleft palate, the situation is different. The frequency of this defect is much lower than that of the cleft lip (1:2500 births); it is seen more frequently in females than in males and is not related to maternal age. If the parents are normal and have one child with a cleft palate, the probability of the next child being affected is about 2 per cent. If, however, there is a similarly affected relative or a parent and child with a cleft palate, the probability increases to 7 and 15 per cent, respectively.

Environmental Factors

Although it has been suggested that cortisone during the first trimester of pregnancy may cause a cleft palate,[12] evidence for this suggestion is insufficient. In fact, a number of cases have recently been reported in which the mother received cortisone during early pregnancy and the baby was normal.[13, 14] So far, it has been impossible to implicate any one environmental factor as a cause of cleft palate in man. Nothing is known regarding the etiology of the cleft lip.

Experimental Data

In experimental work, cleft palates in the offspring of the rat and mouse have been produced by a great variety of teratogenic agents.[15] In particular, three experimental procedures have been highly successful in bringing out this defect in almost 100 per cent of the offspring. These are cortisone injections into susceptible strains of mice,[16, 17] hypervitaminosis A in rats,[18] and pteroylglutamic acid deficiency in rats.[19, 20] From these studies it has become evident that congenital clefts of the palate can be produced in several different ways, each influenced by multiple genetic and environmental factors.[15] In addition, these studies have been valuable in analyzing the mechanisms of palate closure,[21] and the possible role of the tongue and the mandible in palate closure.[22-24]

References

1. STARK, R. B., AND EHRMANN, N. A. The development of the center of the face with particular reference to surgical correction of bilateral cleft lip. Plast. Reconstr. Surg., **21**: 177, 1958.
2. PATTEN, B. M. The normal development of the facial region. In *Congenital Anomalies of the Face and Associated Structures*, edited by S. Pruzansky, p. 11. Charles C Thomas, Springfield, Ill., 1961.
3. STARK, R. B. The pathogenesis of harelip and cleft palate. Plast. Reconstr. Surg., **13**: 20, 1954.
4. FOGH-ANDERSON, P. Inheritance patterns for cleft lip and cleft palate. In *Congenital Anomalies of the Face and Associated Structures*, edited by S. Pruzansky, p. 123. Charles C Thomas, Springfield, Ill., 1961.
5. FOGH-ANDERSON, P. *Inheritance of Harelip and Cleft Palate*. Arnold Busck, Copenhagen, 1942.

6. FRASER, F. C. Thoughts on the etiology of clefts of the palate and lip. Acta Genet. (Basel), 5: 358, 1955.
7. MacMAHON, B., AND McKEOWN, T. The incidence of harelip and cleft palate, related to birth rank and maternal age. Amer. J. Hum. Genet., 5: 176, 1953.
8. NEEL, J. R. A study of major congenital defects in Japanese infants. Amer. J. Hum. Genet., 10: 398, 1958.
9. CURTIS, E. J., FRASER, F. C., AND WARBURTON, D. Congenital cleft lip and palate. Amer. J. Dis. Child., 102: 853, 1961.
10. FRASER, F. C. Genetic counseling in some common paediatric diseases. Pediat. Clin. N. Amer., 5: 475, 1958.
11. FRASER, F. C. Genetics and congenital malformations. In *Progress in Medical Genetics*, edited by A. G. Steinberg, p. 38. Grune & Stratton, Inc., New York, 1961.
12. HARRIS, J. W. S., AND ROSS, J. P. Cortisone therapy in early pregnancy; relation to cleft palate. Lancet, 1: 1045, 1956.
13. PREISLER, O. Is prolonged cortisone treatment in pregnancy damaging to the infant? Zbl. Gynaek., 18: 675, 1960.
14. BONGIOVANNI, A. M., AND McPADDEN, A. J. Steriods during pregnancy and possible fetal consequences. Fertil. Steril., 11: 181, 1960.
15. FRASER, F. C. Experimental induction of cleft palate. In *Congenital Anomalies of the Face and Associated Structures*, edited by S. Pruzansky, p. 188. Charles C Thomas, Springfield, Ill., 1961.
16. FRASER, F. C., WALKER, B. E., AND TRASLER, D. G. Experimental production of congenital cleft palate; genetic and environmental factors. Pediatrics, 19: 782, 1957.
17. KALTER, H. The inheritance of susceptibility to the teratogenic action of cortisone in mice. Genetics, 39: 185, 1954.
18. GIROUD, A., AND MARTINET, M. Tératogénèse par hautes doses de vitamine A en fonction des stades du développement. Arch. Anat. Micr. Morph. Exp., 45: 577, 1956.
19. NELSON, M. M., ASLING, C. W., AND EVANS, H. M. Production of multiple abnormalities in young by PGA deficiency during gestation. J. Nutr., 48: 61, 1952.
20. ASLING, C. W., NELSON, M. M., DOUGHERTY, H. D., WRIGHT, H. V., AND EVANS, H. M. The development of cleft palate resulting from maternal pteroylglutamic acid deficiency during the latter half of gestation in rats. Surg. Gynec. Obstet., 111: 19, 1960.
21. WALKER, B. E. The embryology of cortisone-induced cleft palate. J. Embryol. Exp. Morph., 5: 201, 1957.
22. ASLING, C. W. Congenital defects of face and palate in rats following maternal deficiency of pteroylglutamic acid. In *Congenital Anomalies of the Face and Associated Structures*, edited by S. Pruzansky, p. 173. Charles C Thomas, Springfield, Ill., 1961.
23. TRASLER, D. G. Influence of uterine site on occurrence of spontaneous cleft lip in mice. Science, 132: 420, 1960.
24. TRASLER, D. G., WALKER, B. E., AND FRASER, F. C. Congenital malformations produced by amniotic sac puncture. Science, 124: 439, 1956.

CHAPTER 18

Integumentary System

- **SKIN:** *epidermis; dermis*
- **HAIR**
- **MAMMARY GLAND:** *mammary line; polythelia; polymastia*
- **TEETH:** *cap and bell stage; odontoblasts and dentine; ameloblasts and enamel; cementoblasts and cementum; periodontal ligament*

Skin

The skin has a twofold origin: a superficial layer, the *epidermis*, developing from the surface ectoderm, and a deep layer, the *dermis*, developing from the underlying mesoderm.

Epidermis

Initially the surface of the embryo is covered by a single layer of ectodermal cells (fig. 18-1*A*). In the second month this epithelium divides and a layer of flattened cells, the *periderm*, is laid down on the surface (fig. 18-1*B*). With further proliferation of the cells in the basal layer, a third, so-called intermediate, zone is formed (fig. 18-1*C*). Finally, at the end of the fourth month the epithelial layers constituting the epidermis of the skin acquire their definitive arrangement and four layers can then be distinguished (fig. 18-1*D*). A basal layer, responsible for a continuous stream of new cells toward the periphery, is known as the *germinative layer*. This layer forms ridges and hollows which are filled by the underlying mesoderm, and the pattern so formed is reflected on the surface of the skin in the fingerprint.[1, 2] On top of the germinative layer is a thick *spinous layer* consisting of large polyhedral cells connected by fine tonofibrils. This layer is followed by a *granular layer*, the cells of which contain small keratohyaline granules, the first sign of keratinization. An outermost layer, the *stratum corneum*, forming the tough, scale-like surface of the epidermis, is made up of several layers of closely packed dead cells, loaded with keratin. The flattened

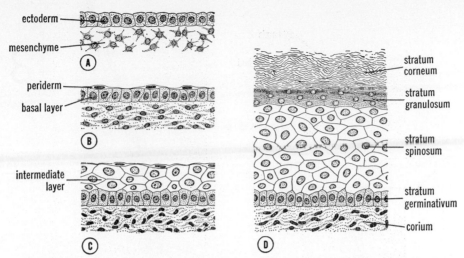

Figure 18-1. *Schematic drawing showing the formation of the skin at various stages of development. A, At 5 weeks; B, 7 weeks; C, 4 months; D, at birth.*

cells of the periderm layer are usually cast off during the second part of intra-uterine life.

During the first 3 months of development the epidermis is invaded by cells of neural crest origin.[3] These cells, known as *dendritic cells*, gradually form melanin pigment, which can be transferred to other cells of the epidermis by way of the dendritic processes. These cells are later known as *melanoblasts*, and after birth cause pigmentation of the skin.[4, 5]

Dermis

The dermis, or deeper layer of the skin, arises from mesoderm of the dermatomes. During the third and fourth months this mesoderm differentiates into connective tissue containing collagenous and elastic fibers. Simultaneously, the superficial layer of the dermis, the *corium*, forms irregular papillary structures, the *dermal papillae*, which project upward into the epidermis. These papillae usually contain a small capillary and a sensory nerve end organ. The deeper layer of the dermis, the *subcorium*, is characterized by the presence of large amounts of fatty tissue.

At birth, the skin is covered by a whitish paste, the *vernix caseosa*, formed by secretion of the sebaceous glands and degenerated epidermal cells and hairs. It is believed to protect the skin against a macerating action of the amniotic fluid.

The skin of the newborn may show varying degrees of keratinization. Sometimes, however, the superficial layers show excessive cornification, giving the skin a scale-like appearance. Such a condition is known as *ichthyosis*.

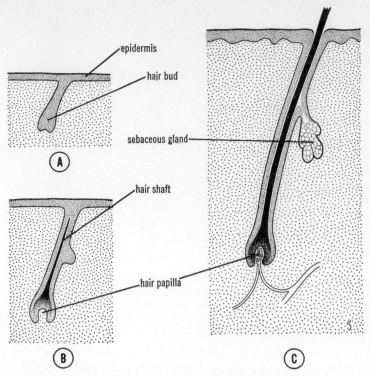

Figure 18-2. *Schematic representation of the development of a hair and a sebaceous gland. A, At 4 months; B, 6 months; C, newborn.*

Hair

In the third month of development the hair appears as solid epidermal proliferations penetrating the underlying corium (fig. 18-2A). At their terminal ends these proliferating buds invaginate, and the newly formed indentations are rapidly filled with mesoderm, forming the *hair papilla* (fig. 18-2B).[6]

Soon, the cells in the center of the hair primordia become spindle-shaped and keratinized, forming the *hair shaft*, while the peripheral cells become cuboidal, giving rise to the wall of the *hair follicle*. Continuous proliferation of the epithelial cells at the base of the shaft pushes the hair upward, and by the end of the third month the first hairs appear on the surface in the region of the eyebrow and upper lip. These hairs, *lanugo hairs*, are shed at about the time of birth and are later replaced by coarser hairs arising from new hair follicles.

The epithelial wall of the hair follicle usually shows a small out-budding penetrating the surrounding mesoderm (fig. 18-2C). The cells in the center of these outbuddings, the *sebaceous glands*, degenerate, thereby forming a fatlike substance which is secreted into the hair follicle.

314   **Special Embryology**

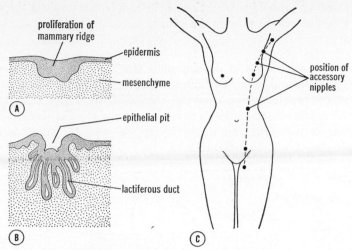

Figure 18-3. *A and B, Sections through the developing mammary gland at the third and eighth months, respectively. C, Diagram showing the position of accessory nipples (broken line indicates position of mammary line).*

Mammary Glands

The first indication of the mammary glands is found in the form of a bandlike thickening of epidermis, the *mammary line* or *ridge*. In a 7-week embryo, this line extends on each side of the body from the base of the forelimb to the region of the hindlimb. Although the greater part of the mammary line disappears shortly after formation, a small portion in the thoracic region persists and penetrates the underlying mesenchyme (fig. 18-3A). Here it forms 16 to 24 sprouts, which in turn give rise to small, solid outbuddings. By the end of prenatal life the epithelial sprouts are canalized, forming the *lactiferous ducts,* while the outbuddings form the small ducts and alveoli of the gland. The *lactiferous ducts* at first open into a small epithelial pit, formed by the original mammary line (fig. 18-3B). Shortly after birth this pit is transformed into the nipple by proliferation of the underlying mesenchyme.

Although normally only a small part of the mammary line persists in the mid-thoracic region, sometimes other fragments persist which then may give rise to accessory nipples. Such a condition, known as *polythelia,* is not uncommon. Accessory nipples may develop anywhere along the original mammary line, but are most frequently seen in the axillary region (fig. 18-3C). Sometimes an abnormally located remnant of the mammary line may develop into a complete mammary gland, an abnormality known as *polymastia.*

Occasionally a patient is seen in whom the lactiferous ducts open into the original epithelial pit, which has failed to evert as a nipple. Such a condition, known as *inverted nipple,* is usually of congenital origin, but may be caused by retraction of the nipple as a result of the presence of a fast-growing tumor in the gland.

Teeth

By the sixth week of development the basal layer of the epithelial lining of the oral cavity proliferates rapidly and forms a bandlike structure, the *dental lamina*, over the region of the upper and lower jaw. This lamina subsequently gives rise to a number of outbuddings which penetrate the underlying mesenchyme (fig. 18-4*A*). These buds, 10 in each jaw, form the primordia of the ectodermal components of the

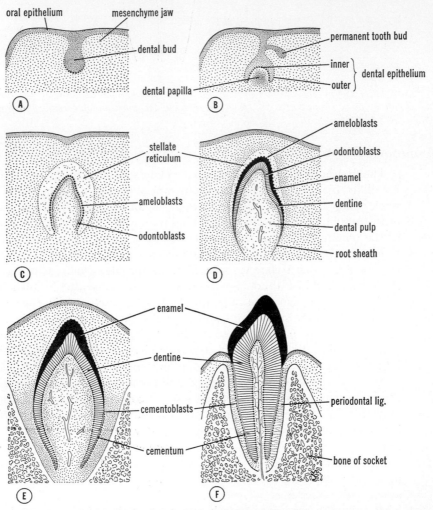

Figure 18-4. *Schematic representation of the formation of the tooth at successive stages of development. A, At 8 weeks; B, 10 weeks; C, 3 months; D, 6 months; E, 8 months; F, after eruption.*

Special Embryology

teeth. Soon the deep surface of the buds invaginates, resulting in the so-called *cap stage* of tooth development (fig. 18-4B). Such a cap consists of an outer convex layer, the *outer dental epithelium*, an inner concave layer, the *inner dental epithelium*, and a central core of loosely woven tissue, the *stellate reticulum*. The mesenchyme located in the indentation lined by the inner dental epithelium proliferates and condenses to form the *dental papilla* (fig. 18-4B).

As the dental cap grows and the indentation deepens, the tooth takes on the appearance of a bell (*bell stage*) (fig. 18-4C). The mesenchyme cells of the papilla adjacent to the inner dental layer then become organized and differentiate into *odontoblasts*. These cells produce the *predentine*, which is laid down immediately below the inner dental layer. With time the predentine calcifies and is transformed into the definitive *dentine*. With the continuous thickening of the dentine layer, the odontoblasts retreat into the dental papilla, thereby leaving a thin cytoplasmic process (*dentinal process*) behind in the dentine (fig. 18-4D). The odontoblast layer persists throughout the life of the tooth and continuously provides predentine, which is subsequently transformed into dentine. The remaining cells of the dental papilla form the *pulp* of the tooth.

In the meantime the epithelial cells of the inner dental layer have differentiated into the *ameloblasts* (enamel formers). These cells produce long enamel prisms which are deposited over the dentine (fig. 18-4D). The contact layer between the enamel and dentine layers is known as the *enamel dentine junction*.[7] This junction determines the final form of the tooth.

The enamel is first laid down at the apex of the tooth and from here spreads gradually toward the neck, thus forming the enamel covering of the crown of the tooth. When, by apposition of new layers, the enamel thickens, the ameloblasts retreat into the stellate reticulum until they finally reach the outer dental epithelial layer. Here they regress, temporarily leaving a thin membrane (the *dental cuticle*) on the surface of the enamel. After eruption of the tooth this membrane gradually sloughs off.

The formation of the root of the tooth begins shortly before eruption of the crown. The inner and outer dental epithelial layers, which are apposed to each other in the region of the neck of the tooth, penetrate deeper into the underlying mesenchyme and form the *epithelial root sheath* (fig. 18-4D).[7] The cells of the dental papilla in contact with this sheath differentiate into odontoblasts, which lay down a layer of dentine continuous with that of the crown (fig. 18-4E, F). As more and more dentine is deposited on the inside of the existing layer, the pulp chamber narrows and finally forms a canal containing the blood vessels and nerves of the tooth.

The mesenchymal cells located on the outside of the tooth and in contact with the dentine of the root differentiate into *cementoblasts* (fig. 18-4E). These cells produce a thin layer of specialized bone, the *cementum*, which is deposited over the dentine of the root. Outside the cement layer, the mesenchyme gives rise to the *periodontal ligament* (fig. 18-4E, F). The fibers of this ligament are embedded in the cementum at one end and in the bony wall of the alveolar socket at the other. Hence, the ligament holds the tooth firmly in position and simultaneously functions as a shock absorber.

With further lengthening of the root, the crown is gradually pushed through the overlying tissue layers into the oral cavity (fig. 18-4F). The eruption of the *deciduous* or *milk teeth* occurs 6 to 24 months after birth.

The buds for the permanent teeth are located on the lingual aspect of the milk teeth and are formed during the third month of development (fig. 18-4B). These buds, which develop in a manner similar to those of the milk teeth, remain dormant until approximately the sixth year of postnatal life. Then they begin to grow, thereby pushing against the underside of the corresponding milk teeth and aiding in their shedding.

Occasionally the two lower central incisors have already erupted at birth. In this instance, they are usually abnormally formed and have little enamel and no roots. Although abnormalities of the teeth are mainly hereditary in nature, environmental factors such as rubella, syphilis, and irradiation have been described as causes for tooth anomalies.[8, 9]

References

1. CUMMINGS, H., AND MIDLO, C. *Fingerprints, Palms and Soles*. Blakiston Co., Division of McGraw-Hill Book Co., Inc., New York, 1943.
2. HALE, A. R. Morphogenesis of volar skin in the human fetus. Amer. J. Anat., 91: 147, 1952.
3. RAWLES, M. E. Origin of melanophores and their role in development of color patterns in vertebrates. Physiol. Rev., 28: 383, 1948.
4. BOYD, J. D. The embryology and comparative anatomy of the melanocyte. In *Progress in the Biological Sciences in Relation to Dermatology*, edited by A. Rook. Cambridge University Press, London, 1960.
5. BILLINGHAM, R. E., AND SILVERS, W. K. Melanocytes of mammals. Quart. Rev. Biol., 35: 1, 1960.
6. PINKUS, H. The embryology of hair. In *Biology of Hairgrowth*, edited by W. Montague and R. A. Ellis. Academic Press, Inc., New York, 1958.
7. ORBAN, B. *Oral Histology and Embryology*, Ed. 4, C. V. Mosby Co., St. Louis, 1957.
8. MILES, A. E. W. Malformations of the teeth. Proc. Roy. Soc. Med., 47: 817, 1954.
9. TÖNDURY, G. Zur Wirkung des Erregers der Rubeolen auf den Menschlichen Keimling. Helv. Paediat. Acta, 1: 105, 1952.

Index

A

Abducens nerve, 263
Abnormal gametes, 13
  implantation site, 25
  ovum, 25
  rotation, intestinal loop, 226
  spermatozoa, 13
  venous drainage, 185
  zygote, 25
Abnormalities, great arteries, 174
Absence, inferior vena cava, 185
Accessory nerve, 262
  pancreatic duct, 217
Achondroplasia, 81
Acrocephalus, 108
Acrosomic granule, 10
Ala orbitalis, 105
  temporalis, 105
Alar plate, 252, 264, 266
  myelencephalon, 262
Alisphenoid bone, 105
Allanto-enteric diverticulum, 39
Allantois, 39, 194
Alveoli, 207
Amelia, 75, 108, 109
Ameloblasts, 317
Aminopterin, 75
Amnioblasts, 31, 67
Amnio-ectodermal junction, 31, 67
Amnion, 67
Amniotic cavity, 31, 68
  fluid, 68
Anal canal, 229
  folds, 138
  membrane, 39, 54, 123, 138, 229
Anencephalus, 257, 275
Anencephaly, 23, 75
Angioblasts, 147
Angiogenetic cell clusters, 48, 150
Annular pancreas, 219
Annulus fibrosis, 102
Anomalies, atrial septum, 162
  atrioventricular canal, 163
  conus arteriosus, 165
  interventricular septum, 164
  lungs, 210

position heart, 167
  semilunar valves, 166
  tongue, 208
  truncus arteriosus, 165
Anomalous pulmonary venous drainage, 187
Anophthalmia, 290
Anorectal canal, 123, 229
Anterior commissure, 273
Antibodies, 76
Antimetabolites, 75
Anus, imperforate, 230
Aorta, arch, 172
  coarctation, 175
  left primitive, 171
  postductal coarctation, 175
  preductal coarctation, 175
  right dorsal, 174
  right primitive, 171
Aortic arch, 171, 177
  double, 176
  fifth, 172
  first, 172
  fourth, 172
  interrupted, 176
  second, 172
  sixth, 172
  third, 172
  sac, 171
  valvular atresia, 167
  stenosis, 167
Aortico-pulmonary septum, 158
Appendicular skeleton, 108
Appendix, 222, 225
  epididymis, 135
  testis, 135
Aqueduct of Sylvius, 250
Artery, carotid, common, 172, 178
  external, 172
  internal, 172
  coeliac, 174
  hepatic, 238
  hyoid, 172
  iliac, common, 174
  internal, 174, 229
  intersegmental, 171
  mandibular, 172

Limbs, 58
  muscles, 114
Liver, 214
Lobster claw deformity, 81, 109
Longitudinal pronephric duct, 118
Loop of Henle, 122
Lung buds, 206
  lobes, ectopic, 210
    agenesis, 210
    anomalies, 210
    congenital cysts, 210
Luteal cells, 22
Lymph glands, 185
Lymphatic system, 185

M

Macroglossia, 208
Macrostomia, 309
Maculae acousticae, 298
Male pronucleus, 17
Malleus, 106, 204, 299
Mammary glands, 315
  line, 315
  ridge, 315
Mammillary body, 269
Mandible, 204
Mandibular arch, 204
  process, 204
  swelling, 51, 303
Mantle layer neural tube, 251
Marginal layer neural tube, 251
Massa intermedia, 269
Maturation division, 7, 9
Maxillary artery, 172
  process, 105, 204
  swelling, 51, 303
Meckel's cartilage, 105, 204
  diverticulum, 222, 225
Median cleft lip, 309
  nerve, 114
Medulla oblongata, 249, 260
Medullary velum, anterior, 265
  posterior, 265
Meiosis, bivalents, 11
  chiasma, 11
  diplotene stage, 11
  leptotene stage, 11
  pachytene stage, 111
  synapsis, 11
  zygotene stage, 11
Meiotic division, 3, 11
Melanoblasts, 313

Membrane, anal, 39, 54, 123, 229
  buccopharyngeal, 39, 51, 197
  cloacal, 39, 52, 123, 229
  tympanic, 199
  urogenital, 39, 54, 123, 229
Membranous labyrinth, 294
  ossification, 98, 105
Meningocele, 75, 258, 275
Meningo-encephalocele, 275
Meningohydro-encephalocele, 275
Meningomyelocele, 258
Menisci, 107
Menses, 22
Menstrual cycle, 23
  phase, 23
Menstruation, 22
Mental retardation, 73, 74
Mesencephalon, 246, 265
Mesenchyme, 46, 94
Mesenteric artery, inferior, 174, 229
  superior, 174
  vein, superior, 180
Mesenteries, 237
Mesentery, dorsal, 238
  primitive, 237
  proper, 238, 241, 243
  ventral, 237
Mesocardium, dorsal, 151
  ventral, 151
Mesoderm, extra-embryonic, 34, 93
  intermediate, 45, 47, 93
  lateral plate, 45, 93
  paraxial, 45, 93
  parietal, 45, 93
  somatic, 45, 47, 93
  splanchnic, 45, 93
  visceral, 45, 47, 93
Mesodermal germ layer, 37, 44, 45
Mesonephric duct, 118, 133
Mesonephros, 118
Mesothelial membrane, 47
Metanephric blastema, 120
Metanephros, 120
Metencephalon, 249, 263
Microcephalus, 74, 81, 108
Microglia cells, 253
Micromelia, 108
Microphthalmia, 73, 290
Microphthalmus, 74
Microstomia, 309
Midbrain, 246
Middle ear, 298
  cavity, 199

Midgut, 54, 194
Milkteeth, 318
Mitotic division, 11
Mitral valve, 157
Mobile cecum, 244
  colon, 244
Mongoloid idiocy, 78
Morula, 19
Mosaicism, 80
Motor neuron, 255
  root, anterior, 255
Müllerian duct, 133
  tubercle, 134
Muscle, cells, 47, 112
  ciliary, 288
  constrictors, pharynx, 205
  cricothyroid, 205
  cross-striated, 111
  digastric, anterior belly, 204
    posterior belly, 205
  dilator, pupillary, 115, 287
  external oblique, 112
  facial expression, 205
  infrahyoid, 113
  intercostal, external, 112
    internal, 112
  intracostal, 112
  mastication, 204
  papillary, 157
  pharyngeal arch, 114
  rectus abdominis, 113
  sphincter pupillary, 115, 266, 287
  stapedius 205, 300
  sternalis, 113
  stylohyoid, 205
  stylopharyngeal, 205
  tensor tympani, 204, 300
  transverse abdominis, 112
    thoracic, 112
Muscular system, 111
Mutation, 82
Myelencephalon, 249, 260
Myelin, 256
Myelination, 256
Myelocele, 258
Myoblasts, 96, 112
Myocardium, 151
Myoepicardial mantle, 151
Myometrium, 137
Myotome, 96, 111
  occipital, 113
  preotic, 113, 114

N

Nasal chambers, 306
  pit, 303
  placode, 303
  swellings, lateral, 303
    medial, 303
Nasolacrimal duct, 304
  groove, 304
Nasopharynx, 203
Neopallium, 273
Nephrogenic cord, 47, 117
Nephron, 122
Nephrotomes, 94, 118
Nerve, abducens, 105, 114, 263
  accessory, 105, 262
  facial, 205, 263
  glossopharyngeal, 105, 202, 205, 262
  hypoglossal, 262
  intercostal, 236
  median, 114
  oculomotor, 105, 114, 266
  optic, 105, 289
  phrenic, 236
  radial, 114
  stato-acoustic, 262
  trigeminal, 263
    bulbospinal portion, 262
    mandibular branch, 202, 204
  trochlear, 105, 114, 266
  ulnar, 114
  vagus, 105, 262
    dorsal motor nucleus, 262
    recurrent laryngeal branch, 205
    superior laryngeal branch, 202
Nervous system, autonomic, 280
  parasympathetic, 283
  sympathetic, 280
Neural crest, 255
  folds, 55, 246
  groove, 55, 246
  plate, 55, 246
  tube, 55, 246
Neurenteric canal, 38
Neurilemma cells, 256
  sheath, 256
Neuroblast, 251, 280
  apolar, 254
  bipolar, 254
  multipolar, 255
  sympathetic, 280
Neurocranium, 103
Neuroglia cells, 253